CANNABIS: A COMPREHENSIVE OVERVIEW:

Volume I - Biology, Cultivation, History and Basics of the Modern Emerging Cannabis Industry

Volume II- ISBN 978-0-578-95187-4

Volume II - Medicine, Science and Industrial Process

Andrea Holmes, Amanda McKinney, Allan Jenkins, Mark Orsag (Editor), Blake Colclasure, Arin Sutlief, Mahesh Pattabiraman and Steven Rothenberger

(Dr. Andrea Holmes)

Chapter Seven: Understanding Perceptions of Hemp and Marijuana and the Linkages of Cannabis to Medicine and Industry
(Dr. Mahesh Pattabiraman and Dr. Allan Jenkins)

Volume One Glossary

Table of Contents (Volume II)

The Medical Cannabis Chapter Group

Chapter Eight: Introduction to Medical Cannabis
(Dr. Amanda McKinney, MD)

Chapter Nine: New Health Options in Cannabinoids and Terpenes...
(Dr. Amanda McKinney, MD)

Chapter Ten: Precautions and Potential Contraindications...
(Dr. Amanda McKinney, MD)

A Detailed Examination of the Multifaceted Cannabis Industry Chapter Group

Chapter Eleven: An Exploration of Cannabis Cultivation and Testing
(Dr. Andrea Holmes)

Chapter Twelve: Cannabis Processing
(Dr. Andrea Holmes and Dr. Mahesh Pattabiraman)

Chapter Thirteen: A New Revolution in Cannabinoids
(Dr. Andrea Holmes and Dr. Mahesh Pattabiraman)

Chapter Fourteen: Cannabis Industry: Business and Professions
(Dr. Andrea Holmes)

Cannabis Testing and Instrumentation Chapter Group

Chapter Fifteen: Cannabis Testing and Instrumentation (Part I)
(Dr. Arin Sutlief)

Chapter Sixteen: Cannabis Testing and Instrumentation (Part II)
(Dr. Arin Sutlief)

Afterword...
(Dr. Andrea Holmes and Dr. Mark Orsag)

Glossary

Brief Author Biographies

The Medical Cannabis Chapter Group, Chapters 8-10

Chapter 8 Introduction to Medical Cannabis
(Dr. Amanda McKinney, MD)

Cannabis has been used by cultures around the world for centuries and in a variety of ways, including medicine. The earliest documented use of cannabis as medicine dates back to approximately ca. 2900 BC, when the Chinese Emperor Fu Hsi is said to have stated that 'Ma', the Chinese word for Cannabis, was a "very popular medicine that possessed both yin and yang."[1] The *Rh-Ya*, the Chinese Pharmacopeia, contains the earliest written reference and dates back to 1500 BC. [2] Medical cannabis was mainstreamed in the West in the 19th Century by, amongst others, a French psychiatrist, Jacques-Joseph Moreau, who found it increased appetite and treated headaches and insomnia in his patients. By 1850, cannabis had been added to the *United States Pharmacopeia*, the primary reference for prescription and over-the-counter medications. [3] Cannabis was even used to treat opiate withdrawal per an 1889 journal article published in *The Lancet.* [4]

Despite this, cannabis was never thoroughly researched for its potential in the evolving field of medicine, because in 1906, cannabis was lumped in with alcohol, morphine, opium, cocaine, heroin, alpha or beta eucaine, chloroform, chloral hydrate and acetanilide for regulation by the Pure Food and Drugs Act, which required all medicines with these ingredients to be labeled as such. [5] From that point forward, cannabis was seen as a drug and began to be outlawed state by state with Massachusetts becoming the first in 1911. [6] At the national level, cannabis was targeted by the 1937 Marijuana Tax Act and was listed as a Schedule 1 drug by the Controlled Substances Act of 1970. As a Schedule 1 drug, cannabis was classified along with cocaine, heroin and methamphetamine as a most dangerous drug with no recognized medicinal value. It is still listed as a Schedule I drug, despite there being no fatal dose for cannabis.[7] The Schedule 1 designation severely constrained research and it was 1998 before the system by which cannabis and its constituents act within the body, the endocannabinoid system (ECS), was discovered. The importance of this system was characterized by Professor Vincenzo diMarzo, when he summarized the ECS functions as "relax, eat, sleep, forget and protect." [8]

Endocannabinoid System

The endocannabinoid system (ECS), is composed of endocannabinoids, receptors and enzymes and is one regulator of nearly every physiologic process in the body including pain sensitivity and immune function. The clinical and physiologic effects of cannabis on basic body functions have been observed for more than 4500 years, but due to legal and technological limitations, the chemical constituents responsible for these actions were unknown until Isreali chemist, Dr. Raphael Mechoulam, identified and isolated delta-9-THC in 1964.[9] Then, in 1988, the receptor to which THC binds and through which it acts, the CB1 receptor, was discovered. The CB1 receptor was identified at high levels in areas of the brain that control cognition, emotions, appetite and motor coordination, explaining many of the psychotropic effects of cannabis but not its peripheral actions. This mystery was solved. In 1993, when the CB2 receptor was identified in the immune system, gut and other peripheral tissues.[10]

Questions then emerged regarding the purpose of these receptors as nature is known only to conserve what is useful physiologically. This question led to the discovery of the endocannabinoids, anandamide and 2-AG, in the mid-1990s. As a result of this and subsequent research, it has been well established that the ECS serves to maintain homeostasis within the body and its various other systems, ensuring that cellular communication is sufficient yet not excessive.[11]

As previously mentioned, one component of the ECS is made up of endocannabinoids-made from lipid precursors, receptors and enzymes. Currently Anandamide and 2-AG are the known endocannabinoids but are unlikely to be the only ones. The cannabinoid receptors to which these substances bind, include, but are not limited to CB1 and CB2. The enzymes of the ECS tightly control the levels of anandamide and 2-AG, determined by a balance of endocannabinoid synthesis and degradation which is enzymatically controlled. [11]

While the ECS functions much like other systems in the body which utilize receptors and ligands, it is unique in that endocannabinoids (ligands) are produced on demand in response to the number of endocannabinoid receptors present in states of injury or illness. Within the brain, the endocannabinoids are synthesized in the postsynaptic neurons rather than in the presynaptic neuron. This requires that the endocannabinoids then travel in a retrograde fashion back to the receptors in the presynaptic neuron. Binding of the post-synaptically produced endocannabinoids to their receptors in the presynaptic cell results in an inhibition of the release of other various neurotransmitters.

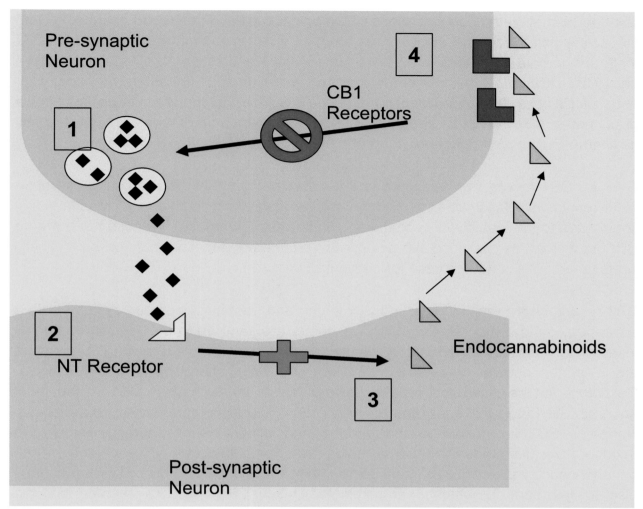

Figure 1. *1) An excitatory neurotransmitter is being released from a presynaptic cell of a neuronal synapse. 2) The neurotransmitter binds and activates the receptor on the postsynaptic neuron. 3) This stimulation triggers the synthesis and release of endocannabinoids. 4)These endocannabinoids travel in a retrograde fashion back across the synapse where the CB1 is bound in the presynaptic cell membrane. Once activated, the CB1 receptor inhibits further release of the stimulating neurotransmitter eliciting a relaxing effect (Figure Credit: Amanda McKinney).*

In the figure: Pre-synaptic Neuron, 1, CB1 Receptors, 4, 2, NT Receptor, 3, Endocannabinoids, Post-synaptic Neuron

Cannabinoid receptors

As previously noted, there are two primary receptors within the ECS, the cannabinoid receptor type 1 (CB1) and cannabinoid receptor type 2 (CB2). CB1 receptors are found primarily in the brain, more specifically in the basal ganglia, hippocampus, amygdala, striatum and cerebellum, where they are involved in cellular signaling.[12] As such, activation, or lack of activation, of these receptors can impact speech, movement, emotions and memory, posture, balance, coordination and speech. CB1 receptors are also found in elevated concentrations in the spinal cord and peripheral nervous system (impacting pain), itch and muscle tone, and, to a lesser extent, are also found in the male and female reproductive systems, anterior eye and retina. In the gastrointestinal tract, CB1 receptors modulate propulsion and secretion. CB1 receptors are most well-known for binding tetrahydrocannabinol (THC) which results in the psychoactive effects of cannabis. CB1 receptors are also found in the autonomic nervous system, thereby having an impact on respiratory, heart and metabolic rates.[13]

Of note, CB1 receptors are absent in the medulla oblongata, the portion of the brain stem responsible for critical respiratory and cardiovascular functions. This critical fact contributes to the inability of cannabis to cause a fatal overdose. Because there are no CB1 receptors in the medulla oblongata, respiratory function cannot be critically suppressed. This is not the case for opioid narcotics.

CB2 receptors are mainly found in the immune and peripheral nervous systems with a subpopulation in the cerebellum. CB2 receptors are involved in the regulation of local inflammatory and anti-inflammatory responses and pain. Both CB1and CB2 receptors are G-protein-coupled receptors (GPCRs) and they share 44% overall identity. Receptors in this class are replaced every two to three days.[13] CB1 is the most abundant GPCR in the brain and plays a critical role in cerebral health and disease. However, CB2 is present in the brain during conditions of traumatic injury and degenerative diseases. The same holds true for inflammatory conditions in the periphery such as liver cirrhosis and certain heart and kidney disorders.[13] CB2 receptors also activate bone formation when stimulated.[14] Both CB1 and CB2 receptors and the ECS, writ large, are critical in the control of gut functions.[13]

Another GPCR, GPR-55, is suspected of being the CB3 receptor because it, too, is activated by the body's endocannabinoids. It is widely expressed in the brain, particularly in the cerebellum, as well as the jejunum and ileum in the intestinal tract. GRP55 is also expressed by osteoblasts and osteoclasts and appears to regulate bone cell function. GPR55 promotes bone resorption via facilitation of osteoclast cell function. Therefore, osteoporosis is associated with overactive GPR55 receptor signaling.[15] GRP55 is also involved in modulating blood pressure and, when activated, promotes cancer cell proliferation.[16]

When not a GPCR, the transient receptor potential vanilloid-1 (TRPV-1), is intimately involved with the ECS. TRPV-1 is an ion channel receptor involved in pain perception, regulation of body temperature, bladder function, itching and pulmonary diseases. It is activated by acids, noxious heat, and capsaicin, a compound found in hot peppers.

TRPV-1 receptors are expressed in the limbic regions of the brain, associated with control of emotion and response to stress. While both CB1 and TRPV-1 receptors are expressed in several regions of the brain, they appear to have opposing roles within the ECS. The endocannabinoid, anandamide, interacts with CB1 receptors to inhibit anxiety-like behavior while anadamine promotes anxiety when it binds TRPV1 receptors. When TRPV-1 activation occurs, it causes the breakdown of bone, pain and inflammation. This results in a directly proportional increase in CB2 receptor production. The inverse happens during bone development.[17]

Table 1 [18]

Body Location	CB1 Receptor Physiology	CB2 Receptor Physiology
Brain	Nociception Drug Addiction Neuroprotection Neurotransmission Appetite and Food Intake Control of Motor Function Mood, Cognition, Perception	Nociception Neurogenesis Neuroprotection Neuroimmune modulation
Liver	Steatosis Fibrogenesis Insulin Resistance	Anti-steatosis Anti-fibrogenesis
Skeletal Muscle	Energy expenditure/oxygen consumption Insulin Resistance	
Bone		Regulation of bone strength and mineral density
Cardiovascular System	Heart rate Hypotension Cardiac dysfunction Decrease in myocardial contractility	Cardiac protection
Spleen	Immunomodulation	Immunomodulation
Immune System	Immunomodulation	Immunomodulation
Gastrointestinal System	Motility Energy balance	

Endocannabinoids

There are two endocannabinoids produced in the body. The first, commonly known as anandamide (N-arachidonoylethanolamine (AEA)), is often called "the bliss molecule" and its name is derived from the word "ananda," which in Sanskrit means joy, bliss or delight. Anandamide (AEA) activates CB1 in the central nervous system and CB2 in the periphery, primarily in the immune system. Anandamide is a partial or full agonist of CB1 receptors. While it binds CB2 receptors, it has very low efficacy and may act as an antagonist.[19] AEA has been shown to negatively impact working memory in rats[20] and early stage embryo development.[21] Anandamide gets its name as the "bliss molecule" because of the role it plays in neural generation of motivation and pleasure as well as feeding behaviors; it enhances the pleasure responses to taste and food intake.[18] In a **murine model**, the "runner's high" seen with exercise also appears to be mediated by anandamide. [22] Anandamide also seems to have anticancer properties as it has been shown to inhibit the proliferation of human breast cancer cells.[23] Chocolate consumption has long been thought to be a pleasurable experience, which may be due to the anandamide found in chocolate along with two other substances that seem to mimic its effects, *N*-oleoylethanolamine and *N-linoleoyl ethanolamide*.[24]

The second endocannabinoid is 2-arachidonoylglycerol (2-AG). It acts as a full <u>agonist</u> at the CB1 receptor but is the primary ligand for the CB2 receptor.[25] High levels of 2-AG are present in the central nervous system. 2-AG has been identified in both bovine (cow's) and human mother's milk having the essential role in the initiation of suckling.[26] Of note, brain 2-AG levels are 170 times higher than those of AEA.[27]

Table 2

Endocannabinoid	Receptor Activity
N-arachidonoylethanolamine (AEA) "Anandamide"	Partial or full agonist for CB1 Weak partial agonist (possible <u>antagonist</u>) for CB2 Less potent than 2-AG but is also less discriminating (binds more readily to CB receptors)

| 2-arachidonoylglycerol (2-AG) | Shows a greater affinity for the CB-2 receptor than for the CB-1 receptor |
| | Full agonist at the CB1 and CB2 receptors |

(Table Credit: Dr. Amanda McKinney)

Cannabinoid Enzymes

The final component of the ECS are the enzymes responsible for synthesis and degradation of the endocannabinoids. Endocannabinoids are synthesized on demand in the postsynaptic cell in contrast to classical neurotransmitters which are made in the presynaptic cell and stored in vesicles for release into the synaptic cleft. The primary building block of endocannabinoids is arachidonic acid, a **polyunsaturated fatty acid**.[28]

The enzyme that synthesizes the anandamide t is known as *N*-arachidonoyl phosphatidylethanolamine (NAPE); while the enzyme that degrades anandamide is fatty acid amide hydrolase (FAAH). 2-AG is synthesized by two isozymes of diacylglycerol lipase (DAGL), *α* and *β,* and is broken down by monoacylglycerol lipase (MAGL). The synthesis enzymes create endocannabinoids from the available arachidonic acid in the phospholipid membrane. After they bind the receptor and provide their intended signal, the endocannabinoids are released and degraded allowing for the raw materials to be available once again for future use.

Table 3

Enzyme	Function
NAPE	Enzyme that synthesizes AEA at the site of the post synaptic cleft
DAGL-alpha	Enzyme that synthesizes 2-AG at the site of the post synaptic cleft
DAGL-beta	Enzyme that synthesizes 2-AG at the site of the post synaptic cleft.
FAAH	Enzyme that breaks down AEA

MAGL	Enzyme that breaks down 2-AG

(Table Credit: Dr. Amanda McKinney)

Care and Feeding of the Endocannabinoid System

As previously noted, the ECS regulates nearly every physiologic process in the body, maintaining homeostasis. It is well known that lifestyle behaviors, like diet, exercise and substance use, impact the development of many disease states such as cardiovascular disease, type 2 diabetes, obesity and many forms of cancer. Likewise, lifestyle behaviors can impact the ECS and its proper function.[29]

Impacts of Diet on the ECS

Consuming foods with arachidonic acid (AA) increases endocannabinoid levels in certain tissues and is crucial for brain development in both the prenatal and postnatal time periods, explaining why AA is found in breast milk. It is also found in animal foods or can be consumed as alpha-linoleic acid (ALA) such as found in vegetable oils, nuts or seeds, which is then converted to arachidonic acid.

However, AA is a double-edged sword. When consumed, AA from animal products is converted to pro-inflammatory metabolites and is involved in neuroinflammation, cancer, asthma, rheumatoid arthritis and other autoimmune disorders. Consuming high levels of AA quadruples the risk of developing ulcerative colitis, an **inflammatory bowel disease**. Patients with **rheumatoid arthritis** also improve on a vegetarian diet, which is low in AA and, therefore, anti-inflammatory in nature.[30]

The Western diet is very high in both AA and ALA, both polyunsaturated fatty acids (PUFAs), because of the high intake of animal foods and processed foods that contain vegetable oils. Because AA (an **omega-6** PUFA) can be biosynthesized in the body from ALA (an **omega-3** PUFA), the best source is seeds and nuts. There is clear evidence that consuming ALA from whole plant foods promotes health, it has been found that ALA consumption increases hepatic levels of both anandamide and 2-AG, thus signalling that AA consumption is not necessary to maintain the ECS. Additionally, only low levels (approx 1% of calories) of dietary ALA are required and higher levels of 8% were shown to increase the risk of developing obesity in a mouse model.[31]

When the body is under stress (physical or emotional) **inflammation** ensues. The adrenal glands, as part of the hypothalamic-pituitary-adrenal (HPA) axis, release glucocorticoids, or steroids, in response that have a strong anti-inflammatory effect.

These glucocorticoids also send a signal to the body to shift production away from the pro-inflammatory AA response pathway toward use of AA in production of anti-inflammatory endocannabinoids.

Several scientific studies have explored other links between the intake of PUFAs and the ECS. **Docosahexaenoic acid (DHA)**, another omega-3 fatty acid, is the primary long chain PUFA found in human brains. Dietary DHA and **eicosapentaenoic acid (EPA)**, also an omega-3 PUFA, support general health, neurological function, and retinal development, via up-regulation of CB1 receptor gene expression.

Omega-3 PUFAs are found in oily fish, walnuts, flax chia and hemp seeds and are valued for their role in the prevention of heart disease, dementia, cancer cell proliferation, insulin resistance and depression. Premature aging and mental illness are linked to low levels of DHA and EPA. Endocannabinoid-mediated neuronal function is negatively impacted in the face of dietary deficiency of omega-3s and can lead to neuropsychiatric disease. Those with Alzheimer's disease or attention deficit hyperactivity disorder (ADHD) often are deficient in omega-3 fatty acids.[32]

A balance of whole plant-derived omega-3 and omega-6 fatty acids is critical for both prevention and management of obesity and metabolic syndrome and is likely modulated through the ECS. This well-balanced ratio of PUFAs is typically absent in the Standard American Diet (SAD), which is characterized by excessive omega-6 intake and deficient omega-3 consumption. It is recommended that omega-3 intake be increased while decreasing the amount of omega-6 in one's diet. A lower omega-6 to omega-3 ratio is liked to a lower risk of the many chronic, diet-related diseases so prevalent in today's society.[29]

The ratio of dietary omega-6 to omega-3 fatty acids also impacts how CB1 receptors regulate fear and memory. It has been speculated that reducing the omega-6/omega-3 ratio in one's diet could enhance the efficacy of treatments for anxiety and PTSD, as well as metabolic disorders.[33]

In the last 100 years, human diets have changed dramatically, particularly but not exclusively in the developed world. Diets much higher in animal foods as compared to historic diets, and diets high in highly refined and processed carbohydrates, have resulted in a pandemic of chronic disease that includes obesity, type 2 diabetes, heart disease and cancer. While there are many causes of this dietary shift, the endocannabinoid system plays a significant role in this unhealthy, global trajectory. CB1 and CB2 receptors have opposing roles with respect to diet and nutrition. Generally speaking, CB1 receptors promote appetite and food intake while CB2 receptors tend to inhibit them.

CB1 receptor activation is linked to both motivation and reward, encouraging sugar consumption by enhancing the neural responses when sweets are consumed. Research in mice reveals that chronic CB1 receptor activation causes obesity-related insulin resistance. This creates a vicious positive feedback loop. In obese individuals, high levels of AEA and 2-AG are found in the liver, pancrease, adipose tissue and skeletal muscle as a result of chronic CB1 activation. These high endocannabinoid levels contribute to insulin resistance, impaired glucose uptake and general cardiometabolic dysfunction. This chronic CB1 activation also leads to more appetite stimulation and increased food intake, exacerbating the processes. Caloric restriction and weight loss can reduce CB1 expression and, therefore, endocannabinoid levels.[29]

Conversely, CB2 receptors in immune cells, adipose tissue and the peripheral nervous system offer broad anti-inflammatory effects that counter the inflammation present in a variety of disease processes. As such, CB2 receptors play a protective role in diet-induced diseases like obesity, a condition of low-grade inflammation. Research also indicates that CB2 activity can prevent or improve **peripheral neuropathy** associated with diabetes and is neuroprotective in cases of stroke, concussion and neurodegenerative ailments. The CB2 receptor is also able to utilize phytocannabinoids and other compounds (**terpenes, flavonoids** and other **polyphenolic compounds**), found in both cannabis and non-cannabis plants such as kitchen spices, leafy greens and other vegetables. These compounds enhance the activity of CB2 receptors counteracting inflammation.[34]

Probiotics are bacteria that offer health benefits to their human hosts. Probiotics are often found in fermented foods, like kimchi and yogurt. The most well-known organisms are Lactobacillus acidophilus and Bifidobacterium species. Prebiotics such as oligofructose and fiber from whole plant foods are carbohydrates that feed probiotic organisms. Both have a positive impact on the ECS. Obese mice have been shown to express elevated levels of CB1 in the colon but when they are fed prebiotics they CB1 expression and AEA production are reduced, leading to less weight and fat gain.[35]

Food is often contaminated with a variety of pesticides that can alter ECS function. Chlorpyrifos and diazinon are examples. As such, it has been hypothesized that eating pesticide-free, organic foods may promote homeostasis of the endocannabinoid system. Piperonyl butoxide, a synergist chemical added to insecticides such as pyrethrum to enhance their activity, is an antagonist of CB1. Other chemicals commonly found in food packaging such as phthalates and plasticizers, act as endocrine disruptors and carcinogens as well as blocking CB1 receptors.[35]

Exercise and the ECS

As discussed previously, the endocannabinoid system is dysregulated in tissues and cells responsible for the control of food intake and energy metabolism leading to obesity. In a murine model when rats were placed on high-fat diet or standard diet, the high-fat diet led to increased anandamide (AEA) levels, but exercise significantly reduced this diet-induced AEA increase. This means that exercise can help manage some of the endocannaboinoid dysfunction seen in the obese state. It is postulated that the "runner's high" may actually be mediated by the endocannabinoid system, rewarding exercise.[35]

Stress and the ECS

Stress of all kinds impacts a multitude of physiologic processes and systems of the body and research suggests that the stress response is primarily regulated by the ECS. Evidence demonstrates that stress regulates endocannabinoid signaling and changes in endocannabinoid signaling also occur as an effect of stress. This is considered a **bidirectional response**. Studies have generally shown that AEA levels decline in the face of stress, with a concurrent downregulation, or loss, of CB1 receptors while 2-AG levels increase. This decline of AEA activates the HPA axis, which is responsible for glucocorticoid release discussed above, as well as increased anxiety. In contrast, increased 2-AG levels lead to termination of the HPA axis stress response and have negative impacts on memory and pain perception. Because the ECS is so important to stress regulation, impairments in endocannabinoid signaling can put individuals at increased risk of stress-related neuropsychiatric conditions like depression, anxiety and post-traumatic stress disorder (PTSD) [36]

In summary, acute stress upregulates the ECS but chronic stress impairs the ECS. However, management of stress has the potential to reverse the negative impacts of chronic stress on ECS function although more research is required. Despite this, there is some anecdotal evidence that stress management practices, such as meditation, yoga and deep breathing exercises have slight cannabimimetic effects.[37]

Pharmaceuticals and the ECS

Some pharmaceuticals also interact with the ECS.

Table 4

Pharmaceutical/Drug	Interaction with ECS
Non-steroidal anti-inflammatory drugs	Blocks the conversion of anti-inflammatory

(NSAIDs) ex., ibuprofen	AEA and 2-AG into pro-inflammatory prostaglandins Some NSAIDs inhibit FAAH, the enzyme that breaks down AEA, thereby increasing AEA levels NSAIDs may enhance the activity of cannabinoids improving pain management efficacy (Entourage Effect)
Opioids/narcotics	Acute opiate administration enhances the activity of cannabinoids and upregulates CB1 expression. Chronic opiate administration has a deleterious effect on the ECS
Antidepressants SSRIs (selective serotonin reuptake inhibitors, MAOIs (monoamine oxidase inhibitors), and TCA's (tricyclic antidepressants)]	Impacts on the ECS are not definitive, but likely result in CB1 upregulation, in some brain regions.
First Generation Antipsychotic Drugs [Ex., haloperidol and chlorpromazine (thorazine)]	Dopamine D2 receptor inverse agonists. Likely upregulate CB1 expression. Antipsychotic drugs do not impact THC-induced "high" or "euphoria," but dampen dysphoria, worsen verbal recall, and worsen distractibility.
Second-generation "atypical" anti- psychotics (e.g., risperidone, olanzapine, clozapine, and aripipra- zole)	Antagonize D2 and 5-HT2A Upregulate CB1 expression Antipsychotic drugs do not impact THC-induced "high" or "euphoria," but dampen dysphoria, worsen verbal recall, and worsen distractibility.
Alcohol	Acute alcohol consumption enhances endocannabinoid release and signaling.

	Alcohol dampens the effects of the ECS. Chronic alcohol consumption and binge drinking desensitize or downregulate CB1 and impair endocannabinoid signaling, except perhaps in areas involved in reward and motivation to self-administer this substance of abuse, contributing to the process of addiction.

(Table Credit: Dr. Amanda McKinney) [29]

Endocannabinoid System Dysfunction

When functioning properly, the ECS maintains homeostasis in the body. However, when it is not, disease processes and disorders can occur, because the ECS has a role in so many physiologic processes including, but not limited to, intestinal function, glucose metabolism, and the stress response. ECS dysregulation has been implicated in metabolic and bowel pathologies and many other diseases. The role of the ECS in obesity and glucose management has been previously mentioned. Another main function of the ECS is modulation of mitochondrial function. Because mitochondria contain their own DNA, mutations can occur resulting in disorders such as Alzheimer's disease, Lou Gehrig's disease, diabetes and cancer.[38]

Evidence also now exists for a "clinical endocannabinoid deficiency" (CED) syndrome which includes common conditions such as migraine headache, fibromyalgia and irritable bowel syndrome (IBS). The common factor that characterizes these conditions is "central sensitization," which is to say that sensations, which are otherwise normal in an unaffected individual, are instead perceived as painful. These disorders also tend to be co-morbid, afflicting the same individuals at various points in their lives and there is growing clinical evidence these same conditions all benefit from treatment with cannabinoids. Those with one or more of these conditions also have low levels of AEA in the brain, gastrointestinal and musculoskeletal systems.[39]

Dysfunction of the ECS has also been implicated in mental illness, with greater dysfunction leading to a more severe illness. Many mental illnesses such as depression, anxiety, and schizophrenia, share symptoms including sadness, suicidal thoughts, body dysmorphia and panic attacks. Often, AEA levels can also be used as an indicator to determine the degree of ECS dysfunction as it pertains to mental illness.[41]

The state of the ECS and its concurrent level of endocannabinoids in the body, whether deficient or sufficient, can also be described as "endocannabinoid tone". Additional conditions, which may be secondary to reduced endocannbinoid tone, include PTSD,

complex regional pain syndrome, **causalgia**, **postherpetic neuralgia**, interstitial cystitis, and infertility and early miscarriage.[41]

Conversely, excessive endocannabinoid tone, especially CB1 activity, is present in the states of morbid obesity, metabolic syndrome with increased inflammation, insulin resistance or diabetes and hepatic (liver) fibrosis. As a result, CB1 inverse agonists have been developed to treat obesity by lowering endocannabinoid tone. However, like many drugs that target one specific mechanism or pathway, unforeseen side effects can develop. Take the case of rimonabant (Acomplia® or SR141716), a CB1 inverse agonist developed as an appetite suppressing anti-obesity drug. It was first approved for use in Europe in 2006, but was withdrawn in 2008 due to serious psychiatric side effects.[40] It was effective at reducing hunger and weight gain, however, functional antagonism of the CB1 receptor led to depression and suicidality.

Normal endocannabinoid tone can, in part, be restored through diet and lifestyle modification. In cases where care of the ECS through diet and lifestyle is not sufficient, exogenous cannabinoids (i.e., medical cannabis) can be utilized.

Pharmacology of Cannabis and Physiologic Effects of Phytocannabinoids

Over the last several thousand years, humans co-evolved with other species, such as dogs, cats and bacteria, developing relationships that are mutually beneficial. Likewise, because humans have been using cannabis for thousands of years, co-evolution between humans and cannabis has also occurred. Cannabis is a highly adaptable plant and grows in a wide variety of environments. As it adapted to harsher climates and conditions, the plant began to produce a multitude of terpenes and cannabinoids which the human ECS has come to rely upon.

This coevolutionary process occurs through the process of epigenetics. **Epigenetics** is the mechanism by which our environment has impacts on our own genes. When these epigenetic changes occur, they can be passed on to our offspring. Cannabis is a good example of this process. As we coevolved, humans bred cannabis plants that suited our needs, changing the plant itself. The use of the plant also created epigenetic changes, honing our endocannabinoid systems in the process, and these changes were then passed down through the generations, fine tuning themselves all along the way.

Cannabis contains over 100 phytocannabinoids and over 300 more other chemical compounds (terpenes, polyphenols, flavonoids, etc) that have impacts on various systems of the body, beyond the ECS, that impact health and disease states. Other impacted systems include the **endorphin system**, the **vanilloid system**, the

glutaminergic/catecholamine/serotonin and **HPA systems**, the **P-PAR gamma system** and the immune system. Likewise, there are non-cannabis plants, such as *Piper nigrum* (black pepper) and *Echinacea purpurea* (purple coneflower), that contain cannabinoids and terpenes also impact the ECS.

Terpenes, aromatic compounds found in plants including cannabis, enhance phytocannabinoid activity resulting in the "**entourage**" **or** "**ensemble effect**", which is the principle that cannabis works better when used in full spectrum forms. In other words, cannabinoids are more effective at lower doses when an array of cannabinoids, terpenes, flavonoids and other compounds present in cannabis are taken simultaneously rather than as isolated molecules. This principle is critical in medical cannabis and will be examined in further detail later in this chapter.

Below, there are details on the major and minor cannabinoids and their **acidic, neutral** and **varin** phases.

Neutral Phase Cannabinoids

Tetrahydrocannabinol (THC)

THC is an intoxicating and psychoactive cannabinoid. It comes in two forms, delta-9-THC and delta-8 THC. Delta-9-THCis the most well-known cannabinoid and is typically referred to as "THC". THC is primarily, but not solely, responsible for the psychosensory effects of cannabis that include a sense of euphoria, heightened sensory awareness and distortion of time, but it also has therapeutic benefits.

THC is also only activated once it has been **decarboxylated** from its original chemical structure, THCA, to THC. There will be more on THCA and other "acidic" cannabinoids to follow. THC is the most sought-after cannabinoid for recreational purposes for its euphoric effects. THC binds and activates the CB1 receptors, found mainly in the central nervous system, leading to THC intoxication and other cerebral effects.

Delta-8-THC is found at very low concentrations in the cannabis plant and is, therefore, considered a minor cannabinoid. Delta-8 is not produced in the cannabis plant, but rather, delta-9-THC degrades into delta-8-THC during storage. Selective breeding and advanced extraction methods are being used to produce large quantities of delta-8-THC.

While delta-8-THC is an analog of delta-9-THC, there are some notable differences. Both forms bind the CB1 receptor in the central nervous system (CNS) and have been reported to stimulate appetite, reduce nausea and soothe pain. However, delta-8-THC has only about half the psychotropic potency of delta-9-THC. In addition, delta-8 is more stable than delta-9; delta-9 is easily oxidized to either cannabinol (CBN) or delta-8. As such, delta-8 is a desirable medicinal compound, as it does not oxidize to CBN and has a long shelf life.

Medical Uses of THC (Delta 9 THC)

1. **Pain Relief:** THC's relieves pain primarily via CB1 receptor activation in the brain region responsible for pain management for the entire body. Delta 9 is the most potent analgesic cannabinoid.[41]
2. **Appetite Stimulation**: THC interacts with the hormones **ghrelin** and **leptin** to stimulate appetite.
3. **Antiemetic:** THC is highly effective in reducing nausea and vomiting in cancer patients receiving chemotherapy.
4. **Muscle Spasticity**: Cannabis has been shown to be effective in treating multiple sclerosis (MS) related to muscle spasticity. THC, as part of a whole plant extract, can reverse the progression of MS through CB1 receptor activation. [42]
5. **Addiction Treatment:** THC has the capacity to reduce the abuse of other substances, particularly opioid narcotics, despite it being a rewarding substance itself.[43]
6. **Metabolic:** Cannabis users tend to have lower body mass index (BMI), lower rates of fatty liver disease and lower rates of diabetes than individuals who do not use cannabis.[44]
7. **Neuroprotective**: THC has the capacity to protect neurons, promote cellular growth and regulate **neuroplasticity** (a process involved in learning and forgetting) in the brain. THC eliminates beta-amyloid and blocks beta-amyloid induced inflammation and prevents nerve cell death in the brain. These are hallmarks of Alzheimer's disease and THC appears to be potentially preventative as well as a possible therapeutic agent.[45] In addition, THC has been shown to reduce gene expression of a heritable and fatal neurodegenerative disorder called Huntington's disease.[47]
8. **Anti-inflammatory**: THC reduces local inflammation by binding to the CB2 receptor.
9. **Cancer:** THC can be used to treat the side effects of cancer treatment such as nausea, vomiting and pain but also has the potential to destroy cancer cells while sparing normal cells, limiting tumor growth, unmasking cancer to the immune system and strengthening the immune system.[43]

Medical Potential (Delta 8 THC)

1. **Pain and Anti-Inflammatory Effects:** Delta-8 has been shown, when applied topically, to reduce pain inflammation in mice with corneal injuries. This is

mediated through the CB1 receptor. [46] Another murine study found that, while delta-8 provides analgesia, tolerance develops quickly.[47]

2. **Anxiety:** Delta-8 reduces anxiety at similar levels as delta-9, however, this evidence is largely anecdotal. It has been reported that "consumption of delta-8-THC results in a very calm and focused high, without the anxiety that can sometimes accompany delta-9-THC".[48]

3. **Anti-Nauseant Effects:** Delta-8 was found to eliminate vomiting in pediatric cancer patients when it was taken immediately before and for 24 hours after administration of chemotherapy. This was a small study of eight patients followed for two years with very few side effects noted.[49]

4. **Appetite Stimulant:** Like delta-9, delta-8-THC has been shown to stimulate appetite, perhaps even better than delta-9, according to a murine study in which administration of low-dose delta-8-THC over a period of 50 days led to a 22% increase in food intake as compared to controls. This result was also significantly higher than for delta-9. [50]

Metabolism of THC

Once in the body, most cannabinoids are metabolized in the liver by an enzyme called CYP2C9. When THC is ingested concurrently with CYP 2C9 inhibitors, this leads to extended intoxication. Some of these inhibitors include...

1. Antifungal Drugs (fluconazole, miconazole and voriconazole)
2. Amentoflavone (constituent of Ginkgo biloba and St. John's Wort)
3. Sulfaphenazole, Sulfamethoxazole (antibacterials)
4. Valproic Acid (anticonvulsant, mood-stabilizing)
5. Antihistamines (Cyclizine, Promethazine)
6. Chloramphenicol
7. Cholesterol Lowering Drugs (fenofibrate, fluvastatin
8. SSRI Antidepressants (fluvoxamine, sertraline)
9. Isoniazid (in tuberculosis)
10. Lovastatin (statin)
11. Phenylbutazone (NSAID)
12. Zafirlukast (leukotriene antagonist)
13. Quercetin (anti-inflammatory)

Because cannabinoids are fat-soluble, lipophilic (fat-loving) molecules, some THC is also stored in body fat in addition to being metabolized in the liver. As a result, its metabolite can remain, and be detected, for several weeks after use (typically one month). Antibody-based drug tests detect these metabolites but do not represent intoxication as is the case with ethanol, breath tests that measure current blood alcohol levels. Rather, these tests portray past consumer use.

Side Effects (Delta 9) THC

With regard to side effects ..."On the cognitive domain, it impairs the human capacity to discriminate between time intervals and spatial distances, vigilance, memory and the performance for mental work. In the psychic area, Δ9-THC may induce unpleasant reactions such as disconnected thoughts, panic reactions, disturbing changes in perception, delusions and hallucinatory experiences. It has been proposed by the World Health Organization that Δ9-THC should be rescheduled to schedule IV (lowest risk) of the United Nations Convention on Psychotropic Drugs, as it does not constitute a substantial risk to public health and its abuse is rare if at all."[51]

Other side effects can include unwanted intoxication. Intoxication is often sought-after, but it can cause temporary yet unpleasant physical and mental effects. Physical effects can include increased, and sometimes rapid, heart rate, red eyes and hyperphagia ("the munchies"). The most common unpleasant mental effect is a feeling of paranoia.

Keep in mind that every person's response to THC and other cannabis compounds is influenced by their unique endocannabinoid system. For instance, scientists have discovered nine variations of the CB1 receptor gene, which opens the door for varied responses to THC. In other words, not everyone will experience the same side effects, or the same level of adverse side effects, associated with THC. For more information about over-intoxication, see the section entitled, "Precautions and Potential Contraindications" below.

CBD (Cannabidiol)

Cannabidiol (CBD) is considered "non-psychoactive", however, it clearly has some psychological effects, as demonstrated by its effectiveness in anxiety disorders. After THC, it is the second-most abundant cannabinoid in cannabis and is created by decarboxylating cannabidiolic acid (CBDA).

CBD's actions within the brain and body are quite complicated. It is very likely that the beneficial effects of CBD operate through diverse biological pathways, rather than by a single action. More research is needed to fully understand the mechanisms by which CBD relieves ailments such seizures.

Here is a summary of the receptor interactions.[52]

1. CBD has an affinity for both the CB1 and CB2 receptors, but very little of its activity is mediated through CB1 and CB2.

2. CBD antagonizes (blocks) GPR55, alpha-1 adrenergic and mu-opioid receptors.
3. CBD is an agonist at 5-HT1A, TRPV1 and TRPV2 receptors.
4. CBD acts as an **allosteric receptor modulator,** meaning it can either enhance or inhibit signal transmission by altering receptor shape. CBD inhibits the uptake of the neurotransmitters **norepinephrine, dopamine, serotonin,** gamma-Aminobutyric acid (**GABA**) and anandamide; thus increasing circulating levels of these compounds making them more available to perform their functions.
5. CBD is a **positive allosteric modulator** of the GABA-A receptor[53] enhancing the receptor's binding affinity for its principal **endogenous** agonist, GABA, the main inhibitory neurotransmitter in the central nervous system. As such, CBD reduces anxiety by amplifying the natural calming effect of GABA.
6. CBD is a **negative allosteric modulator** at the CB1 receptor, changing the shape of the receptor in a way that reduces THC's ability to bind it, which functionally reduces THC's effects.[54]
7. CBD influences mitochondrial calcium stores which can induce apoptosis, or programmed cell death, in cancer cells.[55]
8. CBD inhibits the uptake and breakdown of anandamide, thereby increasing the endocannabinoid levels in the brain's synapses. This has the effect of increasing endocannabinoid tone. This is, perhaps, the primary way in which CBD confers neuroprotection in the face of seizures and other neurodegenerative diseases, like Alzheimer's and Huntington's.[56]

It has been documented that whole-plant CBD-rich extract, containing other cannabinoids and terpenes, is far more potent than single-molecule CBD isolate, making the whole-plant extract therapeutically superior, exemplifying the entourage effect. Additionally, the efficacy of CBD is quite low at both very low and very high doses as indicated by the **dose-response curve**. [57]

Furthermore, because CBD is a **negative allosteric modulator** at the CB1 receptor, using CBD and THC together reduces the psychoactivity and other side effects (anxiety/paranoia) of THC while simultaneously enhancing THC's benefits.[58] CBD displaces some THC from binding to the CB1 receptor, reducing but not eliminating, some of the psychotropic and other unwanted side effects of THC, while allowing more THC to be free to bind other receptor types, such as CB2, which offers neuroprotective, anti-inflammatory and other beneficial effects.[59] CBD also minimizes THC's negative effects on memory. Memory recall is also improved in users with higher CBD intake as compared to those who use cannabis with little or no CBD. Full spectrum cannabis users are also less likely to develop dependence as compared to those who use THC only.[60]

Medical Uses

CBD is being utilized by a large swath of consumers for a variety of symptoms and conditions but largely in an unsupervised way. This is due to the dearth of knowledge of medical cannabis on the part of medical practitioners. Fortunately, research is currently being performed to identify the effectiveness of CBD for various conditions and disease processes. As of this writing, there are 79 clinical trials[61] underway, which will determine the effectiveness of CBD for a panoply of conditions. Unlike many pharmaceuticals with single mechanisms of action, CBD works through multiple pathways and receptors and has a high safety profile which offers great therapeutic potential for a multitude of conditions some of which are detailed below.

1. **Pain Relief:** CBD binds TRPV-1 receptors, which confer information about pain perception, inflammation and body temperature. Other agonists of TRPV-1 reduce pain perception and include capsaicin (found in hot peppers) and anandamide.[62]

2. **Anxiety**: At high concentrations, CBD is a direct agonist at the 5-HT1A receptor, conferring anti-anxiety effects.[63] CBD has been shown to ameliorate situational anxiety, such as public speaking at doses of 400 to 600 milligrams. [64] High in CBD, low in THC strains appear to have the best cannabinoid profile for alleviating depression.[65] CBD's anti-anxiety effects are partly due to its inhibition of the uptake of the neurotransmitter, **adenosine**. This has the effect of increasing adenosine levels in the brain. Adenosine plays a significant role in cardiovascular function as it regulates the consumption of oxygen by the myocardium (heart muscle) as well as coronary artery blood flow. CBD also lowers heart rate and blood pressure in a setting of anxiety.[66]

3. **Cancer**: CBD is a GPR55 antagonist, thereby reducing bone resorption (and, theoretically, osteoporosis) and cancer cell proliferation.[67] CBD also imbues anti-cancer effects via activation of PPAR-gamma which has an anti-proliferative effect on cancer cells and has been shown cause regression of human lung and brain cancer cells.[68] CBD also directly targets mitochondria and alters their capacity to handle calcium causing mitochondrial calcium overload and cell death in acute lymphoblastic leukemia T cells (T-ALL) while sparing healthy T cells. It has been suggested that CBD be included in chemotherapeutic protocols for T-ALL treatment.[69]

4. **Anti-inflammatory:** Inhibition of adenosine reuptake also contributes to CBD's anti-inflammatory effects, as the A1A and A2A adenosine receptors exact broad anti-inflammatory effects throughout the body. Likewise, through the TRPV-1 receptor, reuptake of anandamide is inhibited, increasing anandamide levels and

suppressing pain and inflammation.[70] CBD's activation of PPAR is yet another pathway by which it fights inflammation.[71]

5. **Epilepsy and Seizures:** Due to its demonstrated anticonvulsant activity, CBD was approved by the Food and Drug Administration (FDA) in 2018 for use in severe forms of childhood epilepsy. However, the mechanisms by which CBD confers its anti-seizure activity are still not fully understood. One possibility is CBD's interaction with **glutamate** receptors, "which play a key role in the type of neuronal activity that is a hallmark of epilepsy".[72] CBD also enhances GABA receptors, acts as an anti-inflammatory, and as a neuroprotectant, which also likely contribute to its effectiveness.[73]

6. **Special Note on Epilepsy:** In addition to CBD, the cannabinoids THC, THCA and CBDV all have anti-seizure properties as does the terpene alpha linalool. However, any compound that can prevent seizures or treat seizure disorders can paradoxically also worsen seizures. It is unclear why, but in certain patients at certain dosages, both CBD and THC have been observed to worsen seizures. Cannabis can also impact the metabolism of anti-epileptic drugs, raising or lowering blood levels and must be closely monitored. A 2017 study reported that approximately 86% of 272 epilepsy patients who failed to respond fully to conventional treatment, who then tried cannabis, were likely to receive some benefit. Ten percent (10%) became seizure free and 45% experienced a greater than 50% reduction in seizures. Fourteen percent (14%) did not benefit from the cannabis treatment and approximately 4% became worse after adding cannabis. Optimal dosing of cannabis in seizure disorders is challenging and a **biphasic** dose response is noted.[74]

7. **Addiction Treatment**: CBD has also been reviewed as a potential intervention in the treatment of addiction. It has been shown that CBD can be helpful in cases of opioid, cocaine, psychostimulant[75] and tobacco[76] addictions. This is due, in part to CBD's anxiolytic potential in cases where anxiety leads people to use drugs such as heroin in a process of self-medication.[77]

8. **Cardiovascular Diseases**: CBD has shown the ability to relax arteries particularly in the setting of **endothelial dysfunction**. CBD treatment does not affect resting blood pressure or heart rate but does reduce these cardiovascular parameters in the face of various types of stressors. CBD also has a role in protecting the cardiac muscle after cardiac ischaemia (heart attack) and **reperfusion** and can also reduce the cardiac dysfunction seen in diabetic patients. Likewise, CBD offers neuroprotection in cases of stroke, by helping maintain blood flow in the affected areas of the brain.[78]

Metabolism

Like THC, CBD is metabolized in the liver by way of the hepatic CYP 450 enzyme system. THC is metabolized specifically by the CYP2C9 enzyme, which is just one of the many enzymes in the CYP 450 enzyme system. Most drugs are metabolized and cleared by the CYP 450 system. It is also, conversely, a significant source of adverse drug effects. When one drug occupies the CYP 450 system, the second drug can accumulate to toxic levels. Warfarin, a powerful blood thinning drug, is one example.[79] Approximately 90% of all commonly used drugs are metabolized by the CYP 450 enzyme system, so drug interactions must be assessed for individuals using CBD.

CBN (Cannabinol)

With time, exposure to ultraviolet (UV) light, and/or heat, THC oxidizes and is converted into cannabinol (CBN). THC gradually converts to CBN even in ideal storage conditions by changing the plant's medicinal properties. With regard to psychoactivity, cannabinol (CBN) is thought to be one-fourth (¼) the potency of THC.[80]

CBN Benefits and Medical Uses

1. **Insomnia**: Because CBN is a degradation product of THC it's often called, "the sleepy cannabinoid in old weed".[81] According to one analysis, 5 mg of CBN is as effective as 10 mg of **diazepam**.[82] CBN-rich products are often used for promoting sleep or relaxation without impairment. Some individuals, however, have infrequently reported higher concentrations of CBN being associated with a stimulating effect. CBN, in conjunction with THC, produces greater sedation compared with either cannabinoid alone in a mouse model.[83]
2. **Pain Relief:** CBN has also been identified as a potential analgesic.[84] CBN is a weak partial agonist of CB1, however, CBN's analgesic effects appear to be modulated through the ion channel receptors, TRPM8 and TRPA1. CBN isolate also has been reported to be able to relieve chronic muscle pain disorders such as temporomandibular disorders and fibromyalgia in an animal model.[85]
3. **Anti-Bacterial**: As with other cannabinoids, CBN has been found to be highly effective against multiple antibiotic resistant bacteria, including methicillin resistant Staphylococcus aureus (MRSA), making it a potentially viable treament.[86]
4. **Anti-Inflammatory**: While CBN is not as widely recognized as CBD and THC for its anti-inflammatory properties, it may have similar anti-inflammatory activity and treatment potential in regard to inflammatory diseases. CBN was identified as a possible treatment for inflammatory disorders like allergic asthma.[87] CBN and

THC (but not CBD) can be used to treat glaucoma, as it fights inflammation that can cause elevated intraocular pressure.[88]

5. **Anticonvulsant**: CBN, like CBD and THC, can be utilized in the treatment of epilepsy, reducing seizures. In another possible example of the entourage effect, CBN may be more effective as an anticonvulsant when used with CBD and THC rather than alone.[89]

6. **Bone Formation**: CBN may also modulate bone formation via stem cell recruitment, and therefore, be an effective cannabinoid in the treatment of osteoporosis and bone fractures.[90]

7. **Appetite Stimulant**: CBN appears to be an effective **appetite stimulant**. In rats, CBN administration can increase both feeding time as well as amount consumed. As such, CBN is a non-intoxicating alternative to THC as an appetite stimulant.[91]

8. **Other**: CBN, in recent studies, has been found to have potential to reduce anxiety, attention hyperactivity deficit disorder (ADHD) and chronic insomnia.[92]

CBC (Cannabichromene)

CBC is also a non-psychotropic cannabinoid with significant anti-inflammatory properties and binds the TRPA1 receptor. CBC does not bind the CB1 receptor. CBC is created from CBG under certain environmental conditions during the plant's growing cycle. Genetics also play a role in this process. There is some evidence that co-administration of CBC with THC could increase the effects of THC, consistent with the entourage effect.[93]

Medical Uses

1. **Cancer**: CBC also inhibits the uptake of anandamide, increasing blood levels. Anandamide has been shown to inhibit breast cancer cell proliferation and induce death of colon cancer cells.[94,95] In a mouse model of skin cancer, CBC was shown to inhibit inflammation and tumor growth.[96] THC is known for its anti-tumor properties for several different forms of cancer;however, its psychotropic qualities can make it difficult to use as a chemotherapy agent. However, CBC has been found to be the second-most-potent non-THC cannabinoid at inhibiting cancer cell growth. (CBG was the most potent).[97]

2. **Acne**: CBC appears to be helpful for treating acne, as it has been shown to significantly reduce lipid production in the skin that contributes to the development of acne. CBC also exhibits powerful anti-inflammatory properties by reducing levels of arachidonic acid (AA), needed for **lipogenesis**.[98]

3. **Anti-Inflammatory and Analgesia**: CBC is a CB2 receptor agonist, by which it modulates inflammation.[99] CBC is reported to be more efficacious than, the nonsteroidal anti-inflammatory drug (NSAID), phenylbutazone, which was

removed from the market due to negative side effects.[100] CBC has been shown to reduce pain and inflammation associated with osteoarthritis in rats [101] without the negative side effects of NSAIDs. CBC also stimulates pathways of anti-**nociception**, relieving pain by interacting with several target proteins involved in nociceptive control. Like other examples of the entourage effect, CBC, when used with THC, has a greater anti-inflammatory response than either cannabinoid alone.[102]

4. **Anti-Microbial**: As with other cannabinoids, CBC has been found to be highly effective against multiple antibiotic-resistant bacteria, including methicillin resistant Staphylococcus aureus (MRSA), making it a potentially viable treament.[86] CBC also has antifungal properties.[103]

5. **Depression**: CBC may be useful in treating depression especially in conjunction with both THC and CBD.[104]

6. **Brain Health:** In a mouse model, CBC improved the health of neural stem progenitor cells (NSPCs) essential to brain plasticity under both normal conditions as well as during the recovery from brain injuries. NSPCs are modulated by surrounding microglial cells, brain immune cells and astrocytes, which produce both pro-inflammatory and anti-inflammatory factors. Because CBC has anti-inflammatory activity, the potential benefit of CBC on NSPCs may occur through its inhibitory action on astrocytes. In the referenced study, CBC inhibited differentiation of NSPCs into astrocytes, which may offer a neuroprotective effect by suppressing reactive astrocytes that play a role in neuroinflammation, Alzheimer's disease and hepatic encephalopathy.[105,106]

CBG (Cannabigerol)

CBG and CBGA (the acidic form of CBG and its precursor) are known as the "Mother of Cannabinoids" since CBGA is the precursor molecule of the THC and CBD branches of the cannabis family tree (see Figure 2). CBG is non-psychotropic and has a low affinity for the CB1 receptor but acts as a partial agonist at the CB2 receptor. CBG is an agonist at the TRPV-1, TRPA-1 and a2-adrenergic receptors and inhibits the uptake of the neurotransmitters serotonin, norepinephrine and GABA.[107]

Medical Uses

1. **Anti-Inflammatory**: CBG's affinity for the CB2 receptor contributes to its anti-inflammatory properties. There is anecdotal human and preclinical murine evidence for CBG having benefit in cases of inflammatory bowel diseases like Crohn's and ulcerative colitis. In the mouse model, CBG was found to reduce bowel inflammation, nitric oxide production (which is generated at high levels in certain types of inflammation) and oxidative stress in intestinal cells.[108]

2. **Neuroprotection**: Inflammation and oxidative stress are both contributors to neurodegeneration, which is linked to diseases such as Alzheimer's. It has been found that CBG may protect against both neuroinflammation and oxidative stress, possibly helping to prevent cell loss.[109] In a 2015 study, CBG was shown to improve motor deficits and preserve neurons in the striatum of mice with **Huntington's disease**.[110] Likewise, in a murine model of virally induced **multiple sclerosis**, CBG was found to alleviate symptoms.[111]

3. **Dermatological**: CBG has therapeutic potential for atopic dermatitis, psoriasis,[112] scleroderma, acne,[98] hair growth and pigmentation disorders, keratin diseases, various tumors, and pruritus (itching).[113] CBG is also being studied for use in inflammatory skin conditions, sunburns and minor wounds.

4. **Antimicrobial**: As has been discussed with other cannabinoids, CBG, too, has been found to offer antimicrobial properties against methicillin resistant Staphylococcus aureus (MRSA) strains. However, its mechanism of action remains elusive. [86]

5. **Cancer**: In a murine colon cancer model, CBG was found to promote cancer cell death and inhibit the growth of tumors.[114] Clinical research will need to provide more significant insights into whether these results can be translated into cancer treatment for humans. Additionally, in vitro research on leukemia has suggested that anti-cancer activity is enhanced when CBG is combined with other cannabinoids.[115]

6. **Bladder Dysfunction**: There is also anecdotal evidence that CBG assists with bladder dysfunction (overactive bladder). Animal studies have also confirmed a reduction in bladder contractions with CBG that supports these anecdotal findings.[116]

7. **Appetite Stimulant**: Individuals living with AIDS and cancer commonly experience anorexia, or reduced appetite and **cachexia**. CBG represents a non-psychoactive alternative to THC that may stimulate appetite as it has been found to work as an appetite stimulant in rats, increasing the number and size of meals consumed.[117] CBG, as part of a whole plant cannabis extract, appeared to work even more effectively than CBG as an isolate, yet again exemplifying the entourage effect.[118]

8. **Glaucoma**: CBG has been shown to help lower intraocular pressure, which causes much of the damage from glaucoma. In a 2009 study, CBG and THC were both found to help reduce intraocular pressure. The study also found that, unlike THC, CBG did not affect certain phases of sleep.[119,120]

Cannabicyclol (CBL)

CBL is a non-intoxicating cannabinoid converted from cannabichromene (CBC) under certain environmental changes, most notably light. As cannabis ages, concentrations of THC and CBD decline while CBC and CBL levels rise. Some, in the broader cannabis community, believe that CBL may have medicinal or therapeutic properties, but not enough research has been done to prove this. Likewise, CBL's receptor activity has yet to be determined.

Cannabacitran (CBT)

CBT is a very rare minor cannabinoid that is gaining more recognition. In addition to cannabacitran, which is on the CBC branch of the cannabinoid family tree, there is another cannabinoid molecule, Cannabitriol, which branches from the THC branch and sometimes causes confusion. This is because it too is commonly referenced by the same three letters in its acronym. Cannabitriol is biosynthesized from THCA and cannabicitran from CBDA. Each molecule, however, has a completely different molecular structure and molecular weight. Very little is known about CBT itself and its potential medicinal properties, however, it is speculated that this cannabinoid contributes to the entourage effect.

Acidic Versus Neutral Cannabinoids

Cannabinoids appear naturally in the cannabis plant in their acidic forms and are thought to confer antioxidant and defense mechanisms (anti-pest and antimicrobial) to the plant. Acidic cannabinoids lose their acid, or carboxyl, group when heated, becoming a neutral cannabinoid. This process is called decarboxylation. For example, tetrahydrocannabinolic acid (THCA) is converted to THC when heat is applied. Some decarboxylation also occurs with passage of time at room temperature and with exposure to light. Cannabis products intended to contain the acidic form of cannabinoids nearly universally also contain low levels of cannabinoids in their neutral forms.

Cannabigerolic Acid (CBGA)

Cannabigerolic acid (CBGA) is the precursor cannabinoid to **THCA**, **CBDA**, and **CBCA**. **CBGA** is decarboxylated into CBG by heat and time, but CBGA is rarely found in mature flowers to any significant extent. A few strains lack the enzyme that converts CBGA into the other cannabinoids. Harvesting hemp very early yields higher levels of CBGA and CBG compared to later in the plant's life when there are lesser amounts. Unless the cultivar has been genetically programmed (bred) to stop the transformation of CBGA into other cannabinoids during the plant's maturation.

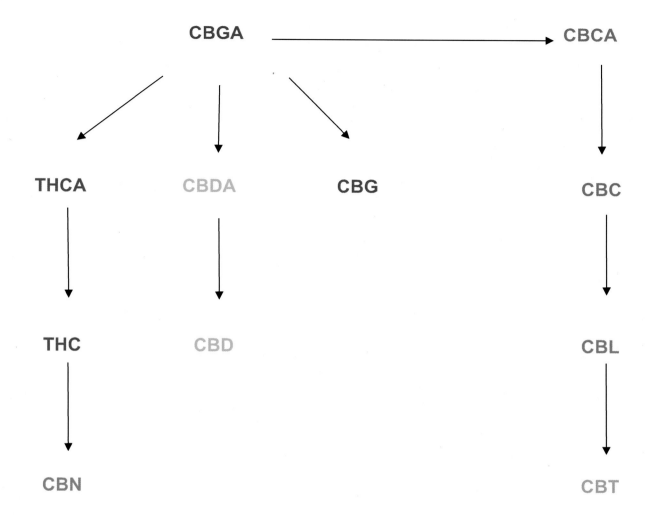

Figure 2 (Figure Credit: Dr. Amanda McKinney).

Medical Uses

1. **Anti-Tumor**: CBGA has been reported to have cytotoxic activity against colon cancer. CBGA may also prevent the growth and proliferation of colon polyps which are colon cancer precursors.[121]

2. **Diabetes**: CBGA may also potentially play a role in controlling diabetes by activating PPARs that, in turn, improve lipid metabolism which reduces excess lipid accumulation in cells, the actual cause of insulin resistance and type 2 diabetes.[122]

3. **Cardiovascular Disease:** Type 2 diabetes is considered a "coronary artery disease equivalent" and most individuals who die from type 2 diabetes actually die from diabetic complications, primarily cardiovascular events like heart attack. CBGA has been found to inhibit the enzyme aldose reductase to a significant degree; aldose reductase is a key enzyme involved in diabetic complications.

Synthetic inhibitors of aldose reductase have severe side effects, so plant-derived CBGA offers a promising alternative.[123]

Cannabidiolic Acid (CBDA)

CBDA is a non-psychotropic cannabinoid typically found at high levels in raw and uncured cannabis. CBDA (or cannabidiolic acid) is the precursor of cannabidiol (CBD) and activates 5-HT1A serotonin receptors and GPR55 receptors significantly more potently than CBD.

Medical Uses

1. **Anti-Nausea:** In mice, CBDA has anti-nausea effects at very low doses. CBD has been shown to reduce anticipated nausea in the animal model, but CBD was not nearly as effective as CBDA. CBDA binds 5-HT1A receptors in a more potent fashion than CBD and can suppress nausea and vomiting caused by toxins and motion sickness. Likewise, CBDA can reduce anticipatory nausea, which is severe nausea that occurs even before a chemotherapy session has been initiated, and it currently has no effective treatment. CBDA combined with ondansetron, a commonly used antiemetic drug, enhances ondansetron's effect, even at very low doses.[124,125]
2. **Anti-Inflammatory**: CBDA has potent anti-inflammatory effects via cyclo-oxgynase (COX) enzyme inhibition, the same mechanism of action as the drug Celebrex. CBDA likely has some of the same mechanisms of action and pharmacologic properties as CBD.[126]
3. **Anti-Tumor**: CBDA, like CBGA, has also been reported to have cytotoxic activity against colon cancer. [127]
4. **Diabetes**: Like CBGA, CBDA activates PPARs that, in turn, improve lipid metabolism, which reduces excess lipid accumulation in cells, the actual cause of insulin resistance and Type 2 diabetes. [128]
5. **Seizures/Epilepsy**: While there are no clinical trials, CBDA is thought to be more effective than CBD in seizure reduction, in certain parameters and at lower doses, according to a patent application by GW Pharmaceuticals, makers of Epidolex.[127] Additionally, clinicians Bonni Goldstein and Dustin Sulak have had great anecdotal success when treating patients with CBDA.

Cannabicyclolic Acid (CBLA)

This is a rare non-intoxicating cannabinoid. Cannabichromenic acid (CBCA) is converted to cannabicyciolic acid (CBLA) during storage and light exposure. CBLA is being studied for its anti-inflammatory properties and other potential benefits.

Tetrahydrocannabinolic Acid (THCA)

THCA is non-intoxicating but, when decarboxylated, is converted to intoxicating THC. Evidence reveals that THCA has its own medicinal potential as an anti-inflammatory, a neuroprotectant and an anti-emetic. Because THCA is non-psychotropic, it is not a banned substance at the federal level. However, because THCA is a precursor to THC, and because no sample of THCA is completely free of THC, possession of it could possibly be prosecuted under the Federal Analogue Act. The detection of THCA in urine could be interpreted as cannabis use, which may have legal implications for users in states where cannabis is still illegal.

Medical Uses

The pharmacology of THCA is unclear, however, it does not appear to act through the CB1 or CB2 receptors. However, some of THCA's activity may be indirectly dependent on them.

1. **Anti-Inflammatory**: The little research that has been performed on THCA reveals it has anti-inflammatory properties mediated by decreased production of tumor necrosis factor alpha (TNF-a4), the cytokine interleukin 10 (IL-10) and inhibition of cyclooxygenase (COX) enzymes. THCA inhibits both COX-1 and COX-2 and modulates immune activity, however, not through CB1 and CB2.[128] Its neuroprotectant activity is through the PPAR-γ pathways. THCA may also inhibit prostate cancer growth in the presence of other non-THC cannabinoids.[129]
2. **Anti-Nausea**: THCA has demonstrated anti-nausea and antiemetic properties in mice at doses much lower than THC, making it a non-psychotropic alternative to THC for nausea and vomiting.[130]
3. **Anti-Seizure**: THCA has potent anti-seizure properties in extraordinarily low doses. Success has been found in four case reports of patients using low dose THCA (0.1-1 mg/kg/day or 0.01% to 0.1% body weight) in conjunction with conventional antiepileptic drugs and full spectrum cannabis. This contrasts with Epidiolex, a pure CBD sublingual spray used for treating epilepsy which is dosed from 5 mg/kg/day to 25 mg/kg/day, making the doses of THCA just mentioned, 10-100 times lower. Increased doses of THCA tend not to improve efficacy. In one of the cases, symptoms and seizure activity worsened after increasing the THCA dose. The terpene, linalool, also contributed significantly to the antiepileptic effect.[131]

4. **Neuroprotection**: THCA possesses neuroprotective properties that could be useful in the treatment of neurodegenerative diseases.[132] THCA was found to improve cognition in one anecdotal report of a patient with Alzheimer's disease while allowing for other medication-use reduction.[131]
5. **Other Possible Medicinal Uses**: Supported by anecdotal reports include insomnia, muscle spasms and pain (irritable bowel syndrome and arthritis), however, pre-clinical and clinical trials still need to be performed.

Chapter 9 New Health Options in Cannabinoids and Terpenes
(Amanda McKinney, MD)

Varin Cannabinoids (THCV, CBDV and others)

The varinolic cannabinoids are considered rare but are now emerging as new targets of selective breeding. None of the various varina from hemp are scheduled as controlled substances, nor are they analogues of any such substances. Varins contain two fewer carbon atoms than their non-varin counterparts (CBD and THC), making these cannabinoids fundamentally different on a molecular level. They therefore have different physiological effects due to different binding in the endocannabinoid system. Two of the varins, CBDV and THCV, have been shown to have medicinal properties.

Cannabidivarin (CBDV)

Medical Uses

1. **Dermatologic**: Recent studies indicate CBDV may help dry skin syndrome as well as acne. Researchers also found that CBDV may reduce allergic inflammation, atopic dermatitis, acne and seborrhea (a.k.a. dandruff).[113]
2. **Seizures/Epilepsy**: Anticonvulsant (anti-seizure) properties of CBDV were reported by suppressing an epilepsy gene providing evidence of the entourage effect as well as the importance of unique ratios and formulations.[133,134] A human trial to treat epilepsy with CBDV is currently being conducted and GW Pharmaceuticals, maker of the first FDA-approved epilepsy CBD drug (Epidolex) is now also developing a CBDV-based drug for epilepsy, GPW42006.
3. **Nausea**: Like THC, CBDV may have therapeutic potential in reducing nausea. CBDV is an inverse agonist at the CB1 receptor. Despite this, it's pharmacology is not characteristic of an inverse agonist at CB1 as CBDV has been shown to to have antiemetic effects like a CB1 agonist but without psychoactivity.[135]
4. **Neurological**: CBDV is currently being investigated as a treatment for symptoms associated with autism spectrum disorder such as repetitive behaviors, cognitive challenges and issues with communication and social functioning.[136] In a murine model, CBDV was also found to reduce or alleviate symptoms associated with the neurodevelopmental disorder, Rett syndrome.[137] CBDV appears to be applicable to both forms of this disease, genetically determined and chemically-induced. CBDV was also found to reverse memory deficits in mice that have the same genetic defect that causes Rett syndrome in humans although the reversal was temporary.[138]
5. **Muscular Dystrophy**: CBDV may also have utility in the treatment of **Duchenne muscular dystrophy (DMD)**. A recently published study suggested that CBDV

could help improve muscle quality and locomotion and help slow muscle degeneration by reducing inflammation.[139]

Tetrahydrocannabivarin (THCV)

THCV is derived from cannabigerovarin acid (CBGVA), one of the two primary cannabinoid precursors, the other being CBGA. Enzymes convert CBGVA to THCVA, which is decarboxylated to the neutral compound, THCV, when exposed to heat or light. THCV is typically found in very small amounts in cannabis flowers, though breeders have worked to develop strains with higher concentrations. THCV binds to both CB1 and CB2 receptors. In rats, it has been shown to be an inverse agonist at the CB1 receptor, blocking the effects of THC at low doses, but stimulating CB1 at higher doses. THCV is a potent partial agonist at CB2.[140]

THCV is considered to have approximately 25% of the psychoactivity as THC,[141] with a faster onset[142] and shorter duration. However, its psychoactive potential is complex and largely dependent upon dosing.[142] At low doses, THCV acts as a **neutral antagonist** at CB1 receptors;[143] where THC activates psychotropic effects, and may inhibit the intoxication associated with THC.[144] Because only trace amounts of THCV are found in most cultivars, a consumer is unlikely to experience any of its inhibiting effects in terms of THC intoxication.

Medical Uses

1. **Anti-Inflammatory**: THCV has been shown to reduce inflammation and pain related to inflammation in mice. This is partially mediated through CB1 activation but primarily through CB2 receptor activation.[145]
2. **Acne**: THCV also has been found to suppress lipid synthesis in the sebaceous glands, assisting acne sufferers whose condition is triggered by excessive oil production. Of all of the phytocannabinoids examined, THCV showed the most promise of becoming a "highly efficient, novel anti-acne agent." [98]
3. **Neuroprotection**: A 2011 study on rats found that THCV's ability to activate CB2 receptors while being a neutral agonist at low doses at the CB1 receptor, and its antioxidant properties, imbue the cannabinoid with neuroprotective properties. Thus, it may potentially be a useful treatment for Parkinson's disease by halting disease progression and alleviating associated symptoms.[146]
4. **Anticonvulsant**: THCV has also been shown to reduce seizure activity in rats.[147]
5. **Diabetes and Glucose Regulation**: Animal studies have shown that THCV has the potential to regulate glucose levels, which could be helpful in treating diabetes. A clinical trial that evaluated the effects of THCV and CBD on 62

subjects with Type 2 diabetes found that THCV has potential to treat symptoms of the disease by modulating glucose activity.[148]

6. **Bone Health**: Through its activity at CB2 receptors in the bone marrow, THCV stimulates bone growth making it potentially useful for treating osteoporosis, fractures and other bone-related conditions.[149]

7. **Weight Loss/Appetite Suppressant**: THCV is often associated with appetite suppressing qualities. However, no clinical trials have pointed to conclusive evidence that THCV, alone or in conjunction with other cannabinoids, aids in appetite suppression or weight loss. In a murine model, THCV improved glucose tolerance and insulin resistance but did not impact weight gain or food intake.[150]

Terpenes

Terpenes are naturally occurring hydrocarbons made of isoprene units ($C_{10}H_{16}$). Through the process of steam distillation, plant material (leaves, roots, flowers, etc.) releases aromatic oils (essential oils) made up of a variety of terpenes. The constituent terpenes of any essential oil are determined by the plant from which they are derived and many are critical as functional defense mechanisms against herbivores and pests. Like the cannabinoids, terpenes have properties that contribute to a plant's medicinal value. While terpenes give fruits, flowers, vegetables and spices their pleasant odors, these molecules also have anti-cancer, anti-inflammatory, anti-anxiety, sleep-inducing and mood-boosting therapeutic properties.

Classification	Isoprene Units	Carbon Atoms
Monoterpenes	2	C10
Sesquiterpenes	3	C15
Diterpenes	4	C20
Sesterterpenes	5	C25
Triterpenes	6	C30

(Credit: Dr. Amanda McKinney)

Each cannabis strain has its own terpene profile creating distinct aromas and flavors. Preservation of terpenes in cannabis at harvest is an important task, because the cultivators want to preserve the best flavor and extend the shelf life. Therefore, cannabis cultivators often choose early morning hours to harvest and sometimes even flash freeze crops to conserve these terpenes.

To further safeguard these special compounds, that are highly sensitive to heat and humidity, cultivators and processors must carefully control environmental conditions to avoid degrading or vaporizing the natural terpenes. Terpenes are affected by the slightest changes in conditions, like wind, sun exposure, mechanical versus manual harvesting, handling and storing.

Terpenes can either be hemp derived or synthetic and can be added into hemp extracts to enhance benefits. There are over 50,000 terpenes that are naturally occurring, but researchers are also making their own terpenes in the lab. This class of compounds has been linked to many pharmaceutical benefits. Terpenes work together with cannabinoids and other plant compounds through the entourage effect. This symbiotic interplay in cannabis has been attributed to improvement of therapeutic effects, because, once again, the whole plant is greater than the sum of the parts.

The table below provides information about some of the most common and best studied terpenes.

Table 6

Terpene	Description	Also Found In	Medicinal Properties
Pinene	Pinene confers the pine tree its primary fragrance. It's often used in insecticides. The two forms of pinene are alpha-pinene and beta-pinene. Alpha-pinene is more common in cannabis and the most abundant terpenoid found in nature.	Pine trees/conifers Dill Basil Rosemary Parsley Pine nuts Lime Orange peel	Anti-inflammatory Anti-cancer Anti-allergy Anti-arthritis Anti-microbial Anti-depressant Bronchodilator Neuroprotective Anti-anxiety
Linalool	Linalool is found in a variety of spices and flowering plants, as	Lavender Frankincense	Respiratory Anti-inflammatory Anti-

	well as some fungi. It's commonly used as a scent, flavoring agent, and in pesticides. Linalool is safe and non-toxic to humans and animals..[151]	Mint Birch Rosewood Laurel Sweet basil Cinnamon Coriander Clove Lemon Mandarin orange	microbial Anti-inflammatory Neurological (Alzheimer's) Sedative Anti-anxiety
Beta-Caryophyllene	Beta-Caryophyllene (BCP) is found extensively in cannabis conferring "herbal spiciness with hints of wood". BCP is unique in that it binds CB2 receptors after consumption.	Black pepper Cinnamon Hops Allspice Fig Clove Basil Ylang ylang Rosemary Black caraway Hops	Neuroprotective Anti-inflammatory Anti-cancer Sleep Pain Diabetes Anti-anxiety Anti-depression
Myrcene	Myrcene, or beta-myrcene, is a monoterpene and found in numerous plants and fruits. Myrcene has "earthy, musky notes, resembling cloves and a fruity, red grape-like aroma". While myrcene is present in many plants, commercial production comes from beta-pinene.	Ylang-ylang Bay Parsley Wild thyme Lemongrass Hops Cardamom Mango fruit	Anti-inflammatory Anti-tumor Sedative Anti-oxidant
Limonene	Limonene confers citrus fragrance, primarily lemon fragrance, to citrus fruits and also many varieties of cannabis. Along with myrcene, the limonene is one of the most abundant terpenes to occur in cannabis.	Lemon Orange Lime Grapefruit Mint Juniper Rosemary Pine Fennel	Anti-anxiety Antioxidant Anti-inflammatory Analgesic Diabetes Anti-cancer Anti-bacterial

Nerolidol	Nerolidol is present in the essential oil of many plants including lavender and jasmine. It is also referred to as peruviol and penetrol. Nerolidol "possesses a floral or woody aroma reminiscent of fresh tree bark". There are two isomers of nerolidol, cis-nerolidol and trans-nerolidol.	Lavender Jasmine Mexican Orchids (Brassavola nodosa) Orange blossom (neroli) Tea tree oil Ginger	Sedative Anti-anxiety Anti-oxidant Anti-cancer Anti-bacterial Anti-fungal Dermatological
Citronellol	Citronellol confers a "fresh, floral-citrus aroma "and is found in rose and other essential oils. Citronellol, as citronella oil, commonly used as an effective mosquito repellent. It's also used in perfumes and beauty products.	Rose Lemongrass plant (Citronella oil)	Anti-inflammatory Anti-tumor Blood pressure lowering
Eucalyptol	Eucalyptol is a monoterpenoid with a "fresh, minty scent and a spicy yet cooling taste". Eucalyptol is also known as cineol. While eucalyptol can be a culinary ingredient in low doses, the terpene is toxic in high doses, adversely affecting the respiratory tract, nervous system, and reproductive system.	Eucalyptus sweet basil Rosemary Sage Bay leaves Camphor laurel Tea tree	Ant-icancer Respiratory Anti-inflammatory Cognitive function
Humulene	Humulene, also known as alpha-humulene, is a monocyclic sesquiterpene. Humulene is a key constituent of the essential oil from hops. Humulene, along with caryophyllene and myrcene, is one of the most common terpenes to occur in cannabis, sometimes as high as 40 percent.	Marsh elders Tobacco Sage	Anti-inflammatory: Anti-allergy Antitumor

Isopulegol	Isopulegol is known for its "potent minty aroma and taste". Isopulegol is the chemical precursor to menthol.	Lemongrass Geranium Ginseng Coriander (cilantro) Hops	Anti-inflammatory Gastroprotective Anti-viral Anti-anxiety Anti-convulsant

(Table Credit: Dr. Amanda McKinney)

Cannabis Roots

While the primary focus of medical cannabis is on the cannabinoids and terpenes produced by the trichomes, small hair-like glands of the cannabis flower or bud, the cannabis roots also have significant medicinal properties worth mentioning briefly.

Since 77 CE, when the Roman naturalist Pliny the Elder documented the medical uses of cannabis roots, herbalists and other practitioners have used them to treat a panoply of conditions, including fever, infections, gout, arthritis, joint pain and postpartum haemorrhage.[152]

The medical value of cannabis roots is due to several chemical constituents. The triterpenoids found in the roots, friedelin and its derivate epifriedelinol, offer significant anti-inflammatory activity. Friedelin also has antipyretic (fever-reducing) properties and appears to work as well as paracetamol, a commonly used antipyretic, at lowering internal body temperature. Friedelin also appears to have estrogenic activity and has been used as an aphrodisiac, for stimulating the onset of menstruation and to manage menopausal symptoms. It also has **cytotoxic** activity against breast, cervical and ovarian cancer cells.[153,154]

Cannabis roots also contain monoterpenes, such as carvone and dihydrocarvone (found in spearmint), and sterols (B-sitosterol, campesterol and P-hydroxy-trans-cinnamamide) which provide analgesic (pain relieving) effects. **Decoctions** and the fresh juice of cannabis roots have been used topically to relieve the pain of arthritis, gout and burns.[155]

Lignans are a class of polyphenol and estrogen precursor molecules that have antioxidant, antiviral, anti-diabetic, anti-tumor and anti-obesity properties. Research reveals that, because lignans are considered phytoestrogens and have anti-cancer properties, they are useful in breast cancer prevention as well as treatment for some hormone-dependent cancers.[156] Unique to cannabis is a group of compounds within the lignanamide class called cannabisins (types A-, B-, C-, D-, E-, F- and G), which don't exist anywhere else in the plant kingdom and are being studied for their anti-cancer properties.[157]

It is important to note, because cannabis roots can **bioaccumulate** pollutants from the soil such as iron, chromium and cadmium, they can be used for **phytoremediation** of the soil. These heavy metals are toxic to humans. Therefore, cannabis roots should only be used medically when the source of the roots has been scrupulously examined.

Delivery and Dosage of Medical Cannabis

Before modern, synthetic chemistry in the 20th Century, humans relied on pharmacognosy, the study and use of medicinal plants. As science evolved, it led to some amazing discoveries. Willow bark has been used for hundreds of years as an antipyretic and analgesic. Modern chemistry identified the "active component", salicylic acid, from which aspirin is now made. This led to the discovery of prostaglandins and an understanding of inflammatory processes in the human body. Cannabis is no exception. Without identification of THC and, later, CBD from cannabis, the endocannabinoid system likely would never have been identified. Humans would have continued to use cannabis medically, however, understanding of how cannabis works and the myriad ways in which it can be used medically would not have been discovered.

While modern science has led us to a better understanding of our own body chemistry and physiology, it has also led to reductionism, which can be described as *"divide and conquer, and it is rooted in the assumption that complex problems are solvable by dividing them into smaller, simpler and thus more tractable units."*[158]

The application of reductionism in modern biomedical research and practice has resulted in some utterly amazing feats, however, reductionism alone is not only inadequate but has created some progress-inhibiting collateral damage. Reducing complex biological or medical phenomena into their individual components improves the chances of identifying a single cause in order to devise a cure. However, this process also effectively eliminates the "greater than the sum of its parts" value of whole plants and the accompanying entourage effects.

The latter emphasis is in contrast to current drug discovery processes, which focus on one key receptor, pathway, process or gene believed to be the root cause of a disease; then developing a single-compound drug to address it. While the resulting drugs can be powerful, they can also have high levels of toxicity (manifesting as unwanted side effects). Additionally, there is rarely one specific mechanism that results in a disease or disorder. A multi-faceted, polymolecular approach to treatment is often required for complex, chronic diseases in order to not only be effective, but also to avoid the development of disease resistance. The concept of disease resistance not only applies to bacteria and viruses exposed to antimicrobial drugs but also to cancers and other chronic diseases. The entourage effect explains the efficacy of low doses of active constituents in combined, whole-plant formulations.

Because of their safety and efficacy, traditional plant (herbal) medicines consisting of plant-derived substances with minimal or no industrial processing are getting significant attention in global health debates. However, pharmacognosy also offers significant benefit to people who don't have access to modern, synthetic drugs. Plants that have medicinal value, can be grown easily, and do not require significant processing can provide much needed treatment for billions of people in the developing world as well as to those who have not had satisfactory outcomes in the prevailing Western medical system. Cannabis is highly amenable to this approach as it grows well in a variety of climates, and it is easy to use. In this section, delivery options and dosing will be discussed.

Cannabis Categories

Human intervention has produced many varieties of cannabis within the species by selecting and breeding plants to either produce plants with more fiber (hemp) or plants with greater THC or other cannabinoid content for medicinal or recreational use. There are four categories of cannabis classified based on their use and levels of chemical constituents.

Categories of Cannabis

Type IV: Cannabis CBG Dominant

Cannabis **cultivars** high in CBG are referred to as Type IV.

Type III: Novice & Medical (CBD Dominant)

Low THC cultivars. Primarily used by medical cannabis patients and new users.

Type II: Functional High/Daytime Use (Mixed-Ratio CBD: THC)

Mixed CBD: THC Ratio Cultivars; usually this gives the user a "functional high". Primarily used by medical cannabis patients for whom THC offers relevant medical benefits and/or for whom intoxication is manageable.

Type I: Functions Affected/Seasoned User (THC Dominant)

Cultivars containing at least 20% THC; these are used recreationally and medically. Individuals at elevated risk for psychosis and/or cardiovascular events should avoid THC, generally and at high doses, specifically.

A variety of products in dispensaries are labeled with a CBD: THC ratio (i.e., 18:1, 4:1, and 1:1) so that patients can choose a product that suits their needs. Many **strains** will also have a "% THC" designation helping to determine the category.

CBD:THC Ratio	Use
18:1	For novice or medical use. Minimal to no psychoactivity.
8:1	For novice or medical use. Minimal to no psychoactivity.
4:1	Considered mid-range. To avoid psychoactivity, it is best used by an individual with some tolerance to THC.
2:1	For individuals who can tolerate THC. Can cause psychoactivity at moderate doses.
1:1	For individuals who can tolerate THC. Can cause psychoactivity at moderate doses.

(Table Credit: Dr. Amanda McKinney)

Another common classification is by indica: sativa ratio, indicating the species (*Cannabis indica* vs *Cannabis sativa*). According to the popular literature, indica strains are considered to be sedating while sativa strains are thought to be invigorating, providing uplifting cerebral effects. The belief that indicas and sativas deliver distinct effects is very deeply rooted in the broader cannabis culture. However, research suggests that there is little evidence indicating indicas and sativas, as classes, consistently reveal chemical profiles which would make indicas sedating and sativas uplifting. According to Ethan Russo, a neurologist and cannabis researcher, "The clinical effects of the cannabis chemovar have nothing to do with whether the plant is tall and sparse vs. short and bushy, or whether the leaflets are narrow or broad." Rather, the effects of cannabis are dependent upon the strain's cannabinoid and terpene constituents, referred to as Total Cannabinoid Profile (TCP).[159]

The purpose of recreational cannabis use is to achieve an altered state, and so strains used are typically high THC and low CBD. Heat must always be applied (or have been applied in processing) in order to decarboxylate the THCA to THC in order to get the desired effect. Conversely, the purpose of medical cannabis is to get well or better manage symptoms. Strains used are high in all cannabinoids (CBD, CBDA, THCA, THC, CBG, CBC, CBN, CBDV, THCV). Because being altered is either not the desired endpoint or is unwanted, applying heat is not always required and is, at times, contraindicated.

Different strains of cannabis offer different TCPs and utilizing different strains can increase the TCP for patients. Additionally, when strains are higher in the non-psychotropic cannabinoids such as CBD, a patient can use these strains in the daytime hours to avoid mental alteration and use higher THC strains at bedtime to assist with sleep.

Evidence for the benefits and effectiveness of medical cannabis for a variety of medical disorders exists; however, there is a dearth of randomized and placebo controlled trials, which are considered the "gold standard" in determining treatment effectiveness. Despite this, medical cannabis can and should be utilized due to its safety and effectiveness in anecdotal, survey, pre-clinica, and observational studies.

Likewise, due to the paucity of clinical trials in which doses of specific cannabinoids and terpenes are studied, the focus of treating patients with medical cannabis is not on dose, per se, but rather on creating a regimen that provides a high TCP while monitoring for disease regression (symptom relief, improvement in laboratory and radiologic evaluations, etc.). Regimens should include a variety of strains delivered in a variety of ways. Good sources of information about the terpene and cannabinoid profiles of cannabis strains can be found at _Leafly.com_ and _Weedmaps.com_.

The goals when starting treatment are to find a tolerable regimen and provide initial symptom relief. As treatment advances, the goals become expanding the TCP and deepening symptom relief. Advanced treatment requires shifting the TCP to avoid tolerance and resistance while simultaneously restoring health and homeostasis.[160]

By far the most common way cannabis has been consumed historically, and still is consumed today, is by smoking a cannabis cigarette or "joint" (also now called a pre-roll when it is prepared commercially) However, there are a plethora of other ways that cannabis can be consumed, all offering benefits and drawbacks depending on the speed of onset desired, the length of effect needed, the cannabinoid profile being sought, social situation, and degree of alteration desired.

Delivery Methods Table

Delivery Method	Description	Onset	Duration	Pros	Cons

Smoking	Dried (cured) cannabis flower or bud is packed into a pipe, water pipe (bong) or rolling paper (joint or pre-roll). A flame is used to combust while the user inhales.	1-5 minutes	1-6 hours	Instant Relief Inexpensive Minimally processed Dosing can be controlled	Respiratory Irritation Socially inappropriate odor
Vaporization or Vaping	Dried (cured) cannabis flower or bud is packed into a vaporizer where it is heated but not combusted while the user inhales.	1-5 minutes	1-6 hours	Instant Relief Minimally processed Less respiratory irritation than smoking Less odor	Vaporizers are expensive and need recharging. Devices take time to heat up
Edibles	Raw or decarboxylated cannabis is added to an array of products like cookies, gummies, lollipops, and chocolate bars.	1-2 hours	4-12 hours	Commercially prepared products have fairly precise dosing. Long lasting relief Easy to consume	Slow onset can lead to overconsumption. Must be kept hidden away from children and pets.
Tinctures or Sublingual Sprays	Extracted cannabinoids in alcohol, glycerine or oil. They are	10-45 minutes	2-8 hours	Easy to use with a mild taste Easy to	Alcohol based tinctures can irritate the mouth

	dropped or sprayed under the tongue and held there to allow absorption through the oral mucosa.			control doses especially for low doses Preferred method for children	Can be expensive, especially at higher doses.
Transdermal Patches	Commercially prepared patch applied to inside of wrist, top of foot or ankle.	Variable	Variable	Easy to use with a variety of dosing options Avoids first pass metabolism in the liver	Can be expensive and hard to find Adhesive can cause skin irritation/react ion
Suppositorie s	Prepared suppositories are inserted in the rectum. Syringes for rectal use are also available	Variable but typically rapid	Variable but typically long	Great alternative to edibles Avoids first pass metabolism in the liver Best absorption Good option for children	Difficult to administer Must be refrigerated
Topicals	Can come as a salve, ointment, lotion, or spray.	Variable	Variable	No "high" Treats skin issues well and provides localized pain relief.	Variable efficacy Local treatment only. No systemic effects.

Consuming Fresh (Raw) Cannabis	Buds and leaves can be juiced, added to smoothies or put in capsules.	2-45 minutes	2-8 hours	Preserves cannabinoids in their acidic forms (like THCA) which offer medicinal properties lost with other forms of delivery.	Requires large amounts of cannabis. (15 leaves plus 1-2 large buds daily...2-4"). Unpleasant "ganja" taste.
Beverages	Commercially prepared cannabis-infused teas, juices, smoothies and sodas. Can also be made at home.	2-45 minutes	2-8 hours	Easy to use and convenient.	Controlling dosing is difficult. Prone to overconsumption.
Dabbing	A "dab" is a cannabis concentrate (hash oil, budder, shatter, wax, etc.) that is heated to a high temperature and inhaled.	1-5 minutes	1-6 hours	Useful for urgent situations. Cost effective for patients who need high-THC	Requires a difficult to use delivery device and often a butane torch which can lead to burns. Higher risk of chemical contamination (solvents) in the concentrate. Risk of overconsumption is high.

(Table Credit: Dr. Amanda McKinney)

Notes on Delivery

Tinctures are a good delivery method to start with given the ability to titrate doses. While tinctures have a long duration of effect, they have a slow onset; patience must be exercised. Vaporization or smoking can be added for quick relief while the patient is waiting for tinctures or edibles to take effect. Raw cannabis (carboxylated) provides the acid form of many cannabinoids (THCA, CBDA, THCVA, etc.), which have medicinal properties of their own in addition to the terpenes. Consuming raw cannabis plants rarely, if ever, causes psychotropic effects and is typically added in the intermediate treatment phase after patients are more comfortable using cannabis. When proceeding to advanced treatment, raw cacao powder, curcumin/turmeric and/or cayenne pepper or other non-cannabis phytocannabinoids, terpenes, spices, etc. can be added to augment treatment by activating the body's endocannabinoid, vanilloid, and immune systems.

Dosing

Like other traditional, herbal medicines, cannabis (especially in whole-plant forms) does not have specific doses. This makes many providers uncomfortable given the standard training in pharmacology that Western medical practitioners receive. Cannabis, unlike most pharmaceuticals, is both effective within a wide range of doses and incredibly safe. However, it is critical that medical cannabis providers spend time learning how to find the correct dose of cannabis for their patients, as it is the most critical factor for success.

Pharmaceuticals are prescribed at specific doses and frequencies based on body weight, age and medical condition. The same cannot be said of medical cannabis. Some patients require only very low doses (e.g. 1 'hit' on a joint or vaporizer), while others require higher doses (e.g. a large joint or a potent edible) to achieve the desired outcome. Anecdotally, practitioners have noticed that patients which use smaller cannabis doses often have more efficacious and sustainable results. Some individuals even display a "threshold dose" of cannabis below which benefits gradually increase over time, and above which tolerance, diminishing benefits and increased side effects are experienced. This exemplifies a biphasic dose-response relationship. It is important for both clinicians and patients to note that more is not always better. In cases where a dose or regimen of medical cannabis is not deemed effective, it is a mistake to assume a higher dose is required when the opposite may be true. This is more commonly seen with THC than with CBD. This principle is illustrated in the graph below.

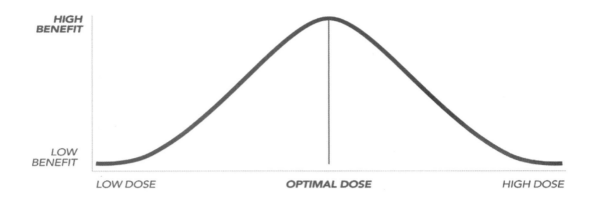

LOW DOSE   OPTIMAL DOSE   HIGH DOSE

Graph courtesy of Dr. Dustin Sulak and Healer.com **Healer**

This phenomenon occurs because low levels or acute administration of phytocannabinoids cause an increase in endocannabinoid production, functionally upregulating the ECS and endocannabinoid tone. Conversely, with long-term and higher doses, down regulation occurs through internalization of the endocannabinoid receptor. In this situation, the cannabinoid receptor is pulled into the cell, so that it can no longer be available for binding and activation.

Dr. Dustin Sulak, who has extensive clinical experience with medical cannabis, has devised a sensitization protocol to "help new users find their optimal dose in 4 days", while helping current users "reset the sensitivity of their endocannabinoid system and achieve much better results with a lower dosage in only 6 days." According to Dr. Sulak, "Afterwards, 90% of patients who try the sensitization protocol are able to decrease their dosage while improving benefits and the average dosage reduction is 56%. This reduction not only improves benefits and reduces side effects – it saves patients a lot of money, and potentially makes more cannabis available for those with limited access."

Dr. Sulak's full sensitization protocol can be found at

https://healer.com/programs/sensitization-protocol/.

Strategies for Avoiding Alteration

Using cannabis, particularly high THC products, 3-5 hours before sleep is advisable in order to prevent situations in which the user must drive or perform executive functions. Other strategies that can be implemented when alteration is not desired include:

1. **Utilizing Low THC Strains**: CBD can counteract the effects of THC, so high CBD strains are commonly used for medical therapy. However, eliminating THC completely is not advisable as THC, CBD, other cannabinoids and terpenes all add to the 'entourage effect'.
2. **Finding Ways to Block the Effects of THC**: CBD is the most useful and readily compound for finding ways to block the effects of THC..
3. **Preventing Decarboxylation of THCA to THC**: The body is unable to decarboxylate THCA to THC, but the body can decarboxylate CBDA to CBD. Therefore, using raw cannabis (with no heat application), can be an effective way of providing a variety of cannabinoids without alteration.

THC Over-Intoxication

There is no lethal dose for cannabis but overconsumption, consuming a dose can result in over-intoxication, unpleasant and unwanted side effects, including panic, paranoia, nausea, vomiting, dysphoria, emotional distress and physical discomfort like elevated heart rate. Over-intoxication is most common after ingesting cannabis, because delta-9-THC is converted by liver enzymes in the digestive system to 11-hydroxy-THC, a far more potent activator of the CB1 receptor, and therefore an intoxicant.[161]

The symptoms of THC over-intoxication can last a few minutes to a few hours, depending on the amount and delivery method of the cannabis consumption. Those affected should be encouraged to find a distraction, such as listening to calming music or watching a lighthearted TV program, while waiting for the symptoms to subside. Hydration with water can help alleviate the frequently accompanying dry mouth. The vast majority of the time, these supportive measures can quell moderate cases of over-intoxication at home. Very rarely is emergency care required and is typically reserved for individuals exhibiting signs of psychosis or cardiovascular distress (chest pain, shortness of breath, facial drooping, arm or leg weakness, etc). If CBD isolate is available, consuming it can counteract the effects of the THC, hastening the alleviation of symptoms. The terpene limonene in lemon zest and chamomile tea can also help.

Levels of Evidence: Assessing the Data

Before diving into the specific disease-related benefits of medical cannabis, it is worth taking some time to examine levels of evidence and how therapeutic effectiveness is determined in Western medicine as well as to evaluate ideas from other traditions about how disease develops and how we can return to health.

The human body can heal itself through nature, *vis medicatrix naturae,* and medical cannabis, especially when used in whole-plant or full-spectrum forms, can provoke this innate capacity. By embracing both the art and science of medical cannabis, individuals can take back responsibility and control for their personal health. While other traditions such as Ayurveda and Traditional Chinese Medicine utilize more holistic and systems based approaches, modern Western medicine has shifted away from holistic, whole-person care toward an allopathic medical model that is more a 'disease-care system' rather than a 'health-care system'. In this model, symptoms of disease are addressed with pharmaceuticals and procedures rather than addressing the actual cause of disease, which might be a problem of poor nutrition or, as we have learned, can result from an imbalance or disturbance of delicate and complicated systems, like the endocannabinoid system.

This allopathic model takes a reductionist approach. Reductionism can be described as *"divide and conquer, and it is rooted in the assumption that complex problems are solvable by dividing them into smaller, simpler, and thus more tractable units. Because the processes are 'reduced' into more basic units, this approach has been termed 'reductionism' and has been the predominant paradigm of science over the past two centuries. Reductionism pervades the medical sciences and affects the way we diagnose, treat and prevent diseases. While it has been responsible for tremendous successes in modern medicine, there are limits to reductionism, and an alternative explanation must be sought to complement it."*[158]

This system of medicine also removes the locus of control over disease from the patient and puts control in the hands of the medical practitioner and the pharmaceutical and insurance industries. Because of negative cultural perceptions, legal regulations and lack of education about medical cannabis in the Western allopathic model, patients lack access and good sound advice about how to use medical cannabis to achieve the desired outcome.

Complicating matters is the way that "efficacy" is determined in medicine. In Western medicine, the practice is considered evidence-based medicine (EBM). According to Sheridan and Julian:

> *"Evidence-based medicine has a long history, but was revived in the early 1990s by a campaign mounted by a movement that took its name. The EBM movement focused attention on the need for greater objectivity in medical decision-making and led to the Cochrane Collaboration, which provides reviews of evidence on the basis of comparative research. Important limitations of EBM's effect on medicine have also emerged. Failure to acknowledge the limitations of clinical trials and systematic*

reviews has limited their applicability to individual patients' circumstances.
***An almost exclusive focus on drugs and devices has left vast areas
of health care in an evidence vacuum.*** *An overdependence on
commissions for its research may have limited its independence in
selecting what it investigates. EBM needs to widen its scope beyond drugs
and devices to address many areas that often lack evidence at present,
notably, health policy, management, and reforms.*"[162]

Without a doubt, medical cannabis falls into one of these *"vast areas of healthcare in an
evidence vacuum."* While there are some studies on medical cannabis and the number
continues to grow, clinical studies are reductionist in nature and incapable of evaluating
all the nuances and potential benefits of medical cannabis on an individual level.

There is clear evidence for a number of disorders for which medical cannabis is of
benefit. For others, while the evidence may be convoluted or mixed, absence of
evidence is not evidence of absence. In other words, just because a particular benefit
has not yet been proven, it may still exist. From a clinician's standpoint, the great value
of medical cannabis is that there is typically no harm in trying it for conditions which
have been resistant to other treatments. Cannabis has such a high safety profile. While
there are still precautions that must be taken, there are very few absolute
contraindications for using medical cannabis.

Medical Cannabis and the Immune System

Our state of health or disease is an expression of our immune systems. Whether health
or disease is expressed is determined by the interactions between our bodies and our
environment as our inner world reflects our outer world. The relationships between
mind, body and our external environment are complex, but the primary purpose of the
push and pull is to maintain internal homeostasis required for survival. Our bodies have
the innate capacity to heal themselves (*vis medicatrix naturae*) and are constantly
working to do so. Natural ecosystems have the same capacity and are constantly
working to do the same, creating a continuously changing nature of the relationships
between humans and our environment.

While this perspective and relationship between our environment and our immunity is
often not acknowledged, particularly in Western, or allopathic medicine, it is critical that
this be acknowledged. Because people have neglected this perspective, there are now
critical levels of chronic disease in the U.S., including obesity, heart disease, diabetes
and cancer. By making this connection between the immune system function and the
environment writ large, there is an opportunity to help people heal.

.

Medical herbalist and author David Hoffmann created a model for four ecological interpretations of the human immune system's relationship with the world. His model, in summary, is that the immune system is an expression of the interface between the body and the environment and that all organisms and ecosystems are working to achieve homeostasis. This striving toward internal homeostasis mirrors the ecological homeostasis of the greater world. Just as more factors stress the planet, (e.g., pollution, overconsumption, climate change) the climate and physical environments must adjust to maintain planetary health. Likewise, the human individual faces new stressors from the adjusted climate and physical environment, to which it must now adapt to achieve internal homeostasis.[163] While these observations are absent from the Western allopathic medical education and model, more research is being done in the area of Planetary Health which is "the health of human civilization and the state of the natural systems on which it depends".[164]

When thinking about disease, disease processes and returning to a state of health, it is helpful to remember that medical practitioners are just the "middle person". The practitioner did not cause the disease, nor does the practitioner cure the patient of their disease. The body does it. The body reacts to external stimuli, such as diet, chemical exposures, psychosocial stressors, etc., in a way that often results in a disease process; too many cheeseburgers and milkshakes equals heart disease and/or Type 2 diabetes. Likewise, when the body rids itself of disease, it does so through a process of an engineered change in the environment which removes the offending agents causing disease, allowing the body's own immune system to function properly and to do its job (removing cheeseburgers and milkshakes from the diet and adding kale and legumes). Practitioners are there to provide advice about what is causing the disease, and what might help the patient to address it. When lifestyle changes are not enough, practitioners can prescribe medications. Those practitioners who are knowledgeable about plant medicines, like medical cannabis, **adaptogens** and other herbal formulations, have an advantage over practitioners who rely solely on synthetic pharmaceuticals as these plant medicines can often help achieve homeostasis unlike pharmaceuticals, which take a more purely reductionist approach to disease treatment.

Endocannabinoid System and Immunity

The endocannabinoid system exhibits complex regulatory effects on the immune system which are beyond the scope of this chapter. However, immune cells have multiple ECS characteristics that include expression of both CB1 and CB2 receptors, endocannabinoid secretion, and the ability to both transport and break down cannabnioids.[165] Therefore, exogenous cannabinoids can be used to regulate the immune system as well.

Diseases of Immunity

Nearly all diseases and conditions are, to some degree, disruptions of immunity and/or induced by inflammation regulated by the immune system. Diseases and disorders of disrupted immunity, for which there are varied levels of evidence for the benefits of medical cannabis, are included below.

Gastrointestinal Disorders[166]

1. Inflammatory Bowel Disease (Crohn's/Ulcerative Colitis)[167]
2. Irritable Bowel Syndrome [170]
3. Autoimmune Hepatitis [168]
4. Non-alcoholic Fatty Liver Disease (NAFLD) [169]
5. Hepatitis C [170]

Disorders of the Urinary Bladder[171]

1. Overactive Bladder (OAB) [172]
2. Interstitial Cystitis (IC) or Painful Bladder Syndrome (PBS) [173]

Skin and Dermatologic Disorders [174]

1. Acne
2. Alopecia areata, effluvium
3. Dermatitis
4. Dry Skin
5. Hirsutism
6. Infection- Methicillin-resistant Staphylococcus aureus (MRSA)[175]
7. Pain and Pruritus[176]
8. Psoriasis

Palliative Care[167,177]

1. Anorexia and weight loss
2. Chemotherapy-induced nausea and vomiting (CINV)
3. Palliative Care Pain Management
4. HIV/AIDS[178]

Disorders of the Endocrine System

1. Type 2 Diabetes (glucose management and prevention/treatment of diabetic neuropathy) [148, 179-181]

Opioid Addiction [182,183]

1. Pain Management
2. Opioid Use Reduction

Chronic Pain [184]
1. Fibromyalgia [185,186]
2. Rheumatoid Arthritis [187]
3. Migraine [188]

Sleep Disorders
1. Insomnia [189]
2. Sleep Apnea [190]

Neurological (Neurodegenerative, Neuropsychiatric, and Movement Disorders) [191]

1. Neuroprotection after Stroke [192,193]
2. Amyotrophic Lateral Sclerosis (ALS) [194]
3. Alzheimer's Disease [195-199]
4. Anxiety [200]
5. Huntington Disease [201]
6. Parkinson's Disease [202-205]
7. Post-Traumatic Stress Disorder(PTSD) [206]
8. Dystonia [207]
9. Tourette's Syndrome [208]
10. Multiple Sclerosis (spasticity) [209-213]
11. Seizures/Epilepsy [214-216]

Cancer

1. Gliomas/Brain Cancer [217-221]
2. Prostate Cancer [222,223]
3. Breast Cancer [224-230]
4. Lung Cancer [231]
5. Skin Cancer [232-234]
6. Lymphoma [235-237]
7. Pancreatic Cancer [238-244]
8. Liver Cancer [245-247]
9. Leukemia [251-253]

10. Bladder Cancer [254,255]
11. Thyroid cancer [256]
12. Endometrial Cancer [257,258]
13. Colon Cancer [259-262]
14. Prostate Cancer [263-265]

There are typically three types of cancer patients seeking medical cannabis as a treatment.

1. Those who are looking for symptom relief from the side effects of their cancer treatment.
2. Those who are looking for both symptom relief from the side effects of their cancer treatment AND who are using medical cannabis as an adjunct to their cancer treatment to help make it more effective.
3. Those who choose to forgo conventional treatment and use only medical cannabis and other alternative therapies to manage symptoms of cancer and treat their cancer as well.

The information provided in this chapter will help guide each of those patient types, and potentially their caregivers, to help them meet their goals with regard to their cancer and cancer treatment. However, generally speaking, patients who are using cannabis to ameliorate the symptoms and side effects of conventional treatment should use cannabis on the days of and following their conventional treatment. Cannabis has the potential to enhance the benefits of both chemotherapy and radiation as well as potentially protect from adverse side effects like neuropathy. This means that patients may be able to tolerate higher doses and longer courses of conventional treatment which could mean better chances of remission.

For individuals using high-dose cannabis as an adjunct to conventional treatment, they will typically need to titrate to higher doses (200 mg to 2000 mg of cannabinoids per day) over the course of 1-4 weeks. THC-heavy products should be used at bedtime and increased gradually. CBD-heavy products can be taken in the morning and the dose increases rapidly due to its tolerability. Effective CBD: THC ratios vary patient to patient and disease process to disease process. Medicine is both an art and a science. There is no one predetermined prescription. Each patient is different with different needs, social situations, disease processes, lifestyle behaviors and personalities that need to be factored into a medical professional's decision-making process and recommendations.

For those choosing to forgo conventional treatment, it is critical to respect their personal decision but also to assess their reasons. Often when people get a cancer diagnosis, it has a profound impact on their psyche. Most people know someone who has gone through cancer treatment or died from cancer, often after an unpleasant treatment course. This can lead some to deem conventional treatment as "not worth it" as it can lead to a significantly decreased quality of life. In some instances that may be so, but not in others. Therefore, it is important to ask some questions regarding their understanding of their prognosis with conventional treatment, what those treatments are and their potential side effects. Helping patients make choices that are not fear-based is one of the most impactful things one can do for them as a practitioner.

Medical cannabis should be used with caution in patients receiving immunotherapy treatments for their cancer. Immunotherapy uses the body's own immune system to target and destroy cancer cells. Because cannabis has many anti-inflammatory properties, there is some unpublished evidence that cannabis and other anti-inflammatory agents can inhibit the effectiveness of immunotherapy treatments. However, oncologists use anti-inflammatory drugs to help patients tolerate the side effects of the treatments. However, they are often used sparingly and in the lowest effective doses.

Because testicular cancers occur more frequently in heavy cannabis users, it is possible that cannabis could make certain types of cancer worse in certain dosages. It is clear that we don't know everything in relation to cancer and cannabis. It is important for those using cannabis, whether or not they are undergoing conventional treatment, to have their disease state monitored to determine if the cannabis is helping or hurting. Cancers that respond well to high dose cannabis appear to grow rapidly after the cannabis dose is reduced, discontinued or once the cancer becomes resistant to an unvaried, low-TCP regimen. Therefore, surveillance is recommended after any dose change or discontinuation or if symptoms return or worsen. Often patients need a TCP of 1000 mg to 2000 mg per day, which can be quite expensive. Therefore, it is critical that commercially-prepared cannabis products be tested for cannabinoid content.

Chapter 10 - Precautions and Potential Contraindications
(Amanda McKinney, MD)

Respiratory [266-272]

Smoking cannabis is associated with airway inflammation similar to that seen in tobacco smokers, which can result in chronic coughing, excess sputum production, wheezing, shortness of breath and an increased incidence of bronchitis and other respiratory infections. These symptoms are present in approximately 30% to 40% of those who smoke cannabis regularly.

There are at least 33 carcinogens released from the combustion of cannabis, such as polycyclic aromatic hydrocarbons, also found in grilled meat and cigarette smoke. Despite this, chronic cannabis smokers have an increased risk of cancers of the lung, oral cavity and larynx but only if they also smoke tobacco. Of 7 studies on the association between smoking cannabis, only one found any association of increased risk of head and neck cancer. Five studies found no association and one study actually found a decreased risk. Additionally, no evidence of long-term lung damage, like emphysema or COPD, was found.

Smoking one cannabis cigarette (joint) daily for ten years is equivalent to smoking a pack of 20 cigarettes per day for six months out of a lifetime. This level of cigarette smoking classifies an individual as a "never smoker", explaining the lack of association between casual cannabis use and lung cancer. However, it is also hypothesized that the antitumor effects of cannabis might also counteract the carcinogenic effects of the smoke, given that a 1975 study found THC could suppress lung cancer cell growth in vitro.

Cannabis use may, however, increase the risk of testicular cancer. Three studies on the subject reveal that for men smoking cannabis once a week or more, or for ten years or longer, there is an approximately 50% increased risk.

With respect to bronchitis and acute lung inflammation, smoking three to four joints per day equates to smoking one pack of 20 tobacco cigarettes per day. This may be because cannabis smoke is often inhaled more deeply and held up to four times longer than tobacco smoke. This results in more deposition of tar in the lungs, causing inflammation. This is exacerbated by the fact that joints are also unfiltered. Smoking cessation (tobacco or cannabis) typically results in resolution of respiratory symptoms. It has been noted that occasional, long-term cannabis smoking has no appreciable negative effects on long-term lung function, however, for those who smoke multiple joints every day, there is a potential risk of accelerated decline in lung function over an extended period (decades). Therefore, regular, heavy cannabis smoking should be avoided.

A viable alternative is inhaling cannabis vapor, or vaping, from the heating (but not combusting) of cannabis flower. This results in the same degree of cannabinoid delivery, but with significantly less carbon monoxide exposure and tar. A study of twenty regular, heavy cannabis smokers with respiratory symptoms who switched to vaping for one month revealed that 60% (12 of 20) experienced a significant improvement of respiratory symptoms. However, 40% still developed a respiratory illness during the trial period.

It is important to note that vapor can contain high concentrations of ammonia if fertilizers were not properly flushed from the plant at harvest. Likewise, waxes used for dabbing or oil concentrates used in vapor pens have been known to have high levels of ammonia, if they have not gone through proper quality assurance during the production process. The cases of acute and serious lung injury after vaping that have been touted in the news and in the medical literature are linked to ammonia. Therefore, it is critical that cannabis flowers and products be sourced from a reputable grower or processor, and that patients be trained to identify the smell of ammonia in their products so that tainted products can be discarded. In addition to ammonia, pesticides also pose a risk to consumers. Pesticide residues have been identified in some cannabis samples at up to a thousand times the legal limit. Because filters are not used, there is a possibility of significant pesticide exposure through cannabis smoking or vaping, which is concerning as using contaminated medical cannabis could exacerbate the condition for which patients are using it. States that have legalized recreational and/or medical marijuana are working to address these issues. For instance, all products that are to be sold to the public in Colorado must be tested for bacteria, mold, pesticide residues and for accuracy of dose in edibles.

Cardiovascular

Cannabis confers bidirectional effects on the cardiovascular system; meaning it can both increase and decrease heart rate and blood pressure. Usage at typical cannabis doses elevates heart rate while slightly decreasing blood pressure. Cannabinoids, particularly those that activate the CB2 receptor like CBD, dilate blood vessels which improves blood flow. Some animal studies even suggest that some cannabinoids have the potential to prevent or help ameliorate atherosclerosis (hardening of the arteries).[273] While high doses of THC can be deleterious in the cardiovascular system, ultra-low doses of THC have actually been shown to reduce heart attack-associated damage, preserving function of the heart muscle and enhancing more rapid healing.[274] Generally speaking, ultra-low and therapeutic doses of cannabis tend to protect the heart, while very high doses of THC, plant-derived and synthetic, have the potential for danger and damage, especially in patients with pre-existing heart conditions and/or elevated cardiovascular event risk.

After consuming a high THC-based product, increased heart rate and blood pressure are often experienced; a phenomenon which lasts typically for 5-10 minutes. This elevated blood pressure and heart rate are collectively responsible for the red, bloodshot eyes seen with cannabis use. But, they have also been implicated in cases of myocardial infarction (heart attack) in those with underlying cardiac disease (both diagnosed and undiagnosed). Therefore, those with known heart disease or who are at high risk of having undiagnosed cardiovascular disease (obesity, Type 2 diabetes, uncontrolled hypertension, etc.) should minimize THC use to the lowest possible effective doses.

With respect to stroke, a nationwide, population-based analysis found that recreational cannabis use is associated with a 17% increased risk of being hospitalized with a non-fatal, acute ischemic stroke for those who smoke cannabis at least once a week. This is compared to those who smoke tobacco (76% increased risk), used cocaine (32% increased risk) and used methamphetamine (221% increased risk).[275,276]

For both heart attack and stroke, there is a temporal relationship between cannabis use and these cardiovascular events, meaning the events occur during, or immediately after, use. However, this is complicated by the fact that cannabis is often used in combination with other drugs, such as alcohol or cocaine, as the risk of heart attack is increased by more than 20 times in the hour after using cocaine, which is five times higher than the risk of heart attack in the hour immediately after using cannabis. This equates to a heart attack risk of 1 in 150,000 in the hour after cannabis use. After the first hour, the risk returns to baseline. [277]

Carbon monoxide in cannabis smoke may also play a role in addition to increased heart rate and blood pressure. Smoking cannabis leads to nearly five times higher carbon monoxide levels in the blood than smoking tobacco. This is, again, due to the more deeply inhaled and longer held smoke of cannabis compared to tobacco. Second-hand cannabis smoke may also be harmful, so it is important to protect vulnerable populations, such as the elderly, disabled, pregnant women, children and pets from cannabis smoke. [278]

Neurological

After smoking marijuana, learning, memory and attention are impaired. This effect remains for a few hours. Research reveals that the hippocampus (the memory center in the brain) is smaller in those who use cannabis than in non-users. Interestingly, in these users, there appear to be structural abnormalities in brain regions that control inhibitions and decision-making which pre-date cannabis use. It is felt that these abnormalities may increase the likelihood an individual would initiate cannabis in the first place. [279]

After prolonged abstinence, hippocampal volume and size can return to normal. According to one study, after use for up to 15 years, the size of the hippocampus was restored after 29 months of abstinence. The same holds true with cognitive impairments, which resolve after 1-2 months of abstinence. Use that begins in adulthood appears not to cause any irreversible neurological problems except in cases of extreme chronic and heavy use, which equates to approximately 16 joints per day or a total lifetime consumption of 75,000 joints.[280]

Persistent cannabis use starting as a teen can lead to a permanent loss of IQ, up to 8 points, after approximately 20 years of persistent use. This is consistent with the level of brain damage seen with low level lead exposure. This is concerning given that marijuana use among adolescents and young adults rose by 50% in Colorado since it's legalization and commercialization. According to the American Academy of Pediatrics:

> "Marijuana is *not* a benign drug for teens. The teen brain is still developing, and marijuana may cause abnormal brain development." Full brain development is generally not complete until approximately age 25. It is also important to note that, because of new breeding techniques, today's marijuana is often six to seven times more potent than in the 1970s, which has the potential to exacerbate these outcomes.[281]

When comparing the impacts of alcohol vs cannabis on the brains of adolescents, alcohol, a neurotoxin, is associated with reduced gray matter volume while cannabis is not. However, another study found that increased cannabis use showed impaired cognitive function in a study of almost 4,000 teens. The researchers did not find this same association with alcohol consumption. Certainly, both alcohol and cannabis should be avoided in adolescence while the brain is still developing.[282]

Increased efforts to delay the use of cannabis onset by young people should be sought, however, Drug Abuse Resistance Education (DARE) programs have been completely ineffectual. Research reveals that these programs have "no beneficial effects in terms of changing drug use or attitudes towards drug use."[284]

Pregnancy/Fertility

While smoking cannabis more than once per week is associated with an approximate 28% lower total sperm count and concentration, no adverse association is seen with use less than once a week. In this same observational study of 1,000 men, cigarettes, alcohol, other drugs and STDs were controlled. A study of infertile couples who had used cannabis more than 90 times, revealed that men had approximately 25% fewer sperm, and egg retrieval was approximately 25% lower for women.[284,285] In men, cannabis use has also been linked to hypoactive sexual desire disorder and erectile dysfunction.

In women, long-term cannabis use may result in oligomenorrhea (infrequent menstruation) due to infrequent ovulation and hypoactive sexual desire and orgasm disorders all resulting in fertility impairment. There is also evidence that cannabis can increase blood testosterone levels in some women which can result in hirsutism (unwanted hair growth of the chin, upper lip, chest, etc). High concentrations of cannabinoids can also inhibit the implantation and development of the embryo.

As such, it is currently recommended cannabis be discontinued by women while attempting conception, and that cannabis not be used during pregnancy and breastfeeding. However, according to the Academy of Breastfeeding Medicine, the benefits of breastmilk outweigh any potential harms even for those women using cannabis while breastfeeding. Current statistics reveal that approximately 4% of pregnant women use cannabis (up from 2.5% in past decades), and that non-pregnant women use cannabis at an approximate 8% rate. [286,287]

Risks of cannabis use during pregnancy include an increased risk of anemia in the infant, lower birth weight and need for intensive care after birth. However, determining the direct effects of maternal cannabis use on the developing fetus is difficult due to confounding factors that cannot always be controlled. Prenatal cannabis exposure may also lead to learning issues that manifest during the school age years. Therefore, it is advisable that pregnant women should either decrease or cease cannabis use entirely, when possible. [288,289]

Cannabis has been rated as extremely effective or effective for morning sickness in pregnancy but should only be used as a last resort. In cases of severe hyperemesis gravidarum that is completely refractory to all other therapies and in circumstances where the mother is contemplating termination of an otherwise wanted pregnancy, cannabis can, and should, be considered.

Morbidity and Mortality

According to a 2017 review from the National Academy of Sciences on the Health Effects of Cannabis and Cannabinoids, there is no (or insufficient) evidence that cannabis use increases mortality from any cause or death from overdose. Of the more than 70,000 drug overdose deaths in the United States in 2017, not one was attributed to cannabis. Rather, opioids, mainly synthetic opioids other than methadone, were responsible for 67.8% of those overdose deaths.[290]

Likewise, there was an average of six daily deaths from alcohol poisoning in the US between 2010 to 2012; an estimated 95,000 people (approximately 70% are men) die from alcohol-related causes each year. This makes alcohol the third leading cause of preventable death in the U.S.[291] preceded by tobacco (1st) and poor diet and physical inactivity (2nd). According to the CDC, "Cigarette smoking is responsible for more than 480,000 deaths (1 in 5) per year in the U.S., including more than 41,000 deaths resulting from secondhand smoke exposure. This is about one in five deaths annually, or 1,300 deaths every day." This means that tobacco is responsible for 25 times more deaths globally than all illicit drugs combined on an annual basis and alcohol kills about 10 times more.[292]

The likelihood of dying from cannabis alone is extremely remote, although marijuana use can lead to death because of the activities, like driving, people might engage in when altered.[293] Additionally, there have been no reported deaths among children from accidental marijuana exposure, though some have required assisted ventilation for respiratory depression. This is typically seen in cases where children have consumed an edible packaged as a candy. An increase in these cases was noted after Colorado legalized recreational marijuana. However, there are still very few of these cases compared to the thousands of Coloradan children who have required treatment each year after accidentally ingesting cosmetics and vitamins.[294,295]

Addiction/Dependence

Long-term cannabis use can lead to addiction in approximately 9% of those who use. Addiction is defined in this context as "a powerful motivation to continually engage in an activity despite persistent negative consequences." For those who begin using in adolescence, the percentage increases to 17%, and rises to 25-50% among those teens who smoke cannabis daily. Strains with high concentrations of THC have been associated with a greater severity of dependence. Legalization has advanced breeding of new cultivars and as such, potency of THC has increased 3-fold in recent years, from 4% to an average of 12%, with some strains as high as 18% to 20%.[296]

Some who try to quit experience withdrawal symptoms, cravings, sleep disturbance, nightmares, anger, irritability and nausea, indicating a physical dependence. Symptoms of withdrawal affect approximately 50% of those who use daily and typically begin one to two days after cessation, peaking at two to six days, and potentially persisting for up to one to two weeks.[297]

Cannabis has a much lower risk of dependence, however, than other drugs, like alcohol, which has a lifetime dependence risk of 16%. Cannabis is less than half as addictive as heroin (23% risk of dependence) and cocaine (17% risk) and less than a third as addictive as tobacco (32% risk).[298] However, it is important to consider the results of substance dependence. There are many who are dependent upon drugs like caffeine, that move them to consume tea or coffee, the latter of which is the number one source of antioxidants in the American diet.[299] Removal of coffee from the American diet would result in an even worse (difficult to imagine) state of health of the American people. Cannabis can be viewed in much the same way. Many people suffering from pain, anxiety, and other disorders of endocannabinoid deficiency would need to turn to other drugs, illicit or prescribed, with higher associated risks and possibly less efficacy in order to address their symptoms.

Cannabinoid Hyperemesis Syndrome (CHS)

Cannabinoid Hyperemesis Syndrome (CHS) is a nausea and vomiting paradox. While cannabis is well known to have antiemetic properties, in the case of CHS, cannabis is actually the culprit. CHS is a syndrome of cyclic vomiting associated with heavy, long-term use of cannabis. Patients describe severe episodes of abdominal pain, vomiting, and, occasionally, diarrhea that is temporarily relieved by taking hot showers or baths. It is unclear how hot baths and showers work to relieve symptoms, but the predominant theory is that cannabis tends to increase the core body temperature while simultaneously reducing skin temperature. Bathing in hot water increases blood flow to skin, allowing heat to dissipate and lowering the core body temperature. CHS typically resolves within days after stopping cannabis use.

While it is unclear what causes CHS, it is suspected to be a product of a dysregulation of the endocannabinoid system. Because delta-9-THC has a long half-life and is lipophilic (stored in fat), chronic and heavy cannabis use may result in an intoxication effect in which stored THC is released from fat into circulation.[300] CBD has also been shown to have a biphasic response in cases of vomiting related to the contemporaneous use of the drugs lithium (in bipolar disorder) and cisplatin (a chemotherapy drug); CBD prevents vomiting at low doses but induces vomiting at higher doses. CBG can also reverse the antiemetic effects of CBD in rodents, apparently through 5-HT1A receptors.[301]

Clinically, CHS appears very similar to cyclic vomiting syndrome (CVS). The disorders can be clinically differentiated, because patients with CVS can abort the episode if cannabis is used immediately at symptom onset. Because, for patients with CHS, cannabis does not relieve the symptoms but rather induces them. Fortunately, some patients with CHS can abstain for 1-2 months, and then resume using medical cannabis at much lower doses.[301]

References:

1. Robert Deitch *Hemp: American History Revisited: The Plant with a Divided History*, 2003
2. National Institute on Drug Abuse (NIDA) *Marijuana Research Findings: 1976*, 1977
3. Richard Glen Boire, JD and Kevin Feeney, JD *Medical Marijuana Law*, 2007
4. Martin Booth *Cannabis: A History*, 2005
5. US Food and Drug Administration (FDA) "FDA History - Part I," FDA website (accessed Jan. 2, 2021)
6. Dale Gieringer, PhD "The Forgotten Origins of Cannabis Prohibition in California," *Contemporary Drug Problems*, Summer 1999
7. https://www.cdc.gov/marijuana/faqs/overdose-bad-reaction.html
8. McPartland JM, Guy GW, Di Marzo V. Care and feeding of the endocannabinoid system: a systematic review of potential clinical interventions that upregulate the endocannabinoid system. *PLoS One*. 2014;9(3):e89566. Published 2014 Mar 12. doi:10.1371/journal.pone.0089566
9. Mechoulam R. Cannabis: The Israeli Perspective. J Basic Pharmacology and Physiology (2015):1-7
10. Atwood BK, Mackie K. CB2: a cannabinoid receptor with an identity crisis. *Br J Pharmacol*. 2010;160(3):467-479. doi:10.1111/j.1476-5381.2010.00729.x
11. Pacher P, Bátkai S, Kunos G. The endocannabinoid system as an emerging target of pharmacotherapy. *Pharmacol Rev*. 2006;58(3):389-462. doi:10.1124/pr.58.3.2
12. Cabral GA, Rogers TJ, Lichtman AH. Turning over a new leaf: Cannabinoid and Endocannabinoid modulation of immune function. J Neuroimmune Pharm. 2015; 10(2):193-203.
13. Moskowitz MH. *Medical Cannabis: A Guide for Patients, Practitioners, and Caregivers*. 2017. p.25
14. Rossi F et al. C2 and TRPV-1 receptors oppositely modulate in vitro human osteoblast activity. Pharmacology Research 99 (2015): 194-201.
15. Lauckner JE, Jensen JB, Chen HY, Lu HC, Hille B, Mackie K. GPR55 is a cannabinoid receptor that increases intracellular calcium and inhibits M current. *Proc Natl Acad Sci U S A*. 2794–801. doi:10.1074/jbc.274.5.2794. PMID 9915812
16. Berrendero, F.; Sepe, N.; Ramos, J. A.; Di Marzo, V.; Fernández-Ruiz, J. J. (1999-09-01). "Analysis of cannabinoid receptor binding and mRNA expression and endogenous cannabinoid contents in the developing rat brain during late gestation and early postnatal period". *Synapse (New York, N.Y.)*. **33** (3): 181–191. doi:10.1002/(SICI)1098-2396(19990901)33:3<181::AID-SYN3>3.0.CO;2-R. ISSN 0887-4476. PMID 10420166
17. Baggelaar MP, Maccarrone M, van der Stelt M. 2-Arachidonoylglycerol: A signaling lipid with manifold actions in the brain. Progress in Lipid Research. 2018; 71:1-17. https://doi.org/10.1016/j.plipres.2018.05.002.
18. Shaan S. Naughton, Michael L. Mathai, Deanne H. Hryciw, Andrew J. McAinch, "Fatty Acid Modulation of the Endocannabinoid System and the Effect on Food Intake and Metabolism", *International Journal of Endocrinology*, vol. 2013, Article ID 361895, 11 pages, 2013. https://2008;105(7):2699-2704. doi:10.1073/pnas.0711278105
19. Hu G, Ren G, Shi Y. The putative cannabinoid receptor GPR55 promotes cancer cell proliferation. Oncogene. 2011 Jan 13;30(2):139-41. doi: 10.1038/onc.2010.502. Epub 2010 Nov 8. PMID: 21057532.

20. Rossi F et al. C2 and TRPV-1 receptors oppositely modulate in vitro human osteoblast activity. Pharmacology Research 99 (2015): 194-201.

21. Dongchen An, et al. Targeting Cannabinoid Receptors: Current Status and Prospects of Natural Products. Int J Molecular Sciences. 2020, *21*(14), 5064; https://doi.org/10.3390/ijms21145064

22. Pacher P, Batkai S, Kunos G (2006). "The Endocannabinoid System as an Emerging Target of Pharmacotherapy". *Pharmacol. Rev.* **58** (3): 389–462. doi:10.1124/pr.58.3.2. PMC 2241751. PMID 16968947.

23. Mallet PE, Beninger RJ (1996). "The endogenous cannabinoid receptor agonist anandamide impairs memory in rats". *Behavioural Pharmacology.* **7** (3): 276–284. doi:10.1097/00008877-199605000-00008. S2CID 143995667

24. Piomelli D (January 2004). "THC: moderation during implantation" (PDF). *Nat. Med.* **10** (1): 19–20. doi:10.1038/nm0104-19. PMID 14702623. S2CID 29207064

25. Fuss J, Steinle J, Bindila L, Auer MK, Kirchherr H, Lutz B, and Gass P (2015). "A runner's high depends on cannabinoid receptors in mice". *PNAS.* **112** (42): 13105–13108. Bibcode:2015PNAS..11213105F. doi:10.1073/pnas.1514996112. PMC 4620874. PMID 26438875.

26. De Petrocellis, Luciano; Melck, Dominique; Palmisano, Antonella; Bisogno, Tiziana; Laezza, Chiara; Bifulco, Maurizio; Di Marzo, Vincenzo (7 July 1998). "The endogenous cannabinoid anandamide inhibits human breast cancer cell proliferation". *Proceedings of the National Academy of Sciences.* **95** (14): 8375–8380. Bibcode:1998PNAS...95.8375D. doi:10.1073/pnas.95.14.8375. PMC 20983. PMID 9653194.

27. di Tomaso E, Beltramo M, Piomelli D (Aug 1996). "Brain cannabinoids in chocolate" (PDF). *Nature.* **382** (6593): 677–8. Bibcode:1996 Nature.382..677D. doi:10.1038/382677a0. PMID 8751435. S2CID 4325706.

28. Sugiura T, Kodaka T, Nakane S, et al. (January 1999). "Evidence that the cannabinoid CB1 receptor is a 2-arachidonoylglycerol receptor. Structure-activity relationship of 2-arachidonoylglycerol, ether-linked analogues, and related compounds". *The Journal of Biological Chemistry.* **274** (5): doi.org/10.1155/2013/361895

29. McPartland JM, Guy GW, Di Marzo V. Care and feeding of the endocannabinoid system: a systematic review of potential clinical interventions that upregulate the endocannabinoid system. *PLoS One.* 2014;9(3):e89566. Published 2014 Mar 12. doi:10.1371/journal.pone.0089566

30. https://nutritionfacts.org/video/inflammatory-remarks-about-arachidonic-acid/

31. Alvheim AR, Torstensen BE, Lin YH, et al. Dietary linoleic acid elevates the endocannabinoids 2-AG and anandamide and promotes weight gain in mice fed a low fat diet. *Lipids.* 2014;49(1):59-69. doi:10.1007/s11745-013-3842-y

32. Lafourcade M, Larrieu T, Mato S, Duffaud A, Sepers M, et al. Nutritional omega-3 deficiency abolishes endocannabinoid-mediated neuronal functions. Nat Neurosci. 2011 Mar;14(3):345-50. PubMed PMID: 21278728.

33. Wood JT, Williams JS, Pandarinathan L, Janero DR, Lammi-Keefe CJ, et al. Dietary docosahexaenoic acid supplementation alters select physiological endocannabinoid-system metabolites in brain and plasma. J Lipid Res. 2010 Jun;51(6):1416-23. PubMed PMID: 20071693; PubMed Central PMCID: PMC3035504.

34. Gertsch J. Anti-inflammatory cannabinoids in diet: Towards a better understanding of CB(2) receptor action?. Commun Integr Biol. 2008;1(1):26-8. PubMed PMID: 19704783; PubMed Central PMCID: PMC2633791.

35. Gamelin FX, Aucouturier J, Iannotti FA, et al. Effects of chronic exercise on the endocannabinoid system in Wistar rats with high-fat diet-induced obesity. *J Physiol Biochem*. 2016;72(2):183-199. doi:10.1007/s13105-016-0469-5

36. Yamada D, Takeo J, Koppensteiner P, Wada K, Sekiguchi M. Modulation of fear memory by dietary polyunsaturated fatty acids via cannabinoid receptors. Neuropsychopharmacology. 2014 Jul;39(8):1852-60. PubMed PMID: 24518289; PubMed Central PMCID: PMC4059893.

37. Gertsch J. Cannabimimetic phytochemicals in the diet - an evolutionary link to food selection and metabolic stress adaptation?. Br J Pharmacol. 2016 Nov 27;PubMed PMID: 27891602.) Morena M, Patel S, Bains JS, Hill MN. Neurobiological Interactions Between Stress and the Endocannabinoid System. *Neuropsychopharmacology.* 2016;41(1):80-102. doi:10.1038/npp.2015.166

38. Nunn A, Guy G, Bell JD. Endocannabinoids in neuroendo psychology: multiphasic control of mitochondrial function. *Philos Trans R Soc Lond B Biol Sci*. 2012;367(1607):3342-3352. doi:10.1098/rstb.2011.0393

39. Russo EB. Clinical Endocannabinoid Deficiency Reconsidered: Current Research Supports the Theory in Migraine, Fibromyalgia, Irritable Bowel, and Other Treatment-Resistant Syndromes. *Cannabis Cannabinoid Res.* 2016;1(1):154-165. Published 2016 Jul 1. doi:10.1089/can.2016.0009

40. Sam, AH; Salem, V; Ghatei, MA (2011). "Rimonabant: From RIO to Ban". *Journal of Obesity.* **2011**: 432607. doi:10.1155/2011/432607. PMC 3136184. PMID 21773005

41. Ramos JA, Bianco FJ. The role of cannabinoids in prostate cancer: Basic science perspective and potential clinical applications. *Indian J Urol.* 2012;28(1):9-14. doi:10.4103/0970-1591.94942

42. de Lago E, Moreno-Martet M, Cabranes A, Ramos JA, Javier Fernández-Ruiz J. Cannabinoids ameliorate disease progression in a model of multiple sclerosis in mice, acting preferentially through CB1 receptor-mediated anti-inflammatory effects. Neuropharmacology. 2012; 62(7):229-2308. https://doi.org/10.1016/j.neuropharm.2012.01.030.

43. Wiese B, Wilson-Poe AR. Emerging Evidence for Cannabis' Role in Opioid Use Disorder. *Cannabis Cannabinoid Res.* 2018;3(1):179-189. Published 2018 Sep 1. doi:10.1089/can.2018.0022

44. Kim D, Kim W, Kwak MS, Chung GE, Yim JY, Ahmed A. Inverse association of marijuana use with nonalcoholic fatty liver disease among adults in the United States. *PLoS One.* 2017;12(10):e0186702. Published 2017 Oct 19. doi:10.1371/journal.pone.0186702

45. Currais, A., Quehenberger, O., M Armando, A. *et al.* Amyloid proteotoxicity initiates an inflammatory response blocked by cannabinoids. *npj Aging Mech Dis* 2, 16012 (2016). https://doi.org/10.1038/npjamd.2016.12

46. Thapa D, Cairns EA, Szcześniak AM, Toguri JT, Caldwell MD, Kelly MEM. The Cannabinoids Δ8THC, CBD, and HU-308 Act via Distinct Receptors to Reduce Corneal Pain and Inflammation. *Cannabis Cannabinoid Res.* 2018;3(1):11-20. Published 2018 Feb 1. doi:10.1089/can.2017.0041

47. Hine B, Toreelio M, Gershon S. Analgesic, heart rate, and temperature effects of delta8-THC during acute and chronic administration to conscious rats. Pharmacology. 1977;15(1):63-72. PMID: 14347.

48. National Center for Biotechnology Information (2021). PubChem Compound Summary for CID 2977, delta8-THC. Retrieved January 28, 2021 from https://pubchem.ncbi.nlm.nih.gov/compound/delta8-THC.

49. Abrahamov A, Abrahamov A, Mechoulam R. An efficient new cannabinoid antiemetic in pediatric oncology. Life Sciences. 1995;56(23-24):2097-2102. https://doi.org/10.1016/0024-3205(95)00194-B.

50. Avraham Y, Ben-Shushan D, Breuer A, Zolotarev O, Okon A, Fink N, Katz V, Berry EM. Very low doses of delta 8-THC increase food consumption and alter neurotransmitter levels following weight loss. Pharmacol Biochem Behav. 2004 Apr;77(4):675-84. doi: 10.1016/j.pbb.2004.01.015. PMID: 15099912.

51. Carlini EA. The good and the bad effects of (-) trans-delta-9-tetrahydrocannabinol (Delta 9-THC) on humans. Toxicon. 2004 Sep 15;44(4):461-7. doi: 10.1016/j.toxicon.2004.05.009. PMID: 15302527.

52. Zhornitsky S, Potvin S. Cannabidiol in humans-the quest for therapeutic targets. *Pharmaceuticals (Basel)*. 2012;5(5):529-552. Published 2012 May 21. doi:10.3390/ph5050529

53. Bakas T, van Nieuwenhuijzen PS, Devenish SO, McGregor IS, Arnold JC, Chebib M. The direct actions of cannabidiol and 2-arachidonoyl glycerol at GABAA receptors. Pharmacol Res. 2017 May;119:358-370. doi: 10.1016/j.phrs.2017.02.022. Epub 2017 Feb 27. PMID: 28249817.

54. Laprairie RB, Bagher AM, Kelly MEM, Denovan-Wright EM. Cannabidiol is a negative allosteric modulator of the cannabinoid CB1 receptor. British J Pharmacology. 2015; 172(20):4790-4805.

55. Olivas-Aguirre, M., Torres-López, L., Valle-Reyes, J.S. *et al.* Cannabidiol directly targets mitochondria and disturbs calcium homeostasis in acute lymphoblastic leukemia. *Cell Death Dis* 10, 779 (2019). https://doi.org/10.1038/s41419-019-2024-0

56. Deutsch DG. A Personal Retrospective: Elevating Anandamide (AEA) by Targeting Fatty Acid Amide Hydrolase (FAAH) and the Fatty Acid Binding Proteins (FABPs). Front Pharmacol. 2016 Oct 13;7:370. doi: 10.3389/fphar.2016.00370. PMID: 27790143; PMCID: PMC5062061.

57. Gallily, R., Yekhtin, Z. and Hanuš, L. (2015) Overcoming the Bell-Shaped Dose-Response of Cannabidiol by Using *Cannabis* Extract Enriched in Cannabidiol. *Pharmacology & Pharmacy*, 6, 75-85. doi: 10.4236/pp.2015.62010.

58. Russo EB. Current Therapeutic Cannabis Controversies and Clinical Trial Design Issues. *Front Pharmacol*. 2016;7:309. Published 2016 Sep 14. doi:10.3389/fphar.2016.00309

59. Dhopeshwarkar A, Mackie K. CB2 Cannabinoid receptors as a therapeutic target-what does the future hold?. *Mol Pharmacol*. 2014;86(4):430-437. doi:10.1124/mol.114.094649

60. Schoeler T, Bhattacharyya S. The effect of cannabis use on memory function: an update. *Subst Abuse Rehabil*. 2013;4:11-27. Published 2013 Jan 23. doi:10.2147/SAR.S25869

61. https://clinicaltrials.gov/ct2/results?term=cannabidiol&Search=Apply&recrs=a&recrs=f&recrs=d&age_v=&gndr=&type=&rslt= (accessed 1/29/21)

62. https://www.projectcbd.org/science/how-cbd-works

63. Linge R, Jiménez-Sánchez L, Campa L, Pilar-Cuéllar F, Vidal R, Pazos A, Adell A, Díaz Á. Cannabidiol induces rapid-acting antidepressant-like effects and enhances cortical 5-HT/glutamate neurotransmission: role of 5-HT1A receptors. Neuropharmacology. 2016 Apr;103:16-26. doi: 10.1016/j.neuropharm.2015.12.017. Epub 2015 Dec 19. PMID: 26711860.

64. Bergamaschi MM, Queiroz RH, Chagas MH, de Oliveira DC, De Martinis BS, Kapczinski F, Quevedo J, Roesler R, Schröder N, Nardi AE, Martín-Santos R, Hallak JE, Zuardi AW, Crippa JA. Cannabidiol reduces the anxiety induced by simulated public speaking in treatment-naïve social phobia patients. Neuropsychopharmacology. 2011 May;36(6):1219-26. doi: 10.1038/npp.2011.6. Epub 2011 Feb 9. PMID: 21307846; PMCID: PMC3079847.

65. Cuttler C, Spradlin A, McLaughlin RJ. A naturalistic examination of the perceived effects of cannabis on negative affect. J Affect Disord. 2018 Aug 1;235:198-205. doi: 10.1016/j.jad.2018.04.054. Epub 2018 Apr 6. PMID: 29656267.

66. Resstel, Leonardo B M et al. 5-HT1A receptors are involved in the cannabidiol-induced attenuation of behavioural and cardiovascular responses to acute restraint stress in rats. British journal of pharmacology vol. 156,1 (2009): 181-8.

67. Hu G, Ren G, Shi Y. The putative cannabinoid receptor GPR55 promotes cancer cell proliferation. Oncogene. 2011 Jan 13;30(2):139-41. doi: 10.1038/onc.2010.502. Epub 2010 Nov 8. PMID: 21057532.

68. Chearwae W and Bright JJ, "PPAR-gamma agonists inhibit growth and expansion of CD133+ brain tumour stem cells," *British Journal of Cancer*, 2008.

69. Gallily, R. , Yekhtin, Z. and Hanuš, L. (2015) Overcoming the Bell-Shaped Dose-Response of Cannabidiol by Using *Cannabis* Extract Enriched in Cannabidiol. *Pharmacology & Pharmacy*, **6**, 75-85. doi: 10.4236/pp.2015.62010.

70. Bisogno T, Hanus L, De Petrocellis L, et al. Molecular targets for cannabidiol and its synthetic analogues: effect on vanilloid VR1 receptors and on the cellular uptake and enzymatic hydrolysis of anandamide. *Br J Pharmacol*. 2001;134(4):845-852. doi:10.1038/sj.bjp.0704327

71. Hegde VL, Singh UP, Nagarkatti PS, Nagarkatti M. Critical Role of Mast Cells and Peroxisome Proliferator–Activated Receptor γ in the Induction of Myeloid-Derived Suppressor Cells by Marijuana Cannabidiol In Vivo. J Immunol June 1, 2015, 194 (11) 5211-5222; DOI: https://doi.org/10.4049/jimmunol.1401844

72. Rodríguez-Muñoz M, Sánchez-Blázquez P, Merlos M, Garzón-Niño J. Endocannabinoid control of glutamate NMDA receptors: the therapeutic potential and consequences of dysfunction. Oncotarget. 2016;7(34):55840-55862. doi:10.18632/oncotarget.10095

73. Jones NA, et al. 2010. Cannabidiol displays anti-epileptiform and anti-seizure properties in vitro and in vivo. Journal of Pharmacology and Experimental Therapeutics 332(2):569-577

74. Sulak D, Saneto R, Goldstein B. The current status of artisanal cannabis for the treatment of epilepsy in the United States. Epilepsy Behav. 2017 May;70(Pt B):328-333. doi: 10.1016/j.yebeh.2016.12.032. Epub 2017 Feb 21. PMID: 28254350.

75. Prud'homme M, Cata R, Jutras-Aswad D. Cannabidiol as an Intervention for Addictive Behaviors: A Systematic Review of the Evidence. *Subst Abuse*. 2015;9:33-38. Published 2015 May 21. doi:10.4137/SART.S25081

76. Morgan CJ, Das RK, Joye A, Curran HV, Kamboj SK. Cannabidiol reduces cigarette consumption in tobacco smokers: preliminary findings. Addict Behav. 2013 Sep;38(9):2433-6. doi: 10.1016/j.addbeh.2013.03.011. Epub 2013 Apr 1. PMID: 23685330.

77. Hurd YL, Yoon M, Manini AF, Hernandez S, Olmedo R, Ostman M, Jutras-Aswad D. Early Phase in the Development of Cannabidiol as a Treatment for Addiction: Opioid Relapse Takes Initial Center Stage. Neurotherapeutics. 2015 Oct;12(4):807-15. doi: 10.1007/s13311-015-0373-7. PMID: 26269227; PMCID: PMC4604178.

78. Stanley CP, Hind WH, O'Sullivan SE. Is the cardiovascular system a therapeutic target for cannabidiol? Br J Clin Pharmacol. 2013 Feb; 75(2): 313–322. Published online 2012 Jun 1. doi: 10.1111/j.1365-2125.2012.04351.x PMCID: PMC3579247 PMID: 22670794

79. Grayson L, Vines B, Nichol K, Szaflarski JP; UAB CBD Program. An interaction between warfarin and cannabidiol, a case report. *Epilepsy Behav Case Rep*. 2017;9:10-11. Published 2017 Oct 12. doi:10.1016/j.ebcr.2017.10.001

80. Huestis MA. Pharmacokinetics and metabolism of the plant cannabinoids, delta9-tetrahydrocannabinol, cannabidiol and cannabinol. Handb Exp Pharmacol. 2005;(168):657-90. doi: 10.1007/3-540-26573-2_23. PMID: 16596792.

81. https://weedmaps.com/news/2017/03/cbn-the-creeper-cannabinoid-in-old-weed/

82. https://www.steephill.com/blogs/34/Cannabinol-(CBD):-A-Sleeping-Synergy

83. Takahashi RN, Karniol IG. Pharmacologic interaction between cannabinol and delta9-tetrahydrocannabinol. Psychopharmacologia. 1975;41(3):277-84. doi: 10.1007/BF00428937. PMID: 168604.

84. Zygmunt PM, Andersson DA, Högestätt ED. Δ9-Tetrahydrocannabinol and Cannabinol Activate Capsaicin-Sensitive Sensory Nerves via a CB1 and CB2 Cannabinoid Receptor-Independent Mechanism. Journal of Neuroscience. 2002; 22(11):4720-4727; DOI: https://doi.org/10.1523/JNEUROSCI.22-11-04720.2002

85. Wong H, Cairns BE. Cannabidiol, cannabinol and their combinations act as peripheral analgesics in a rat model of myofascial pain. Arch Oral Biol. 2019 Aug;104:33-39. doi: 10.1016/j.archoralbio.2019.05.028. Epub 2019 May 28. PMID: 31158702.

86. Appendino G, Gibbons S, Giana A, Pagani A, Grassi G, Stavri M, Smith E, Rahman MM. Antibacterial cannabinoids from Cannabis sativa: a structure-activity study. J Nat Prod. 2008 Aug;71(8):1427-30. doi: 10.1021/np8002673. Epub 2008 Aug 6. PMID: 18681481.

87. Nagarkatti P, Pandey R, Rieder SA, Hegde VL, Nagarkatti M. Cannabinoids as novel anti-inflammatory drugs. *Future Med Chem*. 2009;1(7):1333-1349. doi:10.4155/fmc.09.93

88. Kogan NM, Mechoulam R. Cannabinoids in health and disease. *Dialogues Clin Neurosci*. 2007;9(4):413-430. doi:10.31887/DCNS.2007.9.4/nkogan

89. Chesher, G.B., Jackson, D.M. Anticonvulsant effects of cannabinoids in mice: Drug interactions within cannabinoids and cannabinoid interactions with phenytoin. *Psychopharmacologia* 37, 255–264 (1974). https://doi.org/10.1007/BF00421539

90. Scutt A, Williamson EM. Cannabinoids stimulate fibroblastic colony formation by bone marrow cells indirectly via CB2 receptors. Calcif Tissue Int. 2007 Jan;80(1):50-9. doi: 10.1007/s00223-006-0171-7. Epub 2007 Jan 4. PMID: 17205329.

91. Farrimond JA, Whalley BJ, Williams CM. Cannabinol and cannabidiol exert opposing effects on rat feeding patterns. Psychopharmacology (Berl). 2012 Sep;223(1):117-29. doi: 10.1007/s00213-012-2697-x. Epub 2012 Apr 28. PMID: 22543671.

92. Hergenrather JY, Aviram J, VysotskiY, Campisi-Pinto S, Lewitus GM, Meiri D. Cannabinoid and Terpenoid Doses are Associated with Adult ADHD Status of Medical Cannabis Patients. *Rambam Maimonides Med J*. 2020;11(1):e0001. Published 2020 Jan 30. doi:10.5041/RMMJ.10384

93. O'Neil JD, Dalton WS, Forney RB. The effect of cannabichromene on mean blood pressure, heart rate, and respiration rate responses to tetrahydrocannabinol in the anesthetized rat. Toxicology and Applied Pharmacology 1979; 49(2):265-270.

94. De Petrocellis L, Melck D, Palmisano A, et al. The endogenous cannabinoid anandamide inhibits human breast cancer cell proliferation. *Proc Natl Acad Sci U S A*. 1998;95(14):8375-8380. doi:10.1073/pnas.95.14.8375

95. Patsos HA, Hicks DJ, Dobson RR, et al. The endogenous cannabinoid, anandamide, induces cell death in colorectal carcinoma cells: a possible role for cyclooxygenase 2. *Gut*. 2005;54(12):1741-1750. doi:10.1136/gut.2005.073403

96. Nakajima J, Nakae D, Yasukawa K. Structure-dependent inhibitory effects of synthetic cannabinoids against 12-O-tetradecanoylphorbol-13-acetate-induced inflammation and skin tumour promotion in mice. J Pharmacy and Pharmacology. 2013; 65(8):1223-1230.

97. Ligresti A, et al. Antitumor Activity of Plant Cannabinoids with Emphasis on the Effect of Cannabidiol on Human Breast Carcinoma. Journal of Pharmacology and Experimental Therapeutics September 2006, 318 (3) 1375-1387; DOI: https://doi.org/10.1124/jpet.106.105247

98. Oláh A, Markovics A, Szabó-Papp J, Szabó PT, Stott C, Zouboulis CC, Bíró T. Differential effectiveness of selected non-psychotropic phytocannabinoids on human sebocyte functions implicates their introduction in dry/seborrhoeic skin and acne treatment. Exp Dermatol. 2016 Sep;25(9):701-7. doi: 10.1111/exd.13042. Epub 2016 Jun 15. PMID: 27094344.

99. Udoh M, Santiago M, Devenish S, McGregor IS, Connor M. Cannabichromene is a cannabinoid CB2 receptor agonist. Br J Pharmacol. 2019 Dec;176(23):4537-4547. doi: 10.1111/bph.14815. Epub 2019 Nov 21. PMID: 31368508; PMCID: PMC6932936

100. Turner CE, Elsohly MA. Biological activity of cannabichromene, its homologs and isomers. J Clin Pharmacol. 1981 Aug-Sep;21(S1):283S-291S. doi: 10.1002/j.1552-4604.1981.tb02606.x. PMID: 7298870.

101. Maione S, Piscitelli F, Gatta L, Vita D, De Petrocellis L, Palazzo E, de Novellis V, Di Marzo V. Non-psychoactive cannabinoids modulate the descending pathway of antinociception in anaesthetized rats through several mechanisms of action. Br J Pharmacol. 2011 Feb;162(3):584-96. doi: 10.1111/j.1476-5381.2010.01063.x. PMID: 20942863; PMCID: PMC3041249.

102. DeLong GT, Wolf CE, Poklis A, Lichtman AH. Pharmacological evaluation of the natural constituent of Cannabis sativa, cannabichromene and its modulation by Δ(9)-tetrahydrocannabinol. *Drug Alcohol Depend.* 2010;112(1-2):126-133. doi:10.1016/j.drugalcdep.2010.05.019

103. Turner CE, Elsohly MA. Biological activity of cannabichromene, its homologs and isomers. J Clin Pharmacol. 1981 Aug-Sep;21(S1):283S-291S. doi: 10.1002/j.1552-4604.1981.tb02606.x. PMID: 7298870.

104. El-Alfy AT, Ivey K, Robinson K, Ahmed S, Radwan M, Slade D, Khan I, ElSohly M, Ross S. Antidepressant-like effect of delta9-tetrahydrocannabinol and other cannabinoids isolated from Cannabis sativa L. Pharmacol Biochem Behav. 2010 Jun;95(4):434-42. doi: 10.1016/j.pbb.2010.03.004. Epub 2010 Mar 21. PMID: 20332000; PMCID: PMC2866040.

105. Shinjyo N, Di Marzo V. The effect of cannabichromene on adult neural stem/progenitor cells. Neurochem Int. 2013 Nov;63(5):432-7. doi: 10.1016/j.neuint.2013.08.002. Epub 2013 Aug 11. PMID: 23941747.

106. Bélanger M, Magistretti PJ. The role of astroglia in neuroprotection. *Dialogues Clin Neurosci.* 2009;11(3):281-295. doi:10.31887/DCNS.2009.11.3/mbelanger

107. Navarro G, Varani K, Reyes-Resina I, et al. Cannabigerol Action at Cannabinoid CB1 and CB2 Receptors and at CB1-CB2 Heteroreceptor Complexes. *Front Pharmacol.* 2018;9:632. Published 2018 Jun 21. doi:10.3389/fphar.2018.00632

108. Borrelli F, Fasolino I, Romano B, Capasso R, Maiello F, Coppola D, Orlando P, Battista G, Pagano E, Di Marzo V, Izzo AA. Beneficial effect of the non-psychotropic plant cannabinoid cannabigerol on experimental inflammatory bowel disease. Biochem Pharmacol. 2013 May 1;85(9):1306-16. doi: 10.1016/j.bcp.2013.01.017. Epub 2013 Feb 12. PMID: 23415610.

109. Gugliandolo A, Pollastro F, Grassi G, Bramanti P, Mazzon E. In Vitro Model of Neuroinflammation: Efficacy of Cannabigerol, a Non-Psychoactive Cannabinoid. Int J Mol Sci. 2018 Jul 8;19(7):1992. doi: 10.3390/ijms19071992. PMID: 29986533; PMCID: PMC6073490

110. Valdeolivas S, Navarrete C, Cantarero I, Bellido ML, Muñoz E, Sagredo O. Neuroprotective properties of cannabigerol in Huntington's disease: studies in R6/2 mice and 3-nitropropionate-lesioned mice. Neurotherapeutics. 2015 Jan;12(1):185-99. doi: 10.1007/s13311-014-0304-z. PMID: 25252936; PMCID: PMC4322067.

111. Carrillo-Salinas FJ, Navarrete C, Mecha M, Feliú A, Collado JA, Cantarero I, Bellido ML, Muñoz E, Guaza C. A cannabigerol derivative suppresses immune responses and protects

mice from experimental autoimmune encephalomyelitis. PLoS One. 2014 Apr 11;9(4):e94733. doi: 10.1371/journal.pone.0094733. PMID: 24727978; PMCID: PMC3984273.

112. Wilkinson JD, Williamson EM.Cannabinoids inhibit human keratinocyte proliferation through a non-CB1/CB2 mechanism and have a potential therapeutic value in the treatment of psoriasis. J Derm Sciences. 2007;45(2): 87-92

113. Tóth KF, Ádám D, Bíró T, Oláh A. Cannabinoid Signaling in the Skin: Therapeutic Potential of the "C(ut)annabinoid" System. *Molecules*. 2019;24(5):918. Published 2019 Mar 6. doi:10.3390/molecules24050918.

114. Borrelli F, Pagano E, Romano B, Panzera S, Maiello F, Coppola D, De Petrocellis L, Buono L, Orlando P, Izzo AA. Colon carcinogenesis is inhibited by the TRPM8 antagonist cannabigerol, a Cannabis-derived non-psychotropic cannabinoid. Carcinogenesis. 2014 Dec;35(12):2787-97. doi: 10.1093/carcin/bgu205. Epub 2014 Sep 30. PMID: 25269802.

115. Scott KA, Shah S, Dalgleish AG, Liu WM. Enhancing the activity of cannabidiol and other cannabinoids in vitro through modifications to drug combinations and treatment schedules. Anticancer Res. 2013 Oct;33(10):4373-80. PMID: 24123005.

116. Pagano E, Montanaro V, Di Girolamo A, Pistone A, Altieri V, Zjawiony JK, Izzo AA, Capasso R. Effect of Non-psychotropic Plant-derived Cannabinoids on Bladder Contractility: Focus on Cannabigerol. Nat Prod Commun. 2015 Jun;10(6):1009-12. PMID: 26197538.

117. Brierley DI, Samuels J, Duncan M, Whalley BJ, Williams CM. A cannabigerol-rich Cannabis sativa extract, devoid of [INCREMENT]9-tetrahydrocannabinol, elicits hyperphagia in rats. Behav Pharmacol. 2017 Jun;28(4):280-284. doi: 10.1097/FBP.0000000000000285. PMID: 28125508.

118. De Petrocellis L, Ligresti A, Moriello AS, Allarà M, Bisogno T, Petrosino S, Stott CG, Di Marzo V. Effects of cannabinoids and cannabinoid-enriched Cannabis extracts on TRP channels and endocannabinoid metabolic enzymes. Br J Pharmacol. 2011 Aug;163(7):1479-94. doi: 10.1111/j.1476-5381.2010.01166.x. PMID: 21175579; PMCID: PMC3165957.

119. Tomida I, Pertwee RG, Azuara-Blanco ACannabinoids and Glaucoma, *British Journal of Ophthalmology* 2004;**88**:708-713.

120. Nadolska K, Goś R. Możliwości zastosowania kannabinoidów w leczeniu jaskry [Possibilities of applying cannabinoids' in the treatment of glaucoma]. Klin Oczna. 2008;110(7-9):314-7. Polish. PMID: 19112869.

121. Nallathambi R, Mazuz M, Namdar D, Shik M, Namintzer D, Vinayaka AC, Ion A, Faigenboim A, Nasser A, Laish I, Konikoff FM, Koltai H. Identification of Synergistic Interaction Between Cannabis-Derived Compounds for Cytotoxic Activity in Colorectal Cancer Cell Lines and Colon Polyps That Induces Apoptosis-Related Cell Death and Distinct Gene Expression. Cannabis Cannabinoid Res. 2018 Jun 1;3(1):120-135. doi: 10.1089/can.2018.0010. PMID: 29992185; PMCID: PMC6038055.

122. D'Aniello E, Fellous T, Iannotti FA, Gentile A, Allarà M, Balestrieri F, Gray R, Amodeo P, Vitale RM, Di Marzo V. Identification and characterization of phytocannabinoids as novel dual PPARα/γ agonists by a computational and in vitro experimental approach. Biochim Biophys Acta Gen Subj. 2019 Mar;1863(3):586-597. doi: 10.1016/j.bbagen.2019.01.002. Epub 2019 Jan 3. PMID: 30611848.

123. Smeriglio A, Giofrè SV, Galati EM, Monforte MT, Cicero N, D'Angelo V, Grassi G, Circosta C. Inhibition of aldose reductase activity by Cannabis sativa chemotypes extracts with high content of cannabidiol or cannabigerol. Fitoterapia. 2018 Jun;127:101-108. doi: 10.1016/j.fitote.2018.02.002. Epub 2018 Feb 7. PMID: 29427593.

124. EM Rock et al. Cannabidiolic acid prevents vomiting in Suncus murinus and nausea-induced behaviour in rats by enhancing 5-HT1A receptor activation. Br J Pharmacol. 2013 Mar; 168(6): 1456–1470

125. EM Rock et al. Effect of low doses of cannabidiolic acid and ondansetron on LiCl-induced conditioned gaping (a model of nausea-induced behaviour) in rats. British journal of pharmacology vol. 169,3 (2013): 685-92.

126. S Takeda et al. Cannabidiolic Acid as a Selective Cyclooxygenase-2 Inhibitory Component in Cannabis. Drug Metabolism and Disposition September 2008, 36 (9) 1917-1921

127. https://patents.google.com/patent/WO2017025712A1/en

128. Ruhaak LR, et al. Evaluation of the Cyclooxygenase Inhibiting Effects of Six Major Cannabinoids Isolated from Cannabis sativa. Biological and Pharmaceutical Bulletin. 2011; 34(5): 774-778

129. De Petrocellis L, Ligresti A, Schiano Moriello A, et al. Non-THC cannabinoids inhibit prostate carcinoma growth in vitro and in vivo: pro-apoptotic effects and underlying mechanisms. *Br J Pharmacol*. 2013;168(1):79-102. doi:10.1111/j.1476-5381.2012.02027.x

130. Rock EM, Kopstick RL, Limebeer CL, Parker LA. Tetrahydrocannabinolic acid reduces nausea-induced conditioned gaping in rats and vomiting in Suncus murinus. *Br J Pharmacol*. 2013;170(3):641-648. doi:10.1111/bph.12316

131. Sulak D, Saneto R, Goldstein B. The current status of artisanal cannabis for the treatment of epilepsy in the United States. Epilepsy Behav. 2017 May;70(Pt B):328-333. doi: 10.1016/j.yebeh.2016.12.032. Epub 2017 Feb 21. PMID: 28254350.

132. Moldzio R, Pacher T, Krewenka C, Kranner B, Novak J, Duvigneau JC, Rausch WD. Effects of cannabinoids Δ(9)-tetrahydrocannabinol, Δ(9)-tetrahydrocannabinolic acid and cannabidiol in MPP+ affected murine mesencephalic cultures. Phytomedicine. 2012 Jun 15;19(8-9):819-24. doi: 10.1016/j.phymed.2012.04.002. Epub 2012 May 7. PMID: 22571976.

133. Hill TD, Cascio MG, Romano B, Duncan M, Pertwee RG, Williams CM, Whalley BJ, Hill AJ. Cannabidivarin-rich cannabis extracts are anticonvulsant in mouse and rat via a CB1 receptor-independent mechanism. Br J Pharmacol. 2013 Oct;170(3):679-92. doi: 10.1111/bph.12321. PMID: 23902406; PMCID: PMC3792005.

134. Amada N, Yamasaki Y, Williams CM, Whalley BJ. Cannabidivarin (CBDV) suppresses pentylenetetrazole (PTZ)-induced increases in epilepsy-related gene expression. PeerJ. 2013 Nov 21;1:e214. doi: 10.7717/peerj.214. PMID: 24282673; PMCID: PMC3840466.

135. Rock EM, Sticht MA, Duncan M, Stott C, Parker LA. Evaluation of the potential of the phytocannabinoids, cannabidivarin (CBDV) and Δ(9)-tetrahydrocannabivarin (THCV), to produce CB1 receptor inverse agonism symptoms of nausea in rats. Br J Pharmacol. 2013 Oct;170(3):671-8. doi: 10.1111/bph.12322. PMID: 23902479; PMCID: PMC3792004.

136. https://apps.dtic.mil/dtic/tr/fulltext/u2/1064689.pdf

137. Vigli D, et al. Chronic treatment with the phytocannabinoid Cannabidivarin (CBDV) rescues behavioural alterations and brain atrophy in a mouse model of Rett syndrome. Neuropharmacology 2018; 140:121-129.

138. Zamberletti E, Gabaglio M, Piscitelli F, Brodie JS, Woolley-Roberts M, Barbiero I, Tramarin M, Binelli G, Landsberger N, Kilstrup-Nielsen C, Rubino T, Di Marzo V, Parolaro D. Cannabidivarin completely rescues cognitive deficits and delays neurological and motor defects in male *Mecp2* mutant mice. J Psychopharmacol. 2019 Jul;33(7):894-907. doi: 10.1177/0269881119844184. Epub 2019 May 14. PMID: 31084246.

139. Iannotti FA, Pagano E, Moriello AS, Alvino FG, Sorrentino NC, D'Orsi L, Gazzerro E, Capasso R, De Leonibus E, De Petrocellis L, Di Marzo V. Effects of non-euphoric plant cannabinoids on muscle quality and performance of dystrophic mdx mice. Br J Pharmacol.

2019 May;176(10):1568-1584. doi: 10.1111/bph.14460. Epub 2018 Sep 9. PMID: 30074247; PMCID: PMC6487563.

140. Pertwee RG. The diverse CB1 and CB2 receptor pharmacology of three plant cannabinoids: delta9-tetrahydrocannabinol, cannabidiol and delta9-tetrahydrocannabivarin. *Br J Pharmacol.* 2008;153(2):199-215. doi:10.1038/sj.bjp.0707442

141. Newer Concepts of Cannabis Action and Opiate Dependence. Basel, Karger, 1974, pp 3-11. doi: 10.1159/000400229

142. Gill EW, Paton WD, Pertwee RG. Preliminary experiments on the chemistry and pharmacology of cannabis. Nature. 1970 Oct 10;228(5267):134-6. doi: 10.1038/228134a0. PMID: 5466704.

143. McPartland JM, Duncan M, Di Marzo V, Pertwee RG. Are cannabidiol and Δ(9) - tetrahydrocannabivarin negative modulators of the endocannabinoid system? A systematic review. *Br J Pharmacol.* 2015;172(3):737-753. doi:10.1111/bph.12944

144. Englund A, Atakan Z, Kralj A, Tunstall N, Murray R, Morrison P. The effect of five day dosing with THCV on THC-induced cognitive, psychological and physiological effects in healthy male human volunteers: A placebo-controlled, double-blind, crossover pilot trial. Journal of Psychopharmacology. 2016;30(2):140-151. doi:10.1177/0269881115615104

145. Bolognini D, Costa B, Maione S, et al. The plant cannabinoid Delta9-tetrahydrocannabivarin can decrease signs of inflammation and inflammatory pain in mice. *Br J Pharmacol.* 2010;160(3):677-687. doi:10.1111/j.1476-5381.2010.00756.x

146. García C, Palomo-Garo C, García-Arencibia M, Ramos J, Pertwee R, Fernández-Ruiz J. Symptom-relieving and neuroprotective effects of the phytocannabinoid Δ⁹-THCV in animal models of Parkinson's disease. *Br J Pharmacol.* 2011;163(7):1495-1506. doi:10.1111/j.1476-5381.2011.01278.x

147. Hill AJ, Weston SE, Jones NA, Smith I, Bevan SA, Williamson EM, Stephens GJ, Williams CM, Whalley BJ. Δ⁹-Tetrahydrocannabivarin suppresses in vitro epileptiform and in vivo seizure activity in adult rats. Epilepsia. 2010 Aug;51(8):1522-32. doi: 10.1111/j.1528-1167.2010.02523.x. Epub 2010 Feb 26. PMID: 20196794.

148. Jadoon KA, Ratcliffe SH, Barrett DA, Thomas EL, Stott C, Bell JD, O'Sullivan SE, Tan GD. Efficacy and Safety of Cannabidiol and Tetrahydrocannabivarin on Glycemic and Lipid Parameters in Patients With Type 2 Diabetes: A Randomized, Double-Blind, Placebo-Controlled, Parallel Group Pilot Study. Diabetes Care. 2016 Oct; 39(10):1777-86. doi: 10.2337/dc16-0650. Epub 2016 Aug 29. PMID: 27573936

149. Scutt A, Williamson EM. Cannabinoids stimulate fibroblastic colony formation by bone marrow cells indirectly via CB2 receptors. Calcif Tissue Int. 2007 Jan;80(1):50-9. doi: 10.1007/s00223-006-0171-7. Epub 2007 Jan 4. PMID: 17205329.

150. Wargent ET, Zaibi MS, Silvestri C, Hislop DC, Stocker CJ, Stott CG, Guy GW, Duncan M, Di Marzo V, Cawthorne MA. The cannabinoid Δ(9)-tetrahydrocannabivarin (THCV) ameliorates insulin sensitivity in two mouse models of obesity. Nutr Diabetes. 2013 May 27;3(5):e68. doi: 10.1038/nutd.2013.9. PMID: 23712280; PMCID: PMC3671751.

151. Marnett LJ, Cohen SM, Fukushima S, Gooderham NJ, Hecht SS, Rietjens IM, Smith RL, Adams TB, Bastaki M, Harman CL, McGowen MM, Taylor SV. GRASr2 evaluation of aliphatic acyclic and alicyclic terpenoid tertiary alcohols and structurally related substances used as flavoring ingredients. J Food Sci. 2014 Apr;79(4):R428-41. doi: 10.1111/1750-3841.12407. Epub 2014 Apr 1. PMID: 24689743.

152. Pliny (the Elder). The natural history of Pliny, Volume 4; Bohn's classical library The natural history of Pliny. Translated by John Bostock, Henry Thomas Riley. H.G. Bohn: 1856;XX;298.

153. Chandler RF, Hooper SN. Friedelin and associated triterpenoids. Phytochemistry. 1979;18:711–724.

154. Antonisamy P, Duraipandiyan V, Ignacimuthu S, et al. Anti-diarrhoeal activity of friedelin isolated from Azima tetracantha Lam. in Wistar rats. South Ind J Biol Sci. 2015;1:34–37.

155. Ryz, Natasha R., David J. Remillard, and Ethan B. Russo. "Cannabis roots: a traditional therapy with future potential for treating inflammation and pain." Cannabis and cannabinoid research 2.1 (2017): 210-216.

156. S E McCann, L U Thompson, J Nie, J Dorn, M Trevisan, P G Shields, C B Ambrosone, S B Edge, H F Li, C Kasprzak, J L Freudenheim. Dietary lignan intakes in relation to survival among women with breast cancer: the Western New York Exposures and Breast Cancer (WEB) Study. Breast Cancer Res Treat. 2010 Jul;122(1):229-35.

157. Zhang D, Li C, Zhang L, Li B, Wang Y, Wang R, Chen Z, Xu L, Liu T. Cannabisin D from *Sinomenium Acutum* Inhibits Proliferation and Migration of Glioblastoma Cells through MAPKs Signaling. Nutr Cancer. 2020 Oct 19:1-11. doi: 10.1080/01635581.2020.1836240. Epub ahead of print. PMID: 33076708.

158. Ahn AC, Tewari M, Poon CS, Phillips RS. The limits of reductionism in medicine: could systems biology offer an alternative?. *PLoS Med.* 2006;3(6):e208. doi:10.1371/journal.pmed.0030208

159. https://www.motherearthliving.com/natural-health/botany-of-cannabis-ze0z1011zdeb (Accessed 2/1/21)

160. Moskowitz MH. *Medical Cannabis: A Guide for Patients, Practitioners, and Caregivers.* 2017

161. Sharma P, Murthy P, Bharath MM. Chemistry, metabolism, and toxicology of cannabis: clinical implications. *Iran J Psychiatry.* 2012;7(4):149-156.

162. Sheridan DJ, Julian DG. Achievements and Limitations of Evidence-Based Medicine. J Am Coll Card. Jul 2016; 68(2): 204-213.

163. Hoffmann D, Medical Herbalism: The Science Principles and Practices Of Herbal Medicine. 2003.

164. https://www.thelancet.com/pdfs/journals/lancet/PIIS0140-6736(15)61038-8.pdf (Accessed 2/1/21)

165. Pandey R, Mousawy K, Nagarkatti M, Nagarkatti P. Endocannabinoids and immune regulation. *Pharmacol Res.* 2009;60(2):85-92. doi:10.1016/j.phrs.2009.03.019

166. https://norml.org/marijuana/library/recent-medical-marijuana-research/gastrointestinal-disorders/ (Accessed 2/1/21)

167. Goyal H, et al. Role of Cannabis in Digestive Disorders. Eur J Gastroenterol Hepatol. 2017; 29:135–143

168. Hegde VL, Nagarkatti PS, Nagarkatti M. Role of myeloid-derived suppressor cells in amelioration of experimental autoimmune hepatitis following activation of TRPV1 receptors by cannabidiol. *PLoS One.* 2011;6(4):e18281. Published 2011 Apr 1. doi:10.1371/journal.pone.0018281

169. Kim et al. 2017. Inverse association of marijuana use with nonalcoholic fatty liver disease among adults in the United States. *PLoS One* [open access journal].

170. https://norml.org/marijuana/library/recent-medical-marijuana-research/hepatitis-c/ (Accessed 2/1/21)

171. Tyagi P, Tyagi V, Yoshimura N, Chancellor M. Functional role of cannabinoid receptors in urinary bladder. Indian J Urol. 2010;26(1):26-35. doi:10.4103/0970-1591.60440.

172. https://www.projectcbd.org/cannabis-and-incontinence (Accessed 2/1/21)

173. https://www.marijuanadoctors.com/conditions/interstitial-cystitis/ (Accessed 2/1/21)

174. Bíró T, Tóth BI, Haskó G, Paus R, Pacher P. The endocannabinoid system of the skin in health and disease: novel perspectives and therapeutic opportunities. *Trends Pharmacol Sci.* 2009;30(8):411-420. doi:10.1016/j.tips.2009.05.004

175. https://norml.org/marijuana/library/recent-medical-marijuana-research/methicillin-resistant-staphyloccus-aureus-mrsa/ (Accessed 2/1/21)

176. https://norml.org/marijuana/library/recent-medical-marijuana-research/pruritus/ (Accessed 2/1/21)

177. Johnson JR, Burnell-Nugent M, Lossignol D, Ganae-Motan ED, Potts R, Fallon MT. Multicenter, double-blind, randomized, placebo-controlled, parallel-group study of the efficacy, safety, and tolerability of THC:CBD extract and THC extract in patients with intractable cancer-related pain. J Pain Symptom Manage. 2010 Feb;39(2):167-79. doi: 10.1016/j.jpainsymman.2009.06.008. Epub 2009 Nov 5. PMID: 19896326.

178. https://norml.org/marijuana/library/recent-medical-marijuana-research/human-immunodeficiency-virus-hiv/ (Accessed 2/1/21)

179. Comelli F, Bettoni I, Colleoni M, Giagnoni G, Costa B. Beneficial effects of a Cannabis sativa extract treatment on diabetes-induced neuropathy and oxidative stress. Phytother Res. 2009 Dec;23(12):1678-84. doi: 10.1002/ptr.2806. PMID: 19441010.

180. Wargent ET, Zaibi MS, Silvestri C, Hislop DC, Stocker CJ, Stott CG, Guy GW, Duncan M, Di Marzo V, Cawthorne MA. The cannabinoid Δ(9)-tetrahydrocannabivarin (THCV) ameliorates insulin sensitivity in two mouse models of obesity. Nutr Diabetes. 2013 May 27;3(5):e68. doi: 10.1038/nutd.2013.9. PMID: 23712280; PMCID: PMC3671751.

181. https://norml.org/marijuana/library/recent-medical-marijuana-research/diabetes-mellitus/ (Accessed 2/1/21)

182. Wiese B, Wilson-Poe AR. Emerging Evidence for Cannabis' Role in Opioid Use Disorder. *Cannabis Cannabinoid Res.* 2018;3(1):179-189. Published 2018 Sep 1. doi:10.1089/can.2018.0022

183. https://healer.com/published-data-on-cannabis-treatment-to-reduce-opioid-usage/ (Accessed 2/1/21)

184. https://norml.org/marijuana/library/recent-medical-marijuana-research/chronic-pain/ (Accessed 2/1/21)

185. Fiz J, Durán M, Capellà D, Carbonell J, Farré M. Cannabis use in patients with fibromyalgia: effect on symptoms, relief and health-related quality of life. PLoS One. 2011 Apr 21;6(4):e18440. doi: 10.1371/journal.pone.0018440. PMID: 21533029; PMCID: PMC3080871.

186. https://norml.org/marijuana/library/recent-medical-marijuana-research/fibromyalgia/ (Accessed 2/1/21)

187. https://norml.org/marijuana/library/recent-medical-marijuana-research/rheumatoid-arthritis/ (Accessed 2/1/21)

188. https://norml.org/marijuana/library/recent-medical-marijuana-research/migraine/ (Accessed 2/1/21)

189. Babson KA, Sottile J, Morabito D. Cannabis, Cannabinoids, and Sleep: a Review of the Literature. Curr Psychiatry Rep. 2017 Apr;19(4):23. doi: 10.1007/s11920-017-0775-9. PMID: 28349316.

190. https://norml.org/marijuana/library/recent-medical-marijuana-research/sleep-apnea/ (Accessed 2/1/21)

191. Campos A. C., Fogaça M. V., Sonego A. B., Guimarães F. S. Cannabidiol, neuroprotection and neuropsychiatric disorders. *Pharmacological Research.* 2016;112:119–127. doi: 10.1016/j.phrs.2016.01.033.

192. Hayakawa K, Mishima K, Fujiwara M. Therapeutic Potential of Non-Psychotropic Cannabidiol in Ischemic Stroke. Pharmaceuticals (Basel). 2010 Jul 8;3(7):2197-2212. doi: 10.3390/ph3072197. PMID: 27713349; PMCID: PMC4036658.

193. Ceprián M, Jiménez-Sánchez L, Vargas C, Barata L, Hind W, Martínez-Orgado J. Cannabidiol reduces brain damage and improves functional recovery in a neonatal rat model of arterial ischemic stroke. Neuropharmacology. 2017 Apr;116:151-159. doi: 10.1016/j.neuropharm.2016.12.017. Epub 2016 Dec 21. PMID: 28012949.

194. https://norml.org/marijuana/library/recent-medical-marijuana-research/amyotrophic-lateral-sclerosis/ (Accessed 2/1/21)

195. https://norml.org/marijuana/library/recent-medical-marijuana-research/alzheimers-disease/ (Accessed 2/1/21)

196. Heneka M. T., Carson M. J., Khoury J. El., et al. Neuroinflammation in Alzheimer's disease. The Lancet Neurology. 2015;14(4):388–405. doi: 10.1016/s1474-4422(15)70016-5.

197. Martín-Moreno A. M., Reigada D., Ramírez B. G., et al. Cannabidiol and other cannabinoids reduce microglial activation in vitro and in vivo: Relevance to Alzheimer's disease. Molecular Pharmacology. 2011;79(6):964–973. doi: 10.1124/mol.111.071290.

198. Watt G., Karl T. In vivo evidence for therapeutic properties of cannabidiol (CBD) for Alzheimer's Disease. Front. Pharmacol. 2017;8, article 20

199. Hughes B., Herron C. E. Cannabidiol Reverses Deficits in Hippocampal LTP in a Model of Alzheimer's Disease. Neurochemical Research. 2018 doi: 10.1007/s11064-018-2513-z.

200. https://www.anxiety.org/is-cannabis-an-effective-treatment-for-anxiety-what-research-shows (Accessed 2/1/21)

201. https://norml.org/marijuana/library/recent-medical-marijuana-research/huntingtons-disease/ (Accessed 2/1/21)

202. https://norml.org/marijuana/library/recent-medical-marijuana-research/parkinsons-disease/ (Accessed 2/1/21)

203. Vivekanantham S., Shah S., Dewji R., Dewji A., Khatri C., Ologunde R. Neuroinflammation in Parkinson's disease: Role in neurodegeneration and tissue repair. International Journal of Neuroscience. 2015;125(10):717–725. doi: 10.3109/00207454.2014.982795.

204. Gelders Géraldine, Baekelandt Veerle, Van der Perren Anke. Linking Neuroinflammation and Neurodegeneration in Parkinson's Disease. Journal of Immunology Research. 2018;2018:12. doi: 10.1155/2018/4784268.4784268

205. Hirsch E. C., Vyas S., Hunot S. Neuroinflammation in Parkinson's disease. Parkinsonism & Related Disorders. 2012;18(1):S210–S212.

206. https://norml.org/marijuana/library/recent-medical-marijuana-research/post-traumatic-stress/ (Accessed 2/1/21)

207. https://norml.org/marijuana/library/recent-medical-marijuana-research/dystonia/ (Accessed 2/1/21)

208. https://norml.org/marijuana/library/recent-medical-marijuana-research/tourette-syndrome/ (Accessed 2/1/21)

209. Chiurchiù V, van der Stelt M, Centonze D, Maccarrone M. The endocannabinoid system and its therapeutic exploitation in multiple sclerosis: Clues for other neuroinflammatory diseases. Prog Neurobiol. 2018 Jan;160:82-100. doi: 10.1016/j.pneurobio.2017.10.007. Epub 2017 Oct 31. PMID: 29097192.

210. https://norml.org/marijuana/library/recent-medical-marijuana-research/multiple-sclerosis/ (Accessed 2/1/21)

211. Koudriavtseva T., Mainero C. Neuroinflammation, neurodegeneration and regeneration in multiple sclerosis: Intercorrelated manifestations of the immune response. *Neural Regeneration Research*. 2016;11(11):1727–1730. doi: 10.4103/1673-5374.194804.

212. Chitnis T. The Role of CD4 T Cells in the Pathogenesis of Multiple Sclerosis. *International Review of Neurobiology*. 2007;79:43–72. doi: 10.1016/S0074-7742(07)79003-7.

213. Kaskow B. J., Baecher-Allan C. Effector T Cells in Multiple Sclerosis. *Cold Spring Harbor Perspectives in Medicine*. 2018;8(4):p. a029025. doi: 10.1101/cshperspect.a029025.

214. https://norml.org/marijuana/library/recent-medical-marijuana-research/epilepsy/ (Accessed 2/1/21)

215. Kalant H. Ch 13 Effects of Cannabis and Cannabinoids in the Human Nervous System. The Effects of Drug Abuse on the Human Nervous System. Elsevier, Inc. 2014; http://dx.doi.org/10.1016/B978-0-12-418679-8.00013-7

216. Thiele E., Marsh E., Mazurkiewicz-Bełdzińska M., Halford J.J., Gunning B., Devinsky O., Checketts D., Roberts C. Cannabidiol in patients with Lennox-Gastaut syndrome: Interim analysis of an open-label extension study. Epilepsia. 2019;60:419–428. doi: 10.1111/epi.14670.

217. https://norml.org/marijuana/library/recent-medical-marijuana-research/gliomas-cancer/ (Accessed 2/1/21)

218. Dumitru C. A., Sandikcioglu I. E., Karsak M. Cannabinoids in Glioblastoma Therapy: New Applications for Old Drugs. *Frontiers in Molecular Neuroscience*. 2018;11, article 159 doi: 10.3389/fnmol.2018.00159.

219. Nabissi M., Morelli M. B., Santoni M., Santoni G. Triggering of the TRPV2 channel by cannabidiol sensitizes glioblastoma cells to cytotoxic chemotherapeutic agents. *Carcinogenesis*. 2013;34(1):48–57. doi: 10.1093/carcin/bgs328.

220. Morelli M. B., Nabissi M., Amantini C., et al. The transient receptor potential vanilloid-2 cation channel impairs glioblastoma stem-like cell proliferation and promotes differentiation. *International Journal of Cancer*. 2012;131(7):E1067–E1077. doi: 10.1002/ijc.27588.

221. Dall'Stella P.B., Docema M.F.L., Maldaun M.V.C., Feher O., Lancellotti C.L.P. Case Report: Clinical Outcome and Image Response of Two Patients With Secondary High-Grade Glioma Treated With Chemoradiation, PCV, and Cannabidiol. Front. Oncol. 2018;8:643. doi: 10.3389/fonc.2018.00643.

222. Ramos JA, Bianco FJ. The role of cannabinoids in prostate cancer: Basic science perspective and potential clinical applications. *Indian J Urol*. 2012;28(1):9-14. doi:10.4103/0970-1591.94942

223. Sharma, M. , Hudson, J. , Adomat, H. , Guns, E. and Cox, M. (2014) *In Vitro* Anticancer Activity of Plant-Derived Cannabidiol on Prostate Cancer Cell Lines. *Pharmacology & Pharmacy*, **5**, 806-820. doi: 10.4236/pp.2014.58091.

224. Takeda S, Okajima S, Miyoshi H, et al. Cannabidiolic acid, a major cannabinoid in fiber-type cannabis, is an inhibitor of MDA-MB-231 breast cancer cell migration. *Toxicol Lett*. 2012;214(3):314-319. doi:10.1016/j.toxlet.2012.08.029

225. McAllister SD, Christian RT, Horowitz MP, Garcia A, Desprez PY. Cannabidiol as a novel inhibitor of Id-1 gene expression in aggressive breast cancer cells. Mol Cancer Ther. 2007 Nov;6(11):2921-7. doi: 10.1158/1535-7163.MCT-07-0371. PMID: 18025276.

226. Shrivastava A, Kuzontkoski PM, Groopman JE, Prasad A. Cannabidiol induces programmed cell death in breast cancer cells by coordinating the cross-talk between apoptosis and autophagy. Mol Cancer Ther. 2011 Jul;10(7):1161-72. doi: 10.1158/1535-7163.MCT-10-1100. Epub 2011 May 12. PMID: 21566064.

227. Fraguas-Sánchez AI, Fernández-Carballido A, Simancas-Herbada R, Martin-Sabroso C, Torres-Suárez AI. CBD loaded microparticles as a potential formulation to improve paclitaxel and doxorubicin-based chemotherapy in breast cancer. Int J Pharm. 2020 Jan 25;574:118916. doi: 10.1016/j.ijpharm.2019.118916. Epub 2019 Dec 4. PMID: 31811927.

228. McAllister SD, Murase R, Christian RT, Lau D, Zielinski AJ, Allison J, Almanza C, Pakdel A, Lee J, Limbad C, Liu Y, Debs RJ, Moore DH, Desprez PY. Pathways mediating the effects of cannabidiol on the reduction of breast cancer cell proliferation, invasion and metastasis. Breast Cancer Res Treat. 2011 Aug;129(1):37-47. doi: 10.1007/s10549-010-1177-4. Epub 2010 Sep 22. Erratum in: Breast Cancer Res Treat. 2012 May;133(1):401-4. PMID: 20859676; PMCID: PMC3410650.

229. Murase R, Kawamura R, Singer E, Pakdel A, Sarma P, Judkins J, Elwakeel E, Dayal S, Martinez-Martinez E, Amere M, Gujjar R, Mahadevan A, Desprez PY, McAllister SD. Targeting multiple cannabinoid anti-tumour pathways with a resorcinol derivative leads to inhibition of advanced stages of breast cancer. Br J Pharmacol. 2014 Oct;171(19):4464-77. doi: 10.1111/bph.12803. Epub 2014 Sep 5. PMID: 24910342; PMCID: PMC4209152.

230. Blasco-Benito S, Seijo-Vila M, Caro-Villalobos M, Tundidor I, Andradas C, García-Taboada E, Wade J, Smith S, Guzmán M, Pérez-Gómez E, Gordon M, Sánchez C. Appraising the "entourage effect": Antitumor action of a pure cannabinoid versus a botanical drug preparation in preclinical models of breast cancer. Biochem Pharmacol. 2018 Nov;157:285-293. doi: 10.1016/j.bcp.2018.06.025. Epub 2018 Jun 27. PMID: 29940172.

231. McAllister SD, Soroceanu L, Desprez PY. The Antitumor Activity of Plant-Derived Non-Psychoactive Cannabinoids. J Neuroimmune Pharmacol. 2015 Jun;10(2):255-67. doi: 10.1007/s11481-015-9608-y. Epub 2015 Apr 28. PMID: 25916739; PMCID: PMC4470774.

232. Casanova ML, Blázquez C, Martínez-Palacio J, et al. Inhibition of skin tumor growth and angiogenesis in vivo by activation of cannabinoid receptors. *J Clin Invest.* 2003;111(1):43-50. doi:10.1172/JCI16116

233. Scheau C, Badarau IA, Mihai LG, et al. Cannabinoids in the Pathophysiology of Skin Inflammation. *Molecules.* 2020;25(3):652. Published 2020 Feb 4. doi:10.3390/molecules25030652

234. Blázquez C., Carracedo A., Barrado L., et al. Cannabinoid receptors as novel targets for the treatment of melanoma. *The FASEB journal : official publication of the Federation of American Societies for Experimental Biology.* 2006;20(14):2633–2635. doi: 10.1096/fj.06-6638fje. Bode A. M., Cho Y.-Y., Zheng D., et al. Transient receptor potential type vanilloid 1 suppresses skin carcinogenesis. *Cancer Research.* 2009;69(3):905–913. doi: 10.1158/0008-5472.CAN-08-3263.

235. Benz A. H., Renné C., Maronde E., et al. Expression and functional relevance of cannabinoid receptor 1 in hodgkin lymphoma. *PLoS ONE.* 2013;8(12)e81675

236. Flygare J, Gustafsson K, Kimby E, Christensson B, Sander B. Cannabinoid receptor ligands mediate growth inhibition and cell death in mantle cell lymphoma. FEBS Lett. 2005 Dec 19;579(30):6885-9. doi: 10.1016/j.febslet.2005.11.020. PMID: 16337199.

237. Gustafsson K, Wang X, Severa D, Eriksson M, Kimby E, Merup M, Christensson B, Flygare J, Sander B. Expression of cannabinoid receptors type 1 and type 2 in non-Hodgkin lymphoma: growth inhibition by receptor activation. Int J Cancer. 2008 Sep 1;123(5):1025-33. doi: 10.1002/ijc.23584. PMID: 18546271.

238. Carracedo A., Gironella M., Lorente M., et al. Cannabinoids induce apoptosis of pancreatic tumor cells via endoplasmic reticulum stress-related genes. *Cancer Research.* 2006;66(13):6748–6755. doi: 10.1158/0008-5472.CAN-06-0169.

239. Michalski CW, Oti FE, Erkan M, et al. Cannabinoids in pancreatic cancer: correlation with survival and pain. *Int J Cancer.* 2008;122(4):742-750. doi:10.1002/ijc.23114

240. Sharafi G, He H, Nikfarjam M. Potential Use of Cannabinoids for the Treatment of Pancreatic Cancer. *J Pancreatic Cancer.* 2019;5(1):1-7. Published 2019 Jan 25. doi:10.1089/pancan.2018.0019

241. Dando I, Donadelli M, Costanzo C, et al. . Cannabinoids inhibit energetic metabolism and induce AMPK-dependent autophagy in pancreatic cancer cells. Cell Death Dis. 2013;4:e664.

242. Velasco G, Carracedo A, Lorente M, et al. . Cannabinoids as potential antitumoral agents in pancreatic cancer. In: Pancreatology: From Bench to Bedside.

243. Ferro R, Adamska A, Lattanzio R, et al. . GPR55 signalling promotes proliferation of pancreatic cancer cells and tumour growth in mice, and its inhibition increases effects of gemcitabine. Oncogene. 2018;37:6368–6382

244. Moreau M, Ibeh U, Decosmo K, et al. Flavonoid Derivative of *Cannabis* Demonstrates Therapeutic Potential in Preclinical Models of Metastatic Pancreatic Cancer [published correction appears in Front Oncol. 2020 Aug 21;10:1434]. *Front Oncol.* 2019;9:660. Published 2019 Jul 23. doi:10.3389/fonc.2019.00660

245. Dariš B, Tancer Verboten M, Knez Ž, Ferk P. Cannabinoids in cancer treatment: Therapeutic potential and legislation. *Bosn J Basic Med Sci.* 2019;19(1):14-23. Published 2019 Feb 12. doi:10.17305/bjbms.2018.3532

246. Mukhopadhyay B., Schuebel K., Mukhopadhyay P., et al. Cannabinoid receptor 1 promotes hepatocellular carcinoma initiation and progression through multiple mechanisms. *Hepatology.* 2015;61(5):1615–1626. doi: 10.1002/hep.27686.

247. Berasain C., Perugorria M. J., Latasa M. U., et al. The Epidermal Growth Factor Receptor: A Link Between Inflammation and Liver Cancer. *Experimental Biology and Medicine.* 2009;234(7):713–725. doi: 10.3181/0901-MR-12.

248. Powles T, te Poele R, Shamash J, Chaplin T, Propper D, Joel S, Oliver T, Liu WM. Cannabis-induced cytotoxicity in leukemic cell lines: the role of the cannabinoid receptors and the MAPK pathway. Blood. 2005 Feb 1;105(3):1214-21. doi: 10.1182/blood-2004-03-1182. Epub 2004 Sep 28. PMID: 15454482.

249. Lombard C., Nagarkatti M., Nagarkatti P. S. Targeting cannabinoid receptors to treat leukemia: Role of cross-talk between extrinsic and intrinsic pathways in Δ9-tetrahydrocannabinol (THC)-induced apoptosis of Jurkat cells. *Leukemia Research.* 2005;29(8):915–922. doi: 10.1016/j.leukres.2005.01.014.

250. Jia W., Hegde V. L., Singh N. P., et al. Δ9-tetrahydrocannabinol-induced apoptosis in Jurkat leukemia T cells is regulated by translocation of bad to mitochondria. *Molecular Cancer Research.* 2006;4(8):549–562. doi: 10.1158/1541-7786.MCR-05-0193.

251. Singh Y, Bali C. Cannabis extract treatment for terminal acute lymphoblastic leukemia with a Philadelphia chromosome mutation. *Case Rep Oncol.* 2013;6(3):585-592. Published 2013 Nov 28. doi:10.1159/000356446

252. Kampa-Schittenhelm KM, Salitzky O, Akmut F, Illing B, Kanz L, Salih HR, Schittenhelm MM. Dronabinol has preferential antileukemic activity in acute lymphoblastic and myeloid leukemia with lymphoid differentiation patterns. BMC Cancer. 2016 Jan 16;16:25. doi: 10.1186/s12885-015-2029-8. PMID: 26775260; PMCID: PMC4715874.

253. Scott KA, Dalgleish AG, Liu WM. Anticancer effects of phytocannabinoids used with chemotherapy in leukaemia cells can be improved by altering the sequence of their administration. Int J Oncol. 2017 Jul;51(1):369-377. doi: 10.3892/ijo.2017.4022. Epub 2017 May 29. PMID: 28560402.

254. Amantini C., Ballarini P., Caprodossi S., et al. Triggering of transient receptor potential vanilloid type 1 (TRPV1) by capsaicin induces Fas/CD95-mediated apoptosis of urothelial cancer cells in an ATM-dependent manner. *Carcinogenesis.* 2009;30(8):1320–1329. doi: 10.1093/carcin/bgp138.

255. Bettiga A, Aureli M, Colciago G, et al. Bladder cancer cell growth and motility implicate cannabinoid 2 receptor-mediated modifications of sphingolipids metabolism. *Sci Rep.* 2017;7:42157. Published 2017 Feb 13. doi:10.1038/srep42157

256. Shi Y, Zou M, Baitei EY, Alzahrani AS, Parhar RS, Al-Makhalafi Z, Al-Mohanna FA. Cannabinoid 2 receptor induction by IL-12 and its potential as a therapeutic target for the treatment of anaplastic thyroid carcinoma. Cancer Gene Ther. 2008 Feb;15(2):101-7. doi: 10.1038/sj.cgt.7701101. Epub 2007 Dec 21. PMID: 18197164.

257. Fonseca BM, Correia-da-Silva G, Teixeira NA. Cannabinoid-induced cell death in endometrial cancer cells: involvement of TRPV1 receptors in apoptosis. J Physiol Biochem. 2018 May;74(2):261-272. doi: 10.1007/s13105-018-0611-7. Epub 2018 Feb 13. PMID: 29441458.

258. Taylor AH, Tortolani D, Ayakannu T, Konje JC, Maccarrone M. (Endo)Cannabinoids and Gynaecological Cancers. *Cancers (Basel).* 2020;13(1):37. Published 2020 Dec 25. doi:10.3390/cancers13010037

259. Cianchi F., Papucci L., Schiavone N., et al. Cannabinoid receptor activation induces apoptosis through tumor necrosis factor alpha-mediated ceramide de novo synthesis in colon cancer cells. *Clinical Cancer Research.* 2008;14(23):7691–7700. doi: 10.1158/1078-0432.ccr-08-0799. Jung C. K., Kang W. K., Park J. M., et al. Expression of the cannabinoid type I receptor and prognosis following surgery in colorectal cancer. *Oncology Letters.* 2013;5(3):870–876. doi: 10.3892/ol.2012.1081

260. Borrelli F, Pagano E, Romano B, Panzera S, Maiello F, Coppola D, De Petrocellis L, Buono L, Orlando P, Izzo AA. Colon carcinogenesis is inhibited by the TRPM8 antagonist cannabigerol, a Cannabis-derived non-psychotropic cannabinoid. Carcinogenesis. 2014 Dec;35(12):2787-97. doi: 10.1093/carcin/bgu205. Epub 2014 Sep 30. PMID: 25269802.

261. Romano B, Borrelli F, Pagano E, Cascio MG, Pertwee RG, Izzo AA. Inhibition of colon carcinogenesis by a standardized Cannabis sativa extract with high content of cannabidiol. Phytomedicine. 2014 Apr 15;21(5):631-9. doi: 10.1016/j.phymed.2013.11.006. Epub 2013 Dec 25. PMID: 24373545.

262. Orrego-González E, Londoño-Tobón L, Ardila-González J, Polania-Tovar D, Valencia-Cárdenas A, Velez-Van Meerbeke A. Cannabinoid Effects on Experimental Colorectal Cancer Models Reduce Aberrant Crypt Foci (ACF) and Tumor Volume: A Systematic Review. Evid Based Complement Alternat Med. 2020 Jul 20;2020:2371527. doi: 10.1155/2020/2371527. PMID: 32765628; PMCID: PMC7387981.

263. Sarfaraz S, Afaq F, Adhami VM, et al. . Cannabinoid receptor agonist-induced apoptosis of human prostate cancer cells LNCaP proceeds through sustained activation of ERK1/2 leading to G1 cell cycle arrest. J Biol Chem. 2006;281:39480–39491

264. Singh K, Jamshidi N, Zomer R, Piva TJ, Mantri N. Cannabinoids and Prostate Cancer: A Systematic Review of Animal Studies. Int J Mol Sci. 2020 Aug 29;21(17):6265. doi: 10.3390/ijms21176265. PMID: 32872551; PMCID: PMC7503992.

265. Orellana-Serradell O, Poblete CE, Sanchez C, Castellón EA, Gallegos I, Huidobro C, Llanos MN, Contreras HR. Proapoptotic effect of endocannabinoids in prostate cancer cells. Oncol Rep. 2015 Apr;33(4):1599-608. doi: 10.3892/or.2015.3746. Epub 2015 Jan 21. PMID: 25606819; PMCID: PMC4358087.

266. Roth MD, Arora A, Barsky SH, Kleerup EC, Simmons M, Tashkin DP. Airway inflammation in young marijuana and tobacco smokers. Am J Respir Crit Care Med. 1998 Mar;157(3 Pt 1):928-37. doi: 10.1164/ajrccm.157.3.9701026. PMID: 9517614.

267. Tashkin DP. Effects of marijuana smoking on the lung. Ann Am Thorac Soc. 2013 Jun;10(3):239-47. doi: 10.1513/AnnalsATS.201212-127FR. PMID: 23802821.

268. Newmeyer MN, Swortwood MJ, Abulseoud OA, Huestis MA. Subjective and physiological effects, and expired carbon monoxide concentrations in frequent and occasional cannabis smokers following smoked, vaporized, and oral cannabis administration. Drug Alcohol Depend. 2017 Jun 1;175:67-76. doi: 10.1016/j.drugalcdep.2017.02.003. Epub 2017 Mar 29. PMID: 28407543.

269. Abulseoud OA, Zuccoli ML, Zhang L, Barnes A, Huestis MA, Lin DT. The acute effect of cannabis on plasma, liver and brain ammonia dynamics, a translational study. Eur Neuropsychopharmacol. 2017 Jul;27(7):679-690. doi: 10.1016/j.euroneuro.2017.03.006. Epub 2017 Apr 26. PMID: 28456476; PMCID: PMC6091863.

270. Bloor RN, Wang TS, Spanel P, Smith D. Ammonia release from heated 'street' cannabis leaf and its potential toxic effects on cannabis users. Addiction. 2008 Oct;103(10):1671-7. doi: 10.1111/j.1360-0443.2008.02281.x. Epub 2008 Aug 14. PMID: 18705690.

271. Earleywine M, Barnwell SS. Decreased respiratory symptoms in cannabis users who vaporize. Harm Reduct J. 2007 Apr 16;4:11. doi: 10.1186/1477-7517-4-11. PMID: 17437626; PMCID: PMC1853086.

272. Van Dam NT, Earleywine M. Pulmonary function in cannabis users: Support for a clinical trial of the vaporizer. Int J Drug Policy. 2010 Nov;21(6):511-3. doi: 10.1016/j.drugpo.2010.04.001. Epub 2010 May 6. PMID: 20451365.

273. Kicman A, Toczek M. The Effects of Cannabidiol, a Non-Intoxicating Compound of Cannabis, on the Cardiovascular System in Health and Disease. Int J Mol Sci. 2020 Sep; 21(18): 6740. Published online 2020 Sep 14. doi: 10.3390/ijms21186740 PMCID: PMC7554803 PMID: 32937917

274. Carbone F, Mach F, Vuilleumier N, Montecucco. A single ultra low dose of THC before ischemia is a safe and effective treatment that reduces myocardial ischemic damage. Current Medicinal Chemistry. 2014; 21(35): 4046-4058.

275. Rumalla K, Reddy AY, Mittal MK. Recreational marijuana use and acute ischemic stroke: A population-based analysis of hospitalized patients in the United States. J Neurol Sci. 2016 May 15;364:191-6. doi: 10.1016/j.jns.2016.01.066. Epub 2016 Feb 4. PMID: 26874461.

276. Hemachandra D, McKetin R, Cherbuin N, Anstey KJ. Heavy cannabis users at elevated risk of stroke: evidence from a general population survey. Aust N Z J Public Health. 2016 Jun;40(3):226-30. doi: 10.1111/1753-6405.12477. Epub 2015 Nov 11. PMID: 26558539.

277. Thomas G, Kloner RA, Rezkalla S. Adverse cardiovascular, cerebrovascular, and peripheral vascular effects of marijuana inhalation: what cardiologists need to know. Am J Cardiol. 2014 Jan 1;113(1):187-90. doi: 10.1016/j.amjcard.2013.09.042. Epub 2013 Oct 5. PMID: 24176069.

278. Wilson KM. Secondhand Marijuana Smoke Is Not Benign. J Am Heart Assoc. 2016 Jul 27;5(8):e004004. doi: 10.1161/JAHA.116.004004. PMID: 27464789; PMCID: PMC5015313.

279. Maguire EA, Gadian DG, Johnsrude IS, Good CD, Ashburner J, Frackowiak RS, Frith CD. Navigation-related structural change in the hippocampi of taxi drivers. Proc Natl Acad Sci U S A. 2000 Apr 11;97(8):4398-403. doi: 10.1073/pnas.070039597. PMID: 10716738; PMCID: PMC18253.

280. Batalla A, Bhattacharyya S, Yücel M, Fusar-Poli P, Crippa JA, Nogué S, Torrens M, Pujol J, Farré M, Martin-Santos R. Structural and functional imaging studies in chronic cannabis

users: a systematic review of adolescent and adult findings. PLoS One. 2013;8(2):e55821. doi: 10.1371/journal.pone.0055821. Epub 2013 Feb 4. PMID: 23390554; PMCID: PMC3563634.

281. Meier MH, Caspi A, Ambler A, et al. Persistent cannabis users show neuropsychological decline from childhood to midlife. *Proc Natl Acad Sci U S A*. 2012;109(40):E2657-E2664. doi:10.1073/pnas.1206820109

282. Moffitt TE, Meier MH, Caspi A, Poulton R. Reply to Rogeberg and Daly: No evidence that socioeconomic status or personality differences confound the association between cannabis use and IQ decline. *Proc Natl Acad Sci U S A*. 2013;110(11):E980-E982. doi:10.1073/pnas.1300618110

283. Lynam DR, Milich R, Zimmerman R, Novak SP, Logan TK, Martin C, Leukefeld C, Clayton R. Project DARE: no effects at 10-year follow-up. J Consult Clin Psychol. 1999 Aug;67(4):590-3. doi: 10.1037//0022-006x.67.4.590. PMID: 10450631.

284. Gundersen TD, Jørgensen N, Andersson AM, Bang AK, Nordkap L, Skakkebæk NE, Priskorn L, Juul A, Jensen TK. Association Between Use of Marijuana and Male Reproductive Hormones and Semen Quality: A Study Among 1,215 Healthy Young Men. Am J Epidemiol. 2015 Sep 15;182(6):473-81. doi: 10.1093/aje/kwv135. Epub 2015 Aug 16. PMID: 26283092.

285. Klonoff-Cohen HS, Natarajan L, Chen RV. A prospective study of the effects of female and male marijuana use on in vitro fertilization (IVF) and gamete intrafallopian transfer (GIFT) outcomes. Am J Obstet Gynecol. 2006 Feb;194(2):369-76. doi: 10.1016/j.ajog.2005.08.020. PMID: 16458631.

286. Foeller ME, Lyell DJ. Marijuana Use in Pregnancy: Concerns in an Evolving Era. J Midwifery Womens Health. 2017 May;62(3):363-367. doi: 10.1111/jmwh.12631. Epub 2017 May 12. PMID: 28498631.

287. Brown QL, Sarvet AL, Shmulewitz D, Martins SS, Wall MM, Hasin DS. Trends in Marijuana Use Among Pregnant and Nonpregnant Reproductive-Aged Women, 2002-2014. JAMA. 2017 Jan 10;317(2):207-209. doi: 10.1001/jama.2016.17383. PMID: 27992619; PMCID: PMC5595220.

288. Foeller ME, Lyell DJ. Marijuana Use in Pregnancy: Concerns in an Evolving Era. J Midwifery Womens Health. 2017 May;62(3):363-367. doi: 10.1111/jmwh.12631. Epub 2017 May 12. PMID: 28498631.

289. van Gelder MM, Reefhuis J, Caton AR, Werler MM, Druschel CM, Roeleveld N; National Birth Defects Prevention Study. Maternal periconceptional illicit drug use and the risk of congenital malformations. Epidemiology. 2009 Jan;20(1):60-6. doi: 10.1097/EDE.0b013e31818e5930. PMID: 19057385.

290. National Academies of Sciences, Engineering, and Medicine; Health and Medicine Division; Board on Population Health and Public Health Practice; Committee on the Health Effects of Marijuana: An Evidence Review and Research Agenda. The Health Effects of Cannabis and Cannabinoids: The Current State of Evidence and Recommendations for Research. Washington (DC): National Academies Press (US); 2017 Jan 12. PMID: 28182367.

291. https://www.cdc.gov/alcohol/features/excessive-alcohol-deaths.html (Accessed 2/1/21)

292. https://www.cdc.gov/tobacco/data_statistics/fact_sheets/health_effects/effects_cig_smoking/index.htm#smoking-death (Accessed 2/1/21)

293. Salomonsen-Sautel S, Min SJ, Sakai JT, Thurstone C, Hopfer C. Trends in fatal motor vehicle crashes before and after marijuana commercialization in Colorado. Drug Alcohol Depend. 2014 Jul 1;140:137-44. doi: 10.1016/j.drugalcdep.2014.04.008. Epub 2014 Apr 23. Erratum in: Drug Alcohol Depend. 2014 Sep 1;142:360. PMID: 24831752; PMCID: PMC4068732.

294. Murray D, Olson J, Lopez AS. When the grass isn't greener: a case series of young children with accidental marijuana ingestion. CJEM. 2016 Nov;18(6):480-483. doi: 10.1017/cem.2015.44. PMID: 27780499. Cao D, Srisuma S, Bronstein AC, Hoyte CO. Characterization of edible marijuana product exposures reported to United States poison centers. Clin Toxicol (Phila). 2016 Nov;54(9):840-846. doi: 10.1080/15563650.2016.1209761. Epub 2016 Jul 15. PMID: 27418198.

295. Wang GS, Le Lait MC, Deakyne SJ, Bronstein AC, Bajaj L, Roosevelt G. Unintentional Pediatric Exposures to Marijuana in Colorado, 2009-2015. JAMA Pediatr. 2016 Sep 6;170(9):e160971. doi: 10.1001/jamapediatrics.2016.0971. Epub 2016 Sep 6. PMID: 27454910.

296. Elsohly MA, Mehmedic Z, Foster S, Gon C, Chandra S, Church JC. Changes in Cannabis Potency Over the Last 2 Decades (1995-2014): Analysis of Current Data in the United States. Biol Psychiatry. 2016;79(7):613-9.

297. Bonnet U, Preuss UW. The cannabis withdrawal syndrome: current insights. Subst Abuse Rehabil. 2017 Apr 27;8:9-37. doi: 10.2147/SAR.S109576. PMID: 28490916; PMCID: PMC5414724.

298. Degenhardt L, Hall W. Extent of illicit drug use and dependence, and their contribution to the global burden of disease. Lancet. 2012;379(9810):55-70.

299. https://www.webmd.com/diet/news/20050808/coffee-is-no-1-source-of-antioxidants#:~:text=%20new%20study%20shows%20coffee,Scranton%2C%20in%20a%20news%20release. (Accessed 2/1/21)

300. Gunasekaran N, Long LE, Dawson BL, et al. Reintoxication: the release of fat-stored delta(9)-tetrahydrocannabinol (THC) into blood is enhanced by food deprivation or ACTH exposure. Br J Pharmacol. 2009;158(5):1330-1337. doi:10.1111/j.1476-5381.2009.00399.x

301. Dr. Dustin Sulak- Healer.com and Kim HS, Anderson JD, Saghafi O, Heard KJ, Monte AA. Cyclic vomiting presentations following marijuana liberalization in Colorado. Acad Emerg Med. 2015 Jun 22(6):694-9.

Chapter 11- An Exploration of Cannabis Cultivation and Testing
(Dr. Andrea Holmes)

This section partially recapitulates but differently integrates some of the material from Chapters 1 and 2 in Volume I. Similarly, it presages but also introduces, with less specificity, concepts that are dealt with more thoroughly later in Volume II. The perspective within this section is business-based as opposed more purely biological or grounded in applied chemistry.

Differences between Marijuana and Hemp Cultivation

Both marijuana and hemp are part of the same family, Cannabis Sativa, which creates a lot of confusion. The term cannabis is often used for marijuana when in fact hemp is also cannabis. Cultivated marijuana has much broader leaves, tighter buds and grows as a short, thick and bushy plant (5 feet), whereas hemp plants grow taller up to 20 feet for industrial hemp and have thinner leaves, mostly concentrated on top. Hemp mainly grows upwards, while marijuana is trained to grow side branches. While there are indoor hemp cultivation sites, it is mostly grown outdoors and does not usually require as much maintenance as marijuana. Hemp has a growth cycle of 108 to 120 days. Marijuana has a growth cycle of 60 to 90 days and requires highly controlled growing conditions like proper temperature, lighting and humidity for optimal THCA content. Marijuana and hemp are susceptible to diseases, molds, etc. Marijuana is planted at one plant per four square feet and requires more space than hemp, which is planted at about 40 to 60 plants per four square feet. Industrial hemp plants are more densely packed at 100 to 120 plants per four square feet. Advantages of growing CBD hemp indoors includes the prevention of cross pollination and a controlled environment.

Male and Female Plants

Typically, cannabis is known as a dioecious species, meaning individual cannabis plants will have either a female or male characteristic. Occasionally, a female cannabis plant can express male traits under extreme stress. When growing hemp for CBD, the female flower contains the concentrated levels of cannabidiol (CBD) used for extraction. It is important to scout and look for males during the change of photoperiod. Individual male flowers can produce hundreds of thousands of pollen grains that can potentially be dispersed onto neighboring farms or even marijuana facilities. If female cannabis is pollinated, that plant will produce seeds, yields will decrease and CBD concentrations will diminish. Pollination for industrial hemp used to generate grain or fiber is different. Male pollen is required for hemp food, feed or oils.

How is cross-pollination prevented on a property cultivating either hemp or marijuana? (Wizenberg et al. 2020) That is a difficult question to answer and poses a unique set of challenges. Distance between farms is the simplest solution. Studies have shown that pollen concentration decreases as the distance between two farms increases up to 10 miles. Growers should check with the local regulatory agency for other farm locations and make it a point to ensure a 10-mile buffer. Practicing this method is, of course, another story. Variables in pollen transportation can include bees, humans, wind speed and direction, rain, topography and physical barriers. Installing physical barriers like large trees or windbreaks can help mitigate pollen transport, but this technique is not 100% effective. Early scouting for male plants in the field and isolating them is another process that will greatly reduce the pollen dispersal. Cultivators will identify male plants in the field around 3 to 4 weeks into the photoperiod.They will use a plastic covering to prevent the pollen from moving. Once the male plant has been isolated, the cultivator will remove the plant and destroy it or use it for breeding. As more acres of hemp and marijuana are being cultivated all over the world, more research needs to be done to ensure that crop losses don't occur due to cross-pollination.

Breeding

When it comes to the applicable breeding and plant genetics, there's a lot involved. Let's go over some of the basics. Some basic plant genetics important to cultivators are **genotypes** and **phenotypes**. A **genotype** is defined as the plant's genetic code, like an instruction manual with options. Many phenotypes can be revealed from the same genotype.

A **phenotype** is the observable physical characteristics or traits the plant expresses. This includes everything from the shape of the bud structure, to coloring and the smell each individual plant produces. Breeding the old fashioned way is as simple as crossing a pollinating male plant with a female plant to fertilize it and produce seeds.

Cloning

Another popular method used heavily in the cannabis industry is called cloning. (Grace and Roberts, 2020, 2019). What is cloning in this context? Cloning is when you take a cutting of a female plant during the vegetative stage of its life and propagate it into its own plant. It is called a clone, because it has the same genetic code. This practice allows cultivators to replicate their best and highest performing plants.

Depending on a grower's goals, they will have to clone their plant before they know if it is a keeper since a grower can't clone them in the flowering stage. Since a lot of growers wait until the later weeks of flowering or even post-harvest to decide on whether to keep a phenotype, it is important to plan for that by taking clones early in the vegetative stage. Depending on the desired goal, some breeders take several generations and considerable time to find the perfect combination of traits, which is why cloning is important.

When cloning, check that the female plant is healthy before proceeding. Disease ridden or nutrient deficient plants are not suitable, because they may not root and may just waste time and resources. The female plant should be at least four to eight weeks old in the vegetative stage at the time of cloning. But clones can be taken anytime during the vegetative stage. Use extreme caution during the entire process as this is a delicate task.

Hermaphrodites

Hermaphrodites can occur naturally, as a genetic mutation or due to stress.(Punja and Holmes, 2020). When this occurs, the cannabis plant will display both sexes, and there will be visual observation of both pollen sacs and flowering buds on the same plant. Usually, if growing the plant's flower for cannabinoid content, this is undesirable as the seeds will grow in the same space as the bud-- taking away space and energy from the buds themselves.

Below is a list of common plant stressors:

1. Using cold water to water plants
2. Excessive irritations (moving, touching, bending, breaking, cutting)
3. Interruptions or inconsistent light schedule
4. Over and under watering
5. Significant temperature changes in the environment
6. Invasive plants and other pests

Seed Quality

Quality is very important when it comes to selecting seeds and clones. Genetics plays a big part in the success of the plant. It is important to choose seeds from a reputable seller and breeder but also to choose a variety or strain suited for the grower's desired application. Seeds can be purchased as feminized if the grower only plans to grow female plants. However, research shows that feminized seeds have a higher chance of mutating into a hermaphrodite. This is typically a good option instead of wasting money on male seeds. Usually, in a batch of seeds, about half (50%) are male, and a grower can't tell which seeds are male or female until after germination and well into the growing process.

Figure: Photograph of a hemp hermaphrodite showing the flower filled with seed. Image Credit: Shutterstock

Seed health is important and should not be overlooked. Otherwise, a grower could be wasting time trying to use seeds that are not suitable. The healthy cannabis seed will be a darker brown color with dark stripes. Young and immature seeds will appear light brown to white and green in color. Cracked seeds may still germinate and grow, but the stress may cause a grower's plant to grow differently than expected.

The **U.S. Hemp Authority Certification Program** is the hemp industry's regulatory body to assure stable genetics of seed, high standards, best practices and self-regulation. The **Colorado Department of Agriculture** created the country's first hemp seed certification program in 2016.

Growing Key Points

Below are a few key points to remember while growing cannabis:

Hemp does not grow optimally in clay, because it tends to become impacted. Outdoor growers should remember that planting early, the risk of frost can stress out or kill plants.

Growing cannabis takes special care and attention. The slightest changes can be seen overnight! The cannabis plant will "speak to the grower" through its physical appearance. If the fan leaves and overall plant seem droopy and dry, the grower likely missed a watering and needs to change the watering schedule to prevent stressing out the plant. Stressed out cannabis plants tend to produce higher tetrahydrocannabinol or THC content, and with hemp, that can quickly turn into a huge legal hurdle.

Plant the seed about ¼ to one inch below the surface; then add a small amount of water to moisten the soil. When planting hemp for seed or fiber production, one can plant 1,500 to 4,000 plants per acre. Farmers who are growing for the purpose of fiber will plant their seeds or clones much closer together to encourage them to grow taller instead of wide and short.

However, for other types of growing, such as growing for cannabidiol (CBD), outdoor grows usually give seeds four to eight feet for spacing to allow the plant to grow as dense (with branches and flowers) as possible. Cannabis typically likes a cool 75F (23C) temperature during growing stages, but different strains will favor a variety of temperatures.

Plant Disease and Other Stressors

Plant diseases and threats can destroy a potentially profitable crop in a short time. Hemp can be affected and ultimately damaged by over 50 different threats originating from bacteria, viruses, fungi, pests and invasive plants and more, if a truly global purview is considered! Plant diseases spread fast and should be taken very seriously; as they can destroy all of a grow's plants, not just one or two! It is imperative to be proactive and prevent the presence of any such threats. All the money and hard work put into a grow operation can be destroyed in a matter of days depending on the threat. Precautions should be taken from day one. The more plants, the higher the chance of multiple diseases and pests being present.

Hemp grows extremely fast from seed to harvest, much faster than most plants. Due to their speedy rate of growth and hardiness, hemp plants can actually persevere through the attacks of most diseases and pests, but that does not mean growers should rely on that happening.

Invasive plants or weeds are not a disease, but they do pose a threat to cannabis crops and must be dealt with early in the growing season. Cannabis is a natural repellant, and in some climates, will not experience the presence of weeds once it starts growing. However, that isn't the case everywhere and depends on climate and soil conditions.

The use of chemicals such as pesticides should be avoided whenever possible, as testing of the biomass for pesticides and heavy metals will be required.

Chemical Drift

Cannabis has a very limited number of products that can be used to control pests. However, cultivators growing other agricultural crops have more options for pest control. For example, if a grower's hemp farm is located next to a large-scale soybean or corn operation, that farmer legally can apply control products to their fields. These control products can aid in controlling pests resulting in better plant health and increased yields. If these agricultural control sprays migrate to a grower's hemp field from a neighboring property, the final hemp product could fail local and state testing. Also, depending on the control product used, it could also cause damage or death to the hemp crop.

Similar to cross-pollination, agricultural drift can occur through human error, wind speed, and direction, topography and location. Preventing agricultural drift onto your field is extremely difficult. Windbreaks, physical barriers and indoor cultivation facilities are the best options to prevent agricultural drift from damaging your hemp crop but are not 100% effective. Neighboring farms should implement best management practices to reduce the risk of agricultural drift. Examples of best management practices are increasing the droplet size of the spray, reducing the spray volume and applying control products during early morning or late evening hours while the wind speeds are often reduced. As a hemp cultivator, a grower can also follow the previous application techniques to keep any acceptable control products on their property.

Mold

Microbial growth, such as mold, is a huge problem for a lot of growers. Grey mold scientifically known as *Botrytis cinerea* and white mold scientifically known as *Sclerotinia sclerotiorum* are two of the most common molds that affect hemp. They are often seen affecting other crops such as beans and sunflowers. When handling diseases such as mold, it is important to consider the long term consequences. If the grower is rotating crops between fields, it is important to note whether the predecessor plant dealt with molds such as these. Harvesting equipment, any tool, or areas that have come in contact with the disease should be cleaned and sanitized in such a way that completely kills mold spores and growth. If these extra steps aren't taken, the grower will continue to see this problem in potentially every growing plant.

In one Canadian study, canola was planted and eventually infested with white mold; after rotating the crop out and replacing the field with hemp, 10% of the hemp grown in the same white mold-infested field was also infested with white mold. Farmers recommend crop rotation as a practice to cut back on invasive plants, pests and diseases (Yanchev et al., 2000). Crop rotation has many benefits and will help keep the soil productive and rich with plant nutrients. In Canada, it is recommended not to plant hemp on the same land after canola, beans or sunflowers due to the threats those three crops attract.

Powdery white mildew is a common problem that afflicts indoor grows with high humidity. The strain of fungi seen to affect cannabis in these conditions is called *Golovinomyces* and also known as Erysiphe (Wiseman et al., 2021). Just one centimeter of growth can produce 300,000 spores a day! It is imperative to treat this threat as soon as it is noticed.

Phytoremediation with Hemp

Soil pollution is a global problem. Studies have shown that hemp could be a major factor in remedying our polluted lands, making them cleaner to grow food. Hemp is considered a phytoremediator, because it will bioaccumulate or trap toxins like heavy metals, solvents, pesticides and other contaminants left over in the soil from previous crops grown in the same space (Yanchev et al., 2000).

A great historical example of hemp being used as a bioaccumulator was the cultivation of hemp crops following the Chernobyl Nuclear Disaster. This event is considered the world's biggest radioactive disaster ever recorded. Researchers found great success in removing toxins from the soil over the past decades by cultivating hemp to clean up the radioactive land. Studies even suggest that hemp is the ideal crop for phytoremediation compared to other crops with similar abilities. The United States Environmental Protection Agency (EPA) estimates there are over 30,000 sites that need remediation in the U.S.

Successful reports of using hemp to absorb cadmium in soil have been published. Cadmium poses a threat to humans because it permeates into food. Cadmium is a toxin that can cause severe pain in various human joints and the spine. It can negatively affect the kidneys and has been linked to cancer. In recent years, Italy has been using hemp to clean up nickel and lead that has contaminated their lands. It is believed those metals have caused higher rates of cancer and kidney diseases throughout the population.

Researchers have dubbed hemp a "carbon sink" for its ability to capture carbon emissions (Arrigoni et al., 2017). For every ton (2,000 pounds) of hemp harvested, over 1.6 tons of carbon dioxide is pulled out of the atmosphere. Some say that hemp can help cool our increasingly warming planet and could be a huge tool to combat climate change. Hemp could help end acid rain and reverse the greenhouse effect.

When it comes to cleaning up oil spills in our oceans, while hemp is capable of this task, it takes a lot of hemp to absorb the oils. Unfortunately, producing "toxic" chemicals to clean up oil spills seems to be more cost-effective than growing and harvesting hemp. However, research says these toxic chemicals (called "dispersants") can unfortunately also be detrimental to human and animal health. It is not fully understood the long term human and planetary health effects that they can have.

Hemp used for phytoremediation purposes shouldn't be used for food or cannabinoids, but it can be used for biofuels such as ethanol or gasoline (Akahoshi et al., 2007; Kamireddy et al., 2013). These biofuels are made from the plant's cellulose, which makes up 80% of the hemp plant; whereas in wood that number is closer to 60%. Using cellulosic gasoline could reduce our greenhouse gas emissions by 85% compared to traditional petroleum gasoline.

Many researchers agree that hemp is the perfect crop to be used in a rotation with traditional non-cannabis crops (Adesina et al., 2020). Hemp crops help keep the next rotation of non-cannabis crops healthier by fighting against pests and weeds. Hemp has also proven to improve soil conditions by absorbing toxins and depositing organic matter. Additionally, the complex, deep and broad root system that hemp plants grow encourages aeration in the soil.

According to the Ontario Ministry of Agriculture, Food and Rural Affairs, hemp that is grown outside is estimated to return 42% of its nutrients back to the soil. The chart below shows the nutrient uptake of nitrogen, phosphorus, potassium, magnesium and calcium in hemp. Growing conditions and biological processes may vary from climate to climate, and thus affect nutrient uptakes and returns.

Cultivation

Hemp can be successfully grown using a variety of different methods. The main difference between indoor versus outdoor hemp cultivation is that indoor growing has more "tools" to regulate environmental conditions during the plant's life cycle than outdoor growing.

Typically, indoor hemp cultivators can manipulate the growing environment by adding supplemental lighting, regulating ambient temperature or relative humidity, adding CO2, using high yielding potting soils and even changing the photoperiod. Successful indoor operations use large scale glass or plastic greenhouses. This will also allow for the possibility of year-round cultivation, or at the very least with light deprivation techniques, generation of a few harvests per year. When deciding whether to cultivate indoors, the price is a major concern. Because, the cost to build the indoor structures, utility bills and labor utilization are more expensive than growing outdoors.

Most cultivators that grow hemp outdoors use traditional agricultural methods of growing such as soil modification, crop rotation and planting equipment. Outdoor cultivators are more susceptible to environmental conditions and pest infestations. They typically harvest once per year. Outdoor cultivation is less expensive to operate, however, and cultivation operations can occur much more quickly. Harvesting one crop a year can be labor intensive, however, if the weather does not cooperate during the harvest season. Poor weather can really hinder yields and quality. Consider the distribution market as well. During the harvest season when all the other farms in the region are harvesting, the tremendous amount of product flooding the market could influence selling prices.

Cultivating indoors versus outdoors is going to be a personal preference for many growers based on a variety of factors. A small indoor grow is a great space to get results from seeds or developing clones. Indoor space also works great for breeding and genetics programs. Growing starts during the winter/off season, however, will give your outdoor farm a much better successful early season establishment. Consider operating a hybrid system of both indoor and outdoor cultivation.

Hemp is usually grown in the summer outdoors unless indoor conditions are facilitated in such a way to allow for year round cultivation. Hemp is extremely sensitive to light, and outdoor plants will switch from vegetative to flowering life stages on their own depending on the length of daylight to which they are exposed to. Usually, mimicking the summer's timeline of about 18 hours of light and six hours of lights off keeps the plant in the vegetative stage. Once autumn arrives, and there is about 12 hours of light and 12 hours of dark, the outdoor hemp plant will switch to its flowering stage.

To do this in an indoor grow, once satisfied with the crops' vegetative growth, switch, using a timer, to 12 hours of light on and 12 hours of lights off. This change will trigger the plant to begin its' flowering stage. Once in the flowering stage, the grower will see the hemp plant buds begin to grow clear to an end-stage of white resin-filled projections called trichomes.

Trichomes are the glandular structures located on the flower and leaves and contain many phyto-compounds. Most notably, however, they contain cannabinoids and terpenes. Preservation of the cannabinoids and terpenes in cannabis at harvest is an important task, because the cultivators want to preserve the distinctive flavor profiles and bioactive attributes of these fragile and easy to degrade plant compounds in the trichomes. Cannabis cultivators often choose early morning hours to harvest and sometimes immediately flash-freeze their crops to conserve these terpenes.

To further safeguard these special compounds highly sensitive to heat and humidity, cultivators and processors must carefully control environmental conditions during handling to avoid degrading or vaporizing the natural terpenes in cannabis and other botanicals. During a plant's growth and maturation, cannabinoids and terpenes are affected by even moderate changes in conditions. Wind, sun exposure, temperature cycling and precipitation can all produce unwelcome effects. Mechanical versus manual harvesting, excess handling and careless storing practices will diminish the terpene profile of a medicinal plant. Process controls, Quality Assurance testing, experienced master growers and extractors, Standard Operating Procedures and other protocols typical in the pharmaceutical and food manufacturing industries can ensure not just the terpenes, but also flavonoids, polyphenols and all the other plant compounds are consistently retained, batch to batch.

Introduction to Harvesting and Post-Processing

Growing hemp is similar to growing corn or wheat, but when it comes to harvesting, it is much more difficult to manage for any application. Growing hemp is not an overly expensive endeavor, though it does require special care and labor. It is in the processing and refinement of hemp where major challenges are faced. Preventative maintenance and repair of equipment used in harvesting and processing are unavoidable and costly after initial investments are made in equipment. Due to the strength and toughness of hemp fibers, the plant has a tendency to damage harvesting equipment. Modern technology and equipment built specifically for hemp, however, have solved some of these problems more recently.

Harvesting for Hemp Seeds

When harvesting for seeds, six weeks into flowering is usually when seeds are most ripe and ready. Like fiber, seed harvesting is typically done with a combine, but there are other methods and new technologies on the market. Seeds should be separated from the buds carefully, so they aren't damaged in the process.

Harvesting Hemp for Fiber

Harvesting hemp for fiber varies from farmer to farmer. Fiber grown from hemp is set up into two categories: the long outer bast and the short inner hurds.

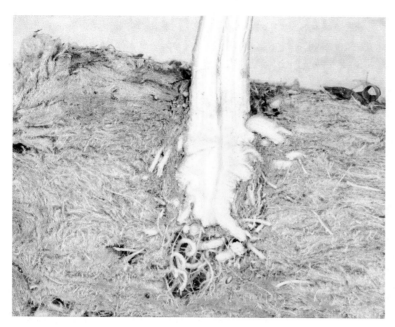

Figure: This photograph shows the cross section of the stem of a hemp plant. Image Credit: Shutterstock

For fiber grown specifically for textiles, the grower should harvest early, before the end of its true flowering season. The science behind this is the longer the grower waits for harvesting, the more lignin and pectin build up in the cell walls making the cells harder to break down. Fiber with too high of a lignin content will only be suitable for some limited industrial applications.

When harvesting for fiber, it is common for smaller plots to be harvested manually without the use of machinery. Special care should be taken when harvesting plants that have an end goal of producing fiber. In order to preserve long fibers which are perfect for fabric textiles, the plant stalks shouldn't be cut up in pieces.

After cutting the stem a few inches above the soil, hemp for fiber must be retted. There are several ways to rett hemp. Using nature, water, chemicals or mechanical separating are all options used today.

Drying and Curing

Drying and curing are part of another method of processing hemp plants. After chopping the plant a few inches from the soil, usually, the next step involves hanging the plant upside down in a cool, dry and dark space for a number of weeks. The plants should be in an environment of about 60F to 75F (15C to 23C) with about 60% humidity.

Good ventilation is the key to drying hemp properly. A trick to prevent trapped moisture from building up and growing mold during this stage is to break or cut segments of whole plants and hang them individually. With the nature of how the plant hangs upside down, it is all too easy for the plant to close in on itself and not allow for an even and effective dry.

Figure: Photograph of drying and curing hemp. Image Credit: Shutterstock

Some cultivators will only take a few days to complete this process, whereas others may take several weeks or months. There are many specialty machines and tools on the market to accomplish drying and curing in a more efficient and controlled manner. The ideal moisture content to move onto milling or grinding of the plant is about 4% to 6% and, depending on resources and environment, the time it takes to accomplish this could vary. Any mold or mildew present from an improper dry will lower the quality of a plant and could ultimately render it useless.

Whatever methods growers choose to process their hemp plants, they must be cautious about touching or agitating the buds and their trichomes. Every touch opens more trichomes and exposes the resin inside. This sticky and smelly substance is actually rich with terpenes (which are what growers smell when handling hemp) and cannabinoids. The more compromised buds the growers have, the less potent their plants will be.

If growers opt to bale their hemp after harvesting, they should wait for the moisture content to be no more than 10% to 15%. It is usually recommended to use balers that create a large round softcore, because it will allow for air movement and, in turn, allow the hemp to dry quickly after being put in storage. Tightly packed square bales can eventually be ruined, because they can hold too much moisture for a long period. Another good practice for preserving the growers' hemp from rotting is to store it in a dry indoor area off the ground.

Predicting yields will vary greatly, because each variable involved will affect the outcome no matter the intended application. Many farmers with outdoor grows recommend starting the season early and using diverse strains to produce high yields. Plant variety and genetics, weather conditions, soil fertility, moisture and growing techniques are some of the ways yields are directly affected.

Harvesting for CBD

Harvesting for cannabidiol, also known as CBD, is usually done 8 to 10 weeks into the flowering stage. A good indication of the flowering states is when the trichomes have all mostly turned to an amber color. Another way to know exactly when to harvest is by taking a sample of a bud each week, and having it tested in a lab for cannabinoid and terpene profile levels. Besides those two things, it is also possible to test for microbes, pesticides and heavy metals.

Harvesting late can cause a crop to have higher THC levels which can cause legal problems for hemp growers, higher myrcene levels (this is a terpene with sedative effects) (Do Vale et al., 2002) and higher CBN levels (a cannabinoid known for sedative effects) (DeLong et al., 2010), as THC synthesizes into CBN naturally.

After harvesting, drying and curing, hemp grown for cannabinoids is milled for extraction. The mill size will vary per method, but the goal is to increase the surface area for solvent extraction. Trimming may also be deemed necessary in some situations. This involves cutting as much of the fan and sugar leaves as possible to expose the bud. There will be trichomes on these leaves, but they aren't as important as the ones directly on the bud.

It is important for the grower not to grind the plant material too small. Once milled hemp biomass is extracted, it produces crude hemp oil, a very thick, brown to dark brown, tar-like oil. Crude hemp oil will vary in quality depending on the processor.

Purifying for Cannabinoids

Purifying for cannabinoids such as CBD usually involves heat and pressure via distillation. Another method used is chromatography, but this is usually too slow of a process for large scale production.

There are also many different types of chromatography methods that allow for the purification or the removal of individual cannabinoids. For example, the cannabis industry is removing THC via gravity chromatography, centrifugal partition chromatography or other advanced filtration techniques. Small scale chromatography for analytical testing occurs with gas chromatography and high-performance liquid chromatography.

Short path distillation and molecular distillation are also popular methods to refine and purify crude hemp oil into CBD rich distillate. The distillate is typically orange to gold-colored thick oil rich in CBD, with potency levels ranging from 50% to 95% and the average being about 65% to 80%. Distillation is done in many ways, but typically adding heat to the crude oil under a low vacuum allows for efficient refinement to take place.

Often when industry professionals say this, it refers to distillates containing other small percentages of major and minor cannabinoids such as tetrahydrocannabinol (THC), cannabinol (CBN) and cannabigerol (CBG). Depending on strain genetics and harvest times, you will see these cannabinoids range as low as .01% to as high as 15% or more in some cases. The distillate, like crude oil, can be so pure that it is often subject to crystallization without any interventions.

The next step in a more pure product beyond distillate referred to industry-wide as isolate. Isolate is a white crystallized form of cannabidiol (CBD). Usually, the crystals are encouraged to grow with the use of a solvent and cryo temperatures that are typical for crystal growth. Once formed, they are often washed and purged of any residual solvents with a vacuum oven. Tests should be performed to check the solvent levels before selling isolate to consumers or as a wholesale product. Isolate is typically 90% to 100% CBD with the highest quality on the market being 97.5% CBD or higher with no THC content. Isolate can then be diluted and added into formulations for a long list of products including capsules, tinctures, food products, pet products, topical products and more.

Cannabinoid Testing and Research

There are over 400 compounds in the cannabis plant. One accurate method to ensure the production of high quality and consistent hemp products is to take samples during each step to test. Most cannabis regulating programs require compliance and testing at many levels and intervals.

There are many different types of analytical instruments on the market used today to test cannabinoids, terpenes, microbial growth, heavy metals and pesticides in hemp biomass and processed hemp products. There is more than one method or instrument to test for everything and opinions vary on what is truly the best and most appropriate method or instrument. As with other aspects of the fast-moving cannabis industry, technologies and standards are improving and changing daily.

Whether cannabis is ingested, inhaled, eaten or topically applied, the standards of growing and processing cannabis will determine whether a person's health will benefit from all the cannabinoids or if dangerous contaminants will adversely affect their health. In fact, during extraction and refinement processes, the contaminants can be concentrated and contaminated CBD products will be, effectively, made worse by practices such as smoking, dabbing or vaping.

Cannabis absorbs heavy metals from the soil, fertilizer and water. Therefore, cadmium, arsenic, nickel, lead, mercury and other heavy metals accumulate in the plant and therefore testing is absolutely necessary. Other contaminants found in hemp include highly-toxic pesticides. Suspect or unverifiable growing practices, internationally and domestically, can introduce known carcinogens into your CBD product. Sloppy or poor processing methods can leave any number of residual solvents in a CBD tincture, soft gel or lotion. Harmful yeasts and molds, mycotoxins and other microbial pathogens are capable of causing disease and even death if contaminated cannabis is not rejected prior to processing.

Testing facilities should be state audited and ISO 17025 certified to assure that calibration and testing laboratories are delivering good services and consistent data. They should follow pharma-level QA/QC programs, use analytical testing with HPLC (high-performance liquid chromatography) and GC-MS (gas chromatography mass spec) instruments used by professional lab technicians, employ bar-coded tracking systems for full traceability, enforce strict standard operating procedures and confirm final product quality with multiple levels of oversight.

Below is a chart that lists some appropriate instruments to use for different categories:

Substance	Compounds	Application	Instrumentation Used

Cannabinoids	THCA, THC, CBDA, CBD, and all other minor cannabinoids	To determine the concentration of each cannabinoid. This is referred to as potency testing.	HPLC GC-FID (cannot distinguish between THCA and THC or CBDA and CBD as decarboxylation occurs in the instrument due to heat)
Terpenes	Alpha-pinene, *β-caryophyllene, limonene*	Determine concentration terpenes which is important for flavor and aroma and medicinal benefits	GC-FIDGC-MS
Residual Solvents	Butane, Pentane, hexane, Ethanol, Acetone, iso-propanol	Determine if any solvents remain in the product after solvent extraction of cannabis. This protects the consumer.	GC-FIDGC-MS
Pesticides	Organophosphates, carbamates, etc.	Determine if any pesticides are present. This protects the consumer.	HPLC-MS-MS GC-MS-MS
Heavy Metals	Arsenic, mercury, lead, cadmium	Determine if heavy metals are present. This protects the consumer. Heavy metals are used in fertilizers for cannabis.	ICP-MS

Microbial pathogens	Yeast, Molds, Bacteria	To assure there are no harmful pathogens in products like E.coli, salmonella, candida Albicans, etc.	Agar Plates Agar Films PCR

(Chart Credit: Dr. Andrea Holmes)

HPLC (High Performance Liquid Chromatography)

The **order of elution** is a major determining factor in calculating the levels of each individual cannabinoid within a sample. Using a detector, HPLC is sensitive enough to identify compounds down to the parts per trillion. Usually, an ultraviolet wavelength detector known as Diode Array Detector (DAD) or Photodiode Array Detector (PDA) is used in conjunction with HPLC to determine the potency of cannabinoids. A major factor for results is determining the time it takes for a sample to pass through the column to the detector.

Most labs testing for cannabinoid potency today are testing for the most common 10 to 15 cannabinoids. Some of those include:

1. Cannabidiol (CBD)

2. Cannabidiolic Acid (CBDA)

3. Tetrahydrocannabinol (THC)

4. Tetrahydrocannabinolic Acid (THCA)

5. Cannabigerol (CBG)

6. Cannabigerolic Acid (CBGA)

7. Cannabinol (CBN)

8. Cannabichromene (CBC)

9. Cannabitriol (CBT)

10. Delta-9-Tetrahydrocannabinol (d9THC)

11. Delta-8-Tetrahydrocannabinol (d8THC)

12. Tetrahydrocannabivarin (THCV)

13. Cannabidivarin (CBDV)

Analyzing chromatograms, peaks and retention times of each analyte (such as CBD) helps the analyst determine how much of each compound is present in the sample. Potency results can vary significantly per method and per operator, because there are so many variables in the process. A grower can send a homogenized sample of the same batch of product to two different labs using the same type of testing instruments and receive different results. Due to this degree of uncertainty, the industry has accepted a range of +/- 15% in crude hemp oil, distillate, isolate and other cannabinoid products.

Terpene Testing

Terpenes are delicate molecules that pose more challenges to analyze. They are non-polar and very similar to each other structurally, making them harder to separate and identify. In sample collection, transportation and preparation, terpenes are so volatile that they are being lost throughout the process.

Terpenes are characterized by using headspace solid-phase microextraction (SPME) followed by chromatographic separation using a gas capillary column. Terpene peaks are identified by using MS spectral matching against National Standards and Technology (NIST) libraries and confirmed by retention times using terpene standards.

The American Oil Chemists' Society (AOCS) says that mass spectrometry (MS) is less effective at distinguishing terpenes that elute at the same time from a GC (gas chromatograph) column, because many have similar molecular weight and share fragment ions. AOCS recommends another combination of instruments using methods for Full Evaporation Techniques with Head Space by using an Ionization Detector (FET-HS-GC-FID). It is great for terpenes and residual solvents, because it only minimally processes the sample. There are about 38 terpenes being identified using this method.

Residual Solvents

Regulatory bodies in the cannabis industry have determined limits for residual volatile organic chemicals in all consumer products that contain cannabis extracts. To meet these guidelines, producers must monitor solvent levels in finished products, active ingredients and additives. Cannabis processors use various solvents in the extraction processes including, ethanol, isopropanol, butane, heptane, acetone, etc. The solvents can evaporate but sometimes not all of the solvent is removed. Therefore, testing of all cannabis products, except for flowers, is necessary to avoid consumer product contamination with solvents. Two instruments are typically used for residual solvents, GC-FID (gas chromatography-flame ionization detector) and GCMS (gas chromatography mass spectrometry). In order for testing laboratories to handle many samples, these instruments run overnight and an auto-sampler is used that allows the automatic analysis of residual solvents.

Pesticides

Laws vary greatly, but in most places, it is illegal to use any pesticides, insecticides or fungicides to control threats to cannabis crops. Regulations typically require an analysis to prove that these potentially toxic substances were not used during cultivation or processing.

HPLC-MS/MS is suitable for about 95% of pesticides and is typically required for pesticides that can be altered by heat. According to the AOCS, GC in tandem with mass spectrometry (GC-MS/MS) can detect many pesticide classes. Chlorinated pesticides are best seen using a GC with an electron capture detector (ECD). In the U.S., if pesticides are not registered by the U.S. Environmental Protection Agency (EPA), then they are considered illegal. Several states adopted cannabis policies involving federally registered pesticides. Other states have not regulated pesticides, since the EPA has not registered any pesticides for cannabis production. Therefore, different states have different regulations for pesticide limits. The presence of pesticides or failed tests can have serious implications on health as cannabis samples may test often and very high for the active ingredients, pyrethrins and/or piperonyl butoxide. State regulatory agencies are immediately informed whether cannabis samples fail a test in a state-accredited lab. Typically, the testing is repeated one more time to confirm a failed test. State authorities usually mandate that a pesticide-contaminated product is fully destroyed under supervision or remediated to reduce the pesticide concentration.

Examples of pesticide samples that are tested for industry-wide:

1. Abamectin
2. Bifenazate
3. Bifenthrin
4. Daminozide
5. Etoxazole
6. Fenoxycarb
7. Imazazil
8. Imidacloprid
9. Myclobutanil
10. Paclobutrazol

11. Pyrethrins

12. Spinosad

13. Spiromesifen

14. Spirotetramat

15. Trifloxystrobin

Heavy Metals

Hemp is a phytoremediator that can absorb toxins from soil and even water and air. The varieties and levels of these toxins vary from land to land. Heavy metals can be toxic to humans and animals and cause serious health conditions. Any combination of heavy metals such as silver, arsenic, mercury, lead, selenium, cadmium and chromium can be absorbed by the cannabis plants. There are several ways to accomplish heavy metal testing, some can measure elements at parts per millions, while others can detect parts per billion. Instruments used to detect heavy metals are typically inductively coupled plasma ICP MS or ICP-optical emission spectrometry (OES). The literature recommends atomic absorption (AA), inductively coupled plasma optical emission spectroscopy (ICP-OES), and inductively coupled plasma mass spectrometry (ICPMS) to get accurate heavy metal results. Mercury must be measured by cold vapor atomic absorption spectroscopy (CVAAS). Unlike cannabinoid potency testing, regulatory bodies such as the U.S Food and Drug Administration (FDA) have standardized published methods for analyzing heavy-metals. These guides can help the cannabis industry test for heavy metals as well.

Microbials

Quality control testing in cannabis industries is a requirement that involves cell enumeration of bacteria and fungi to comply with state and federal regulations. In U.S. states, where marijuana has been legalized, these regulations include the determination of total yeast and mold count (TYMC) and other bacteria in all consumer-facing products to prevent health problems. There are several methods used for cell enumeration in microbiological testing labs, including plate counting, polymerase chain reaction (PCR) and using a hemocytometer. Plate counting measures viable cells as colony-forming units (CFUs) in dilute liquid culture samples by spreading the sample on agar plates so that a single cell results in a colony which can be counted by the naked eye (See Figure: 3M Below). This process requires little instrumentation but rather a few user skills. PCR is a quick, automated method but requires expertise to perform and interpret, along with costly equipment and supplies, such as a thermal cycler and PCR reagents.

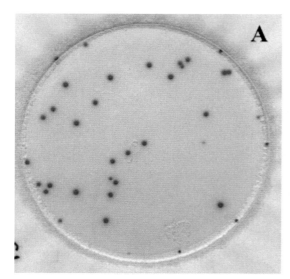

Figure: 3M yeast and mold plate showing an example of a plated film for analysis of yeast and mold that are shown as blue colonies. Image Credit: Andrea Holmes.

Films are sample ready-culture medium systems that contain nutrients, antibiotics, and a water-soluble gelling agent. Yeast and mold colonies on these plates can be distinguished by color. The color change is due to the enzymatic activity of phosphatases. Plate Readers are commercially available for automated quantification of aerobic coliform and E. coli/coliform colonies.

The FDA maintains the Bacteriological Analytical Manual (BAM). This document describes preferred procedures for microbiological analyses of foods, drinks, and cosmetics as well as their containers, contact materials, and production environments.

Cannabis Testing - Hemp

Testing for THC in hemp will be a major research effort. Farmers have to learn how to test their harvest to assure that they do not get over the 0.3% limit. There are portable HPLC instruments, but the accuracy is not very high and these tests are not accepted by state regulators. In addition, research improvement of roadside testing of hemp must be a major research focus. The current testing is not working anymore for law enforcement, because the field tests all test positive for THC. Furthermore, the road tests do not quantify THC concentration.

Genome of Cannabis

DNA sequencing will identify the genes that are responsible for phytochemicals produced by cannabis. The genome is still underexplored and complex, especially the Tetrahydrocannabinol producing gene, and while some people claim they have used Crisper for editing, no peer-reviewed publications exist, only patent disclosures. An article (Dolgin, 2019) states "Within three years," "none of the plants that we're growing currently will continue to be produced, and there will be unbelievable new varieties as a result of marker-assisted hybridization and trait-based selection." This actually presents a market opportunity for states that have already been oversaturated with CBD products. They could distinguish themselves in making a seed that expresses the minor cannabinoids: CBC, CBD, CBG, CBDV, THCV, etc.

Clinical Studies with Cannabis

The National Institutes of Health (NIH) is paying attention to the need for clinical studies and has recently released the first funding announcement for research proposals of how minor cannabinoids and terpenes affect nociception, which is the nervous system's response to harmful stimuli, such as an injury. Furthermore, this request for research proposals encourages an unprecedented interdisciplinary approach between scientists like chemists, biologists, neuroscientists and health professionals, such as physicians, psychologists and psychiatrists.

THC Free Cannabinoids

Removing THC from hemp without negatively affecting the plant's bioactive phytocompounds and nutrients has become a major research focus in the cannabis industry. Many people would like to have THC free products. The term "THC-Free" can range from "non-detect" levels using industry-standard analytical chemistry instrumentation to a level of <0.3%, which is the legal/compliance limit in the U.S. To remove THC from cannabis extracts requires chromatography or other filtration techniques. Current research focuses on the optimization of these processes and upscaling.

Minor Cannabinoids

Cannabinoid science continues to advance, and this presents a prime opportunity for new and innovative product development. THC and CBD have been the most prevalent cannabinoids studied, but there are more than 100 other cannabinoids that have been identified in the cannabis plant. Scientists are now investigating minor, very rare, and emerging cannabinoids, such as CBG, CBN, CBC, CBDA and THCV, among others, to see what possible therapeutic applications these components hold. This largely untapped field offers exciting possibilities for product research and development.

Personalized Cannabis Health and Wellness

Traditional medicine has relied on the one-size fits all philosophy. The advantage of this approach is that it lends itself well for random double-blind controlled trials, while plant-based molecules with their many bioactive compounds do not. This creates research opportunities to study how cannabinoids can affect health and wellness for individuals, not the masses. Personalized cannabis medicine takes into account physiological differences, genetics, upbringing, nutritional history, personal life circumstances, etc. Hundreds of emerging cannabinoids, terpenes, herbs and plant-based omegas thus represent untapped research areas.

Chapter 12-- Cannabis Processing
(Dr. Andrea Holmes and Dr. Mahesh Pattabiraman)

This chapter discusses all processing and refinement methods of cannabis, including marijuana and industrial hemp. Fiber production, extraction methods, distillation techniques and purification methods will be covered. Differences between cannabis products, such as the major and minor cannabinoids, full spectrum versus broad spectrum extracts, distillates, isolates and nano-encapsulated cannabinoids (and their applications) will be discussed. THC remediation will also be covered as well as how these processing methods relate to the environmental issues, economic benefits and challenges the cannabis industry currently faces in the U.S. Newly emerging technologies like biomimetics, fermentations and catalytic enzyme conversions to source cannabis will also be discussed.

Cannabis: Hemp versus Marijuana

The word cannabis refers to the genus of flowering plants in the family *Cannabaceae* with three commonly known species: Cannabis sativa, Cannabis indica, and Cannabis ruderalis. What is often confusing for people to understand is that hemp and marijuana are both considered cannabis. They are distinguished by their concentration of the psychoactive compound called tetrahydrocannabinol (THC), which is the compound that makes a person high. This is also the compound that gives hemp an incorrect stigma when people believe that hemp has THC, can make a person high, and thus is still illegal in many countries. However, hemp does not contain a significant amount of THC (less than 0.3%), but rather contains mostly cannabidiol (CBD) that doesn't make a person high, is considered non-psychotropic and has been legalized at the federal level in the U.S. As the major cannabinoid in hemp, CBD is well known for pain management, anti-inflammatory response, depression and provides an overall feeling of wellness. The first CBD-containing drug, Epidioloex, was recently approved by the FDA to treat epilepsy (Abu-Sawwa & Stehling, 2020; Guan et al., 2020).

Another common classification of cannabis is by the indica/sativa ratio. According to popular cannabis literature:

1. Indica strains are believed to be physically sedating, perfect for relaxing with a movie or as a nightcap before bed.
2. Sativa strains tend to provide more invigorating, uplifting cerebral effects that pair well with physical activity, social gatherings and creative projects.

The belief that indica and sativa deliver distinct effects is very deeply rooted in mainstream cannabis culture. However, research suggests that there is little evidence indicas and sativas exhibit a consistent pattern of chemical profiles which would make one inherently sedating and the other uplifting.

Cannabis Seed for Propagation

Named by Carl Linneaus, the Cannabis Sativa species historically described hemp plants found in Europe and western Eurasia, where it was cultivated for its fiber and seeds. Cannabis is typically known as a dioecious species, meaning individual cannabis plants will have either a female or a male characteristic. Occasionally, a female cannabis plant can express male traits under extreme stress. Male pollen is required for hemp seed, food, feed or oils. When growing cannabis for seed, male flowers must pollinate female cannabis plants. Seed health is important and healthy cannabis seed will be a darker brown color with dark stripes. Young and immature seeds will appear light brown to white and green in color. Cracked seeds may still germinate and grow but the stress may cause the plant to grow differently than expected. These seeds can be what is called "sexed". Experienced seed growers can visually inspect the seed and distinguish males from females based on the shape and other physical properties. When harvesting for seeds, six weeks into flowering is usually when seeds are most ripe and ready. Like fiber, seed harvesting is typically done with a combine.

Cannabis for Roots

Cannabis roots, especially hemp roots, can be four to six feet long and have been used in soil remediation (Adesina et al., 2020; Yanchev et al., 2000). The roots do not contain cannabinoids or terpenes, but they contain medicinal compounds that are bioactive and used for inflammation and other ailments like arthritis (Rodriguez-Leyva & Pierce, 2010). The roots have to be extracted with water to obtain these molecules.

Other Phyto Compounds in Cannabis, Such as Terpenes

The word terpene originates from the word turpentine, which is sap from tapped trees or distilled out of wood. Turpentine was used in ancient Chinese medicine for toothaches and breathing issues. Terpenes are very volatile and evaporate quickly at moderate temperatures, which explains why the air often smells fresher in the morning. Because that is when plants release terpenes as they reach their maximum concentration before the sun evaporates them throughout the day. Preservation of the terpenes in cannabis at harvest is an important practice because the cultivators want to preserve the distinctive flavor profiles and bioactive attributes of these fragile and easy to degrade plant compounds. Cannabis cultivators often choose early morning hours to harvest and sometimes immediately flash freeze their crops to preserve these terpenes. To further safeguard these special compounds that are highly sensitive to heat and humidity, cultivators and processors must carefully control environmental conditions during handling to avoid degrading or vaporizing the natural terpenes in cannabis and other botanicals. During a plant's growth and maturation, terpenes are affected by even moderate changes in conditions, like wind, sun exposure, temperature cycling and precipitation. Obviously, mechanical versus manual harvest, excess handling and careless storing practices will diminish the terpene profile of a medicinal plant. Process controls, QA testing, experienced master growers and extractors, SOPs and other protocols typical in the pharmaceutical and food manufacturing industries can ensure that not just the terpenes, but also flavonoids, polyphenols and all the other plant compounds are consistently retained, batch to batch.

Terpenes, cannabinoids and the other phytocompounds give cannabis, including both marijuana and industrial hemp, its unique medicinal benefit, taste and smell (Baron, 2018). With cannabis, the trichomes are the glands found on the surface of plants and are responsible for producing the plant's terpenes. Terpenes can be either cannabis-derived or made synthetically and can be added into hemp extracts to enhance medicinal qualities. There are over 50,000 terpenes that are naturally occurring, but researchers are also making terpenes as well as combinations of terpenes in the lab, because this class of compounds has been linked to so many pharmaceuticals and health and wellness benefits (Baron, 2018).

Terpenes work together with cannabinoids and other plant compounds through the "entourage effect" (Russo, 2019). This symbiotic interplay of many different naturally occurring molecules in various ratios in different cannabis cultivars has been attributed to the improvement of therapeutic qualities. The "whole-plant" is greater than the sum of the parts. As a result of research on the entourage effect, many people now believe that "whole-plant" and "whole-plant medicine" is superior to highly refined cannabis extracts or isolate-based product formulas. Because of the enhancing synergistic effect when the full array of cannabinoids, terpenes and other phytocompounds like flavonoids, chlorophylls, vitamins and minerals, are consumed together, the whole-plant cannabis oil has aptly been termed "full spectrum" hemp or plant oil. These products often have been found to be more effective in improving health compared to the administration of the same plant compounds individually.

Based on data from internet searches, interest in terpenes has increased five-fold since 2016. Products showcasing and very deliberately incorporating specific terpenes will greatly increase in breadth and number as scientific studies, public awareness and consumer demand rapidly grow. Cannabis will change the landscape at the grocery store as food is no longer about just taste and aroma. Because cannabinoid and terpene-containing foods are all natural, functional therapeutically and appealing to both health-conscious individuals as well as multiple demographics seeking alternative remedies to traditional medicine, these evolving cannabinoid product lines will likely push many legacy foods and drinks right off of the shelves.

Basic Processing Methods

Processing refers to the chemical or physical treatment of raw cannabis plant parts to produce useful substances such as cannabinoids or materials such as fiber. All parts of the plant, except leaves, are processed by the industry to produce raw materials that could be converted to finished products ranging from food, fabric and healthcare products to construction materials.

Hemp for Fiber: Hemp fiber is obtained from the stalk of the plant, which is primarily composed of cellulosic substance (a long biopolymer). In a typical plant, there are two layers; the outer layer is a long, rope-like bast fiber that is easily peeled off, while the inner layer is a woody, pith-like body called the hurd. The outer layer is a skin-like peel that is used for producing fibrous material used in making fabric, paper and even plastic. Processing for fiber first requires specialized decortication equipment to separate the fiber from the wood and rest of the plant, but then depending on quality and coarseness of the fiber desired, further refinement and processing steps or equipment are required. More prevalent in Europe, Russia and China, hemp processing for fiber is still not a strongly established industry in the United States. Although industrial hemp planting and harvesting requires a traditional farm combine to be retrofitted, the change is neither complex nor overly costly.

Cannabis for Seed: Harvesting for seed and grain also requires a combine and other typical farm equipment. Sometimes, the combines need to be retrofitted. Seed harvesting is done primarily to propagate cultivars of specific strains that are pursued for desired genetic traits, such as high cannabinoid content in flowers, specific cannabinoids (CBG or CBN), mood inducing qualities, flavor, disease or drought resistance and whether or not it is grown for cannabinoids or fiber. Seeds are also used as a source of nutrition as they are rich in protein and a number of fatty acids that have nutritional value as well as for extracting hemp seed oil.

Cannabis Roots: The root of the cannabis plant also contains several phytochemicals, which have been used in traditional medicine, especially for treatment of inflammatory pain. More than twenty different compounds belonging to the class of phytochemicals terpenes, alkaloids and steroids are found in hemp root, albeit in small quantities (Ryz *et al*, Cannabis Cannabinoid Res. 2017). While cannabis roots are not utilized as much as the flower, seeds and stalk are in the cannabis industry, there are a few companies that produce finished products from hemp root extract and external fibre. Products such as cosmetics (hair oil, skin cream, salve), toiletries (soap, scrubs), etc. A specialized extraction with water is needed to extract the root components.

Cannabis for Cannabinoids: Harvesting of hemp and marijuana requires specialized farming equipment and requires extraction and refinement equipment, like distillation rigs. Typical costs of extraction depend on size and type of extraction.

Cannabis for Isolated Molecules like CBD and THC: Isolation of THC or CBD requires a crystallization process with solvents. Typical costs of isolation equipment and solvents depend on scaling, types of employed solvents and the type of molecules that are isolated.

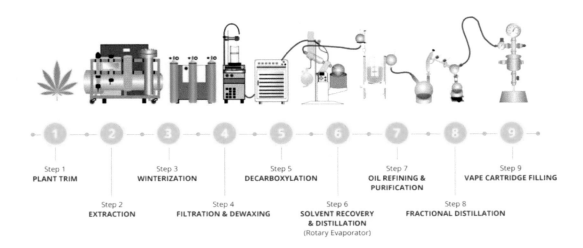

Figure: Schematic that shows all the steps of a cannabis extraction process-- starting from the biomass to extraction, winterization, decarboxylation, refinement to the final product. Image Credit: https://manoxblog.com/2019/11/06/cannabis-full-co2-extraction-process-seed-to-high-purity-extractions/

Conclusion: With this plant, there are so many components and uses. Stalks, leaves, flowers, seeds, roots, fiber, cannabinoids, terpenes and phytochemicals. All have special handling and processing requirements to optimize extraction and preserve precious compounds like the terpenes and root compounds.

Processing for Fiber

Industrial hemp can be used for food, fiber, fuel and personal care products. Industrial hemp that is grown for fiber is very tall and has slender stems with a great amount of fine fibers. Below is a photo of a traditional hemp field used for fiber production.

Figure: Industrial hemp growing under irrigation. Photo Credit: Colorado Department of Agriculture

Combining is the preferred method of harvesting hemp. If also harvesting for seed, the combine header is lifted to cut the crop just below the seed head to minimize the volume of fibre moving through the combine and prevent wrapping of fiber. Often, shorter plants in the canopy may not have mature seed and are not worth cutting low to get the seed head. Growers have reported crops over eight feet high are difficult to harvest.

Fiber extraction processes nearly always involve retting (Centola, 1954). The process whereby naturally occurring bacteria and fungi or chemicals, break down the pectins that bind the hemp fibers to be released after cutting in the field, depending on moisture levels and air temperature. Traditionally, after weeks of field retting, hemp is then gathered for further processing to extract the fibers. Water retting involves soaking the stems in water tanks, ponds or in streams for around 10 days. Most effective in this regard is warmed water laden with bacteria. Dew retting entails laying the crop on the ground for three to six weeks, turning the plants occasionally to allow for even retting.

The separation of hurd and bast fiber is known as <u>decortication</u>. Regardless of the retting techniques used, without sophisticated machinery, manual labor is subsequently required to break, crush or peel the stems and to separate the outer bark and bast fiber material from the 'woody core. Decortication is accomplished by crushing rollers and brush rollers, or by hammer-milling, wherein a mechanical hammer mechanism beats the hemp against a screen until hurd, smaller bast fibers and dust fall through the screen. Depending on the desired material coarseness, fiber has to be processed further after decortication. Fluffier fiber for yarn and clothing needs more processing than coarse fiber used for woody building blocks. Once fiber is processed, storage conditions can significantly affect its quality. Timber racks or other storage systems assure that materials don't get affected by weather or other forms of erosion. Hopper bins with aeration are the best choice of storage. Flat metal bins with aeration flooring are also a good choice for storage. Mini-bulk bags have been used to store hemp seed as long as the moisture content is 8% or less.

PROCESSING STRATEGIES FOR HEMP

Bast fiber of hemp has a high degree of variability but is suitable for many industrial uses. In order to produce competitive and economically feasible products, effective processing methods are critical.

Hemp fiber contains cellulose, hemicellulose, lignin and pectin. Pre-treatment (degumming cellulose) is needed to achieve good quality fiber. Degumming the cellulose can be done by steam explosion, a technique that uses increased pressure and temperature to penetrate the space between bast fibers. This allows the fibers to become soft and water soluble. The pre-treatment can also be done with enzymes, chemically or with ultrasound. Any of these methods can be used in the production of special fibers which can be processed and spun into new types of cotton, yarn or wool. These fibers can also be used for specific technical uses such as non-woven fabrics, filter elements, etc. Steam explosion process use (Vignon et al., 1996) has demonstrated that the cellulose content of hemp fiber increases from 73% to 85% to 90%. The retting process is recommended to be included before steam explosion as well as adding sulfuric acid (H_2SO_4) or Sodium Hydroxide (NaOH). The traditional processing of hemp can generally be divided into three areas:

1. Processing for Long Fiber

The long fiber processing of hemp is used mainly in the production of wet-spun hemp yarns. Due to the dimension of the fibers, only special machinery with a low degree of automation can be employed. New developments in the field of machining technology cannot be expected in the near future due to high investment costs.

After harvesting and retting, the de-leafed hemp stems are dried, and any wood is removed by squeezing, breaking and beating the fibrous material. Hemp softeners or rollers are used to make the fiber softer. A cutting machine is used to reduce the length of the long fibers. A hackling machine combs and smooths the short and long fibers, which are spun to yarns by wet or dry spinning processes.

2. Processing for "Tow"

The term 'tow' pertains to fiber that is mostly wood, dirt particles or trash. Tow processing involves the scutching and hackling to coarse yarn or cord in a dry or wet spinning process. This low quality fiber is unspinnable, but it can be processed to technical products such as insulating material and molds. It still constitutes a great potential for added value of hemp.

3. Processing for Cotton

"Cottonization" of hemp (Moussa et al., 2020) should be ideally carried out with bast fibres arranged in length and characteristics similar to cotton (cottonization). This allows the processing to be performed on cotton machines. Pectin and lignin are very sticky substances and must be removed to get single fibers. This can be done by chemical or mechanical methods as discussed with steam explosion above. The factors of the cottonizing process, such as pre-treatment and sopinnability, dictate the quality of yarn relative to fine versus coarse fibers.

The "bast" part of hemp is used to make all of the materials listed herein. Compared to other synthetic fibres (e.g. glass fibre), hemp has a lower cost and a lower density. Hemp fiber has a higher tensile strength and stiffness compared to cotton and requires less water. Existing machinery for cotton can be used for making cottonized hemp. Below are a few applications of hemp fibers.

Rope

Rope has been made from hemp for more than 10,000 years. Rope was one of the main fibers from hemp produced during the 18th Century. George Washington and Thomas Jefferson grew many acres of hemp. Hemp rope was used during the age of sailing ships as part of the sail's rigging and anchor cord. It is one of the strongest natural ropes in the world. Rope is of paramount importance in fields as diverse as construction, seafaring, exploration, sports and communications.

Hempcrete

Hempcrete is composed of hemp hurds (shives), lime and sand. Hempcrete is used as a material for construction and insulation (Arrigoni et al., 2017). It is also known as Canobiote, Canosmose and Isochanvre. This bio-based product is strong, durable and is an excellent insulator. Homes and other buildings built with hempcrete are robust, sustainable and offer a green alternative to traditional buildings. Hempcrete may also have a future in the construction of recording studios due to its particular acoustical properties.

Hemp Plastics

The cellulose in hemp can be extracted and used to make cellophane, rayon, celluloid and a range of plastic related products. The rigid and strong plastics are used to create super-hard resins for cars, boats and even musical instruments. Hemp fibers can be used to make reusable cloth diapers with higher absorbent efficacy than cotton. Hemp plastics offer a great eco-friendly alternative to non-biodegradable plastics. Due to the fact that hemp fiber can be recycled, automotive industries are increasingly interested in producing hemp-based composite materials instead of glass fiber for interior and exterior automotive body parts.

Hemp Paper

Normal paper is made out of wood pulp. But paper can also be made out of hemp fibers. In order to save trees, hemp paper offers an alternative, because it is faster to grow a new crop of industrial hemp than it is to grow a new forest of trees. The higher quality of hemp **paper** is because **hemp** pulp is much **better** for **paper** than wood pulp. Unfortunately, hemp paper is also more expensive to produce.

Hemp Fuel

Eco-friendly and cost-efficient hemp biodiesel and hemp ethanol/methanol can offer an alternative to petroleum fuels (*Hemp Biofuel*; Kamireddy et al., 2013). Hemp biodiesel is made from the fatty acids in pressed hemp seed oil. Hemp ethanol/methanol is made from the fermented stalk by gasification, acid hydrolysis and enzymes.

Hemp Clothing

Hemp has been used for textiles for thousands of years. Clothing and shoes made from hemp are becoming more and more popular in the mainstream. Hemp boots are strong, comfortable, breathable, flexible and light-weight. They are well suited for people who are focused on vegan lifestyles and these boots keep feet dry and odor free. Within the textile industry, hemp fiber could also be used for carpet backing, upholstery backing and geo-textile products. Competitive materials to hemp textiles are cotton, jute, wool, polyesters and nylon.

Processing Cannabis for Cannabinoids

CO2, Ethanol Hydrocarbon Extraction, Solventless Cannabis Extraction

Process for Extracting Cannabinoids Product with Supercritical Carbon Dioxide (CO_2) Extraction

The extraction of THC or CBD in cannabis depends on the solubility of THC and other cannabinoids in organic solvents, such as hydrocarbons and alcohol. The type of extraction method used is determined by the type and quality of the final product. CO_2-based products range from consumables to pre-filled vaporizers to dabbing products and isolates. Terpenes are isolated during the process and can also be sold separately or reintroduced into the oil extract. One very important aspect of CO_2 extract is that it contains the acidic forms of cannabinoids (THCA, CBDA, etc.).

Supercritical fluid extraction (SFE) is a well-known technology for plant and vegetable extraction of essential oils and other bioactive components, such as cannabinoids from hemp and marijuana. The supercritical (SC) solvent used in cannabis extraction is carbon dioxide (CO_2). It is inexpensive and generally recognized as a safe (GRAS) solvent.

The supercritical fluid extraction pressure for CO_2 during cannabis extraction must reach pressures above 1,000 psi just to enter the supercritical fluid state. Many CO_2 extraction methods call for pressures significantly higher (1,600-4,000 PSI). When pressure decreases, CO_2 returns to the gas state rendering the extracted cannabinoids solvent-free product. Fine tuning of pressure and temperature allows selectivity to the extraction process. Since CO_2 is nonpolar, as dipole moments from carbon to the oxygen cancel out (net zero dipole moment), alcohols or water may be added to maximize extraction yield. SFE can be used for extraction of hemp and marijuana. Processors use different extraction conditions to optimize effects of pressure, plant material composition, time and use of co-solvents to obtain extracts with high cannabinoid content and specific phytocompounds. The Figure shows a phase diagram demonstrating how temperature and pressure changes the physicochemical state of CO_2.

Figure: Phase Diagram for Carbon Dioxide. Image Credit:

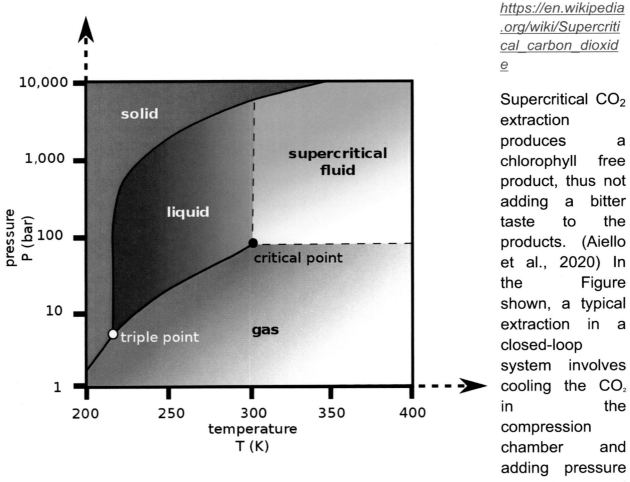

Supercritical CO_2 extraction produces a chlorophyll free product, thus not adding a bitter taste to the products. (Aiello et al., 2020) In the Figure shown, a typical extraction in a closed-loop system involves cooling the CO_2 in the compression chamber and adding pressure to create supercritical CO_2. The supercritical CO_2 is moved into the extraction vessel where the plant is extracted. At this stage of the process, the cannabinoids, terpenes and trichomes are separated. Lastly, the CO_2 evaporates and gets rerouted back to the compression vessel.

Supercritical extraction may affect the terpenes (Sexton et al., 2018). Subcritical extraction may also be used, when pressure is maintained constantly, while the temperature is decreased to the supercritical threshold, causing it to become a (non-supercritical) liquid. Due to the lower temperatures, the volatile and fragile terpenes are prevented from denaturing.

Process for Extracting Cannabinoid Products with Ethanol Extraction

Ethanol is "a colorless volatile flammable liquid C_2H_5OH that is the intoxicating agent in liquors and is also used as a solvent and in fuel. Iit is also called *ethyl alcohol* or *grain alcohol.*" Ethanol is a polar molecule and is capable of extracting many phytocompounds from cannabis, including proteins, fats, lipids, flavonoids, terpenes, major and minor cannabinoids (Tian et al., 2020). This oil type is the best for a tincture or edible infusion to get rid of pronounced cannabis taste and is used in cartridges, tinctures, edibles, topicals, which are common products in CBD brands.

The ethanol method uses either cold, warm or room temperature solvents to extract cannabis. Two types of ethanol can be used; ethanol that has organic solvent constituents to avoid ethanol tax or food grade ethanol which is subject to ethanol tax making the extraction more expensive. The cold ethanol extraction uses cryo temperatures (-150°C to -238°F) to absolute zero (-273°C or -460°F), while leaving behind impurities such as waxes and chlorophyll that are commonly found when extracted with ethanol at room or warm temperatures. The extraction method is very effective and gives more than 90% extraction yield.

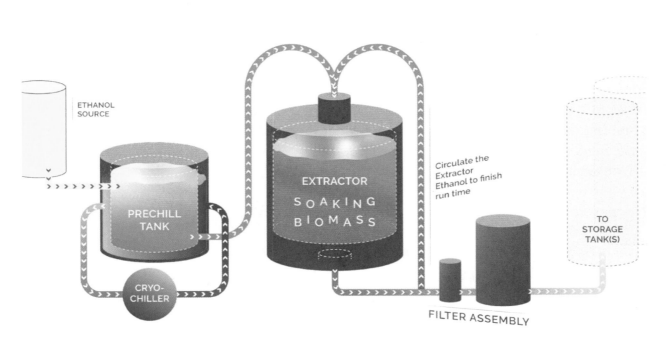

Figure: General concept of how cold ethanol extraction works. Ethanol is chilled with a cryo-chiller and enters the extractor with the cannabis biomass. After the extraction, the cannabinoids are removed and filtered to remove any particles from the biomass. The ethanol is recovered by evaporation and then reused for the next extraction. To maximize extraction efficacy, the ethanol is passed through the biomass multiple times. After the extraction is finished, the ethanol is evaporated by applying heat so that ethanol reaches the gas phase and is then condensed by a chiller or rotoevaporation to recover the liquid solvent. Image Credit: *https://www.edenlabs.com/coldfinger/ethanol-extraction-process/*

Process for Extracting Cannabinoids Products with Hydrocarbon Extraction

Hydrocarbons are very efficient non-polar solvents for cannabis extraction. The most often used hydrocarbons used for extraction are butane (C_4H_{10}) or propane (C_3H_8), but others solvents like methanol, ethanol, chloroform, hexane, etc. are also occasionally applied, although safety considerations related to their toxicity and flammability exist. (Rovetto & Aieta, 2017) Commercially available hydrocarbon equipment is readily available, fully assembled and is often purchased as a complete set to manage everything from the front to the end of processing. These are fully assembled systems, kits, parts, fittings and accessories, making it easy for extraction companies to get started quickly.

The hydrocarbon extraction process starts by packing the cannabis plant material tightly into a vessel to remove any air spaces. A filter screen is attached to the bottom of the vessel to prevent contamination of the extract with the plant material. The solvent is introduced into the vessel and ignited to heat the biomass. The biomass releases its oil, which is then placed into hot water to evaporate the butane. There are several purges of butane to assure the extracts are solvent free. The highly concentrated extract is then used to create cannabis oils, shatter, glass, hash, wax and other products.

Process for Extracting Cannabinoid Products with Solventless Extraction

Solventless extraction relies on mechanical forces (like pressure) to pull out the crude oils. The most often used solventless extraction unit is a rosin press, which uses a type of pneumatic press. Pressure is created from compressed air and heat is applied to create a terpene rich rosin in a short amount of time. Rosin presses have gained a lot of popularity, because of their simple design and limited space requirements. Products of water extracts are called solventless hash oil, kief, rosin, live resin and budder also known as cake batter or a "whipped" rosin.

Process for Extracting Cannabinoid Products with Water Extraction

A lesser known extraction method is critical water extraction or heated water vapor and is considered a "green" solvent extraction process. For critical water, freshly harvested biomass is flash-frozen and placed into an ice water extraction unit and gently agitated to extract the trichomes. (Carraher & Baker, 2021) For water vapor extraction, water is heated or activated in an activation machine to become a gas, which is continuously fed to extract the biomass. Products of water extractions include crude oil, water hash or freeze-dried hash or kief.

Advantages and Disadvantages of Each Extraction Method

When evaluating advantages and disadvantages of extraction methods several criteria need to be considered:

1. Cost of Production and Equipment
2. Quality of the End Product
3. Safety
4. Production Efficiency

EXTRACTION SMACKDOWN RESULTS

Category	Cost of Production & Equipment	Product Quality	Safety	Efficiency
Pros/Cons	Hydrocarbon extraction machines have lower starting costs, while CO₂ equipment is the most expensive.	Hydrocarbon provides full-spectrum extract, while ethanol creates high-potency extract. CO₂ extraction captures flavonoids and carotenoids.	In the wrong hands, hydrocarbon can turn a facility into a fireball. CO₂ can suffocate users, but it is not as explosive.	Ethanol extraction is the most efficient at capturing simple cannabinoids, while hydrocarbon is most efficient at capturing the essence of the whole plant.
Winner	**Hydrocarbon**	**Too close to call**	**CO₂**	**Ethanol**

Figure: Advantages and disadvantages of different extraction methods.
Image Credit: https://mjbizmagazine.com/digital-issues/2018-10-Oct/62/

1. Advantages and Disadvantages of CO_2 Extraction Method

The CO_2 extraction process requires personnel with technical skills. The method is expensive for small scale extractions and becomes profitable for large scale extractions. CO_2 can be used to dissolve substances into "fractions" that can be removed or isolated. Terpenes, for example, can be removed. The CO_2 extraction method is among the safest and the FDA has declared this extraction method as safe, rendering this method much more acceptable than the hydrocarbon based method. The extraction method is also conserving, as the low heat preserves the natural volatile compounds found in cannabis. CO_2 has a pleasant aroma, but the extracts may still need to be further refined with winterization and distillation to change the color from brown to golden.

The start-up costs for CO_2 extractions are, however, high and the throughput is not as scalable as ethanol. The equipment generates a lot of heat and the facility needs a solid air conditioning system to prevent overheating. If there is a leak, employees could suffocate.

2. Advantages and Disadvantages of Ethanol Extraction Method

Ethanol is polar and is able to extract a lot of plant constituents from the plant which leads to a bitter taste and a dark green color that has to be further refined in a dewaxing process called winterization and distillation. Ethanol is extremely flammable, and the temperature needs to be carefully controlled during the entire process, but especially during evaporation. Due to the potential danger the extraction has to occur in a controlled area that is rated as explosion protected and fireproof. Advanced machines are available that can assure this.

Ethanol extraction is a relatively inexpensive method of extracting cannabis and it is easily scalable. The start-up equipment is less expensive than other extraction technology. This makes it particularly attractive for start up companies in the hemp industry where more biomass is required than in the marijuana industry.

The extraction equipment is sold as closed-loop systems, which ensures no solvent escape into the atmosphere and prevents fire hazards and employee exposures. Ethanol is a polar solvent and can dissolve many plant extracts like chlorophyll and some other plant matter as well as terpenes and cannabinoids. The whole cannabis oil extract resembles the chemical profile of the whole plant matter, which many people find important for medicinal purposes as the entourage effect comes into play.

3. Advantages and Disadvantages of Hydrocarbon Extraction

The strict regulatory compliance issues for hydrocarbon extraction systems is based on the regulations of the Occupational Safety and Health Administration (OSHA) and National Fire Protection Association (NFPA). Processors must be in compliance, because hydrocarbons are flammable and can cause explosions. Thus, extraction has to occur in a Class 1, Division 1 (C1D1) extraction/manufacturing space with gas monitoring, zero ignition points, adequate ventilation and a fire-suppression system in place. More regulations apply to drying ovens, refrigeration and further refinement equipment. Start up costs for the equipment are moderate to high but more expensive than for ethanol extraction. The products made with hydrocarbon extraction are crystalline high quality products like shatter.

4. Advantages and Disadvantages of the Water Extraction Method

While this method uses the greenest solvent, water or steam, it is not very efficient, difficult to execute and can damage the plant material. While this method uses an inexpensive and safe solvent, not many processors are using this method. It is also difficult to evaporate the water because of its high boiling point. This often leaves the product wet and many plant constituents heat damaged.

Winterization in Cannabis Processing: Steps to Winterization

Cannabis winterization involves freezing the solution (ethanol) to allow the undesirable compounds to solidify. (Tian et al., 2020) They then can be filtered. In the case of ethanol extracts, this removes the fats and lipids, leaving the oil more refined and of higher quality, because fat and waxes look like a sludgy crude oil.

The method involves several steps. The oil gets dissolved in food grade ethanol (200 proof) and placed into a cryo temperature freezer until the waxes solidify. Then, the waxes are filtered several times. The ethanol is removed by evaporation using heat and can be recycled or reused. After winterization, the oil can be further refined by distillation. This changes the color from brown to gold.

Decarboxylation to Acidic and Neutral Cannabinoids

Decarboxylation is a chemical reaction that uses high temperatures and removes the functional group known as carboxylic acid and releases carbon dioxide. The process of cannabis decarboxylation must convert THCA and CBDA and other acids to CBD or THC, etc. When one smokes cannabis, this decarboxylation occurs and converts the non-psychotropic THCA to the bioactive and psychotropic THC that causes the feeling of a "high". (Rolle, 2020) The decarboxylation also occurs in the extraction process when heat is applied to recover the solvents. Thus, in cannabis flowers, the major cannabinoids are the acids, and in extracts, the major cannabinoids are the neutral forms. The Figure shows the chemical reaction that occurs during decarboxylation.

Figure: Chemical Scheme showing the decarboxylation of THCA to THC producing carbon dioxide   Image   Credit: Shutterstock.

Processing and Refinement Techniques and Cannabinoid Testing for These Products

Separation Science - A Brief Background

Processing cannabis for cannabinoids refers to the processing of hemp flowers to extract phytochemicals. Extraction of cannabinoids from hemp flowers results in a honey-like syrupy substance, which is a mixture of numerous phytochemicals. While the extracted mixture, often referred to as broad spectrum cannabinoids mixture (CBD), predominantly contains cannabinoids, it also contains numerous other classes of compounds (chemically pure substances), such as significant amounts of terpenes and minor amounts of alkaloids and flavonoids. Separation, isolation and purification of these substances is important for commercial, legal, medicinal and research purposes. Below are the various commercial and industrial methods that exist for the purification of cannabinoids. Before that, a brief apprentice level introduction to the basics of separation science will be essential to understanding the relevant industrial processes. While some methods such as chromatography and distillation are used extensively in the cannabis industry, other methods, such as sublimation, are used situationally. Thus, a broad review of separation methods and their scientific bases is presented first followed by the specific methods employed by the cannabis industry. The broader background is presented with the aim of educating the reader, such that they may be in a position to better understand and/or even invent future separation methods based on this scientific foundation. Basic general chemistry knowledge, up to the level of knowing molecular structure and polarity, is required to understand the science behind processing of flowers for cannabinoids and their purification.

Separation Methods: Physical and Chemical

Physical property is any characteristic of a substance that could be determined without changing the chemical identity of the substances, such as boiling point, melting point, density, solubility, viscosity, magnetism, etc. Chemical property is any characteristic of a substance that can only be determined after affecting a chemical change. Examples include acidity, basicity, toxicity, corrosivity, etc. Separation of chemical components in a mixture can be achieved either through <u>physical</u> interactions between substances or through <u>chemical</u> changes affected through reactions.

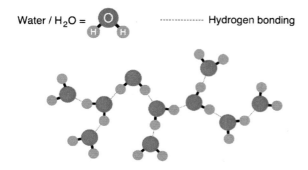

Figure. Molecular structure of water (oxygen in red and hydrogens in grey) and representation of hydrogen bonding between them. Image Credit: Shutterstock.

At the molecular level, all chemical substances engage in weak attractive or repulsive interaction with nearby molecules, called non-bonding interactions. Hydrogen bonding between water molecules is one such well-known non-bonding interaction where a weak, yet significant, force of attraction between partially positive hydrogen in one water molecule and partially negative oxygen in another molecule exists. This attraction is responsible for the very high boiling point of water (100 °C) compared to molecules of comparable, or even higher molecular weight, that lack such non-bonding interactions. Thus, hydrogen bonding is a physical interaction that influences a physical property (boiling point). External physical factors such as introducing another substance (like ethanol, which can hydrogen bond and disrupt H…O bonding between water molecules) or lowering atmospheric pressure (which encourages more evaporation by reducing vapor pressure) would change the physical property of water without changing its chemical structure. Other examples of weak, non-bonding interactions include dipole-dipole, ion-dipole, London dispersion forces, pi-pi, etc.

Physical separation methods are based on disrupting non-bonding interaction between molecules by introducing another molecular type into a mixture or changing external conditions (temp, pressure, etc.). This results in a change in one or more of the aforementioned physical properties of the participating substances. Thus, a chemical separation could be achieved by engineering a physical property change. Distillation is a physical separation method that uses temperature to achieve separation (vide infra). Separating a mixture of compounds over an adsorbent (column chromatography) is a physical method of separation.

A chemical separation is achieved based on differential reactivity towards a common chemical reagent. In such methods, often the chemical change is only slightly modified such as gain/loss of a hydrogen ion (protonation or deprotonation) that confers a positive or negative charge resulting in a significantly modified physical property-- such as aqueous solubility, ability to crystallize or strength of non-bonding interaction. There are fewer chemical separation methods than there are physical. An example of chemical separation is acid/base extraction. The following section will discuss various processing/separation methods and it will be clear to the reader whether a given method of separation is physical or chemical.

Scales of Separation

Separations are often performed on either the **analytical, preparative or industrial scale.** In the analytical scale, a small sample of the substance is used where less than a few milligrams of substance is collected to determine the number of components and their relative quantities in the whole mixture. Preparative scale separations are referred to as operations performed on quantities of a mixture, typically in scales greater than a few grams, with the aim of isolating substances in their pure forms. When the quantity of preparative scale operations exceeds tens of kilograms of substance, it might be referred to as an industrial or large scale separation. In this text, the preparative and industrial scales will be used equivalently. Certain separation methods are more amenable to some scales than others. For example, chromatographic (*vide infra*) separations are employed mostly for analytical purposes, while distillation is exclusively a preparative method.

Qualitative Versus Quantitative Analysis

When analytical scale separations of mixtures are performed, they are done to determine the identity of the substances (qualitative analysis) and/or to determine the relative quantities of substances (quantitative analysis). While theoretically all chemical and physical separation methods could be used analytically, chromatography (*vide infra*) is the most convenient and efficient method available to date, especially for cannabinoids. Analytical methods such as conductivity, mass spectrometry, etc. are available for academic research, but the cannabis industry employs chromatography almost exclusively for this purpose.

Full Spectrum "Crude" Oil

The definitions of "full" versus "broad" spectrum cannabis extracts or tinctures are not clearly distinguished. There are several terms that define the product that is extracted. Sometimes it is called oil, tincture, extract or just plain crude. In general, a "full" spectrum oil, extract or tincture, contains THC and all the other cannabinoids and phyto compounds that are naturally occurring in the plant, including terpenes, essential oils, flavonoids, chlorophyll, proteins, sugars, etc. This is also referred to as "crude extract." This product also has the lowest concentrations of cannabinoids. This "crude" is the most basic, least expensive and least refined product that can be used to infuse consumer facing products, such as hemp or marijuana tinctures, gel caps, tablets, topicals, etc.

After the first step of solvent extraction, the crude oil has a THC (for marijuana) or CBD (hemp) potency of between 50%-60%. In order to obtain the crude full spectrum oil, the milled biomass is extracted by one of the extraction methods detailed earlier, (ethanol, CO_2 hydrocarbon, etc.) After the solvent is evaporated, the acidic cannabinoids are decarboxylated. Crude extract will vary in quality from processor to processor, depending on the equipment and solvent used. Crude hemp oil is usually a very thick, brown to dark brown tar-like oil. Information on the potency testing for crude oil follows.

Broad Spectrum "Crude" Oil

Broad spectrum is more refined and has less phytocompounds or other plant constituents and sometimes less to zero THC, which is called THC-remediated broad spectrum oil. A broad-spectrum oil will probably be winterized to remove the lipids, fats and chlorophylls. This broad-spectrum oil has a slightly higher price point than the raw crude described above. Some hemp processors take this refined broad spectrum oil and treat it with diluent oil like MCT oil to get the THC level below 0.3%, which is compliant to add into hemp infused consumer-facing products. However, this dilution process also dilutes the CBD content and other cannabinoid content. Thus, processors sometimes reintroduce the CBD (usually in isolate form) after dilution.

Distillate

Processing techniques called short path distillation and molecular distillation are popular methods to refine and purify crude hemp oil into CBD or THC-rich distillate. The distillate is typically orange to gold-colored thick oil rich in CBD (hemp) or THC (marijuana) with potency levels ranging from 65% to 80%. Distillation is done in many ways, but typically, adding heat to the crude oil under a low vacuum allows efficient refinement to take place. The Figure shows the golden honey-colored distillate. The distillate is often used in vape pens or sold for dabbing, vaporizing by placing it on an extremely hot metal object called a nail and then inhaling.

Isolate

The next step in a more pure product beyond distillate would be referred to industry-wide as isolate. Isolate is a white crystallized form of cannabidiol (CBD). Naturally plant derived THC isolate does not exist as a white solid, but more as a transparent yellowish shatter-looking substance. It typically contains 70% to 80% THC. Usually, the CBD isolate crystals are grown with the use of a solvent and cryo temperatures. Once formed, they are often washed and purged of any residual solvents with a vacuum oven. Testing must be performed to make sure that there are no residual solvents in the isolate. Isolate is typically 90% to 100% CBD with the highest quality on the market being 97.5% CBD or higher with no THC content.

Distillation

Cannabinoids have different boiling points and this physical property allows their separation by distillation. (Adair et al., 2021) Distillation is based on temperature and vapor pressure and it is a physical method of separation as the chemical structure of the compounds remain unchanged during the process. Distillation is performed only at the preparative scale. Boiling point of a liquid is the temperature at which the vapor pressure of the liquid phase of a compound equals the external pressure acting on the surface of the liquid. The Figure below shows a typical distillation apparatus that can be used to separate cannabinoids from each other, but also from terpenes that have much lower boiling points than cannabinoids. For example, the boiling point for CBD is 160°C to 180°C and for beta caryophyllene (the most abundant and one of the many terpenes found in cannabis) it is 130°C. These different boiling points are far enough from each other to allow for separation.

Heating the cannabinoids and terpenes at these temperatures could cause structural degradation or molecular rearrangement to form other cannabinoids or compounds. That is why distillation for cannabinoids is performed under reduced pressure by applying a vacuum. This allows for the depression of boiling points and the cannabinoids and terpenes are, through this method, preserved.

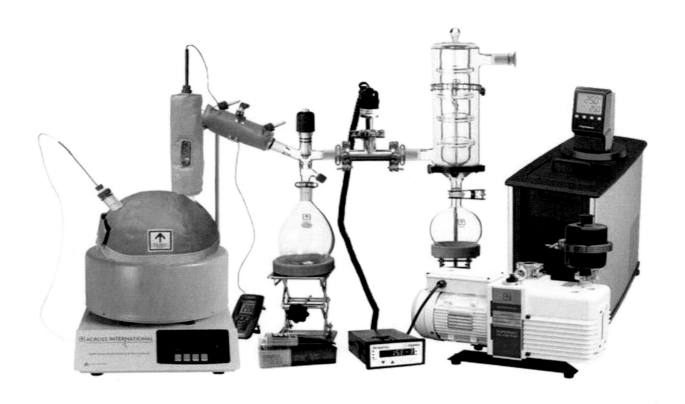

Figure: This picture shows a typical lab setup for a 5 L short path distillation apparatus used in the cannabis industry. It contains a source of heat holding a round bottomed flask. There is a still head with a thermometer. The cooling condenser, with inlets and outlets, is attached to a cooling bath with cooling water or ethylene glycol. There is a distillate/receiving flask that is attached to a vacuum trap filled with dry ice and acetone. The dry ice acetone slurry is very cold, up to -70 °C, and forces vapors of solvents to condense. Picture Credit: https://www.growinglabs.com/products/ai-5l-short-path-distillation-kit-turn-key-packag

There are several different methods regarding isolation to just one single molecule. These processing methods are called distillation, crystallization and chromatography. Distillation can be used to separate cannabinoids based on different boiling points and vapor pressures. For example, CBC with a boiling point of 220°C could be separated from CBD, with a boiling point of 160° to 180°C. However, when the boiling points are very close, distillation is not the best technique to isolate molecules and then methods that are called crystallizations or recrystallizations have to be used.

Isolation of Individual Cannabinoids to make Isolates by Crystallization

Crystallization is the process of aggregation of individual molecules that are dissolved in a solvent to form macroscopic crystalline entities. Crystallization occurs when the attractive influence between molecules dissolved in a solvent overcomes its propensity to remain dissolved. Crystallization of dissolved compounds is induced by concentration (wherein the solvent is evaporated) or by cooling (wherein solubility of the compounds are decreased). It is a great tool in a separation chemist's toolkit, as it is a simple and efficient method of purification. This is due to the fact that when a mixture of two different compounds are dissolved in a solvent (solution), the attractive influence between molecules of the same type would be far greater than the attractive influence between two different types. Thus, when a solution of CBD (90%) and THC (10%) are concentrated and cooled, pure crystals of CBD would precipitate at the bottom, while THC will remain dissolved. As neither the chemical structure of CBD or THC undergoes a chemical change, crystallization is a physical method of separation and it is only used in preparative scales. There are four types of crystallization options that can be adopted after the first stage of crystallization process completion:

1. Cooled Crystallization (Covered as used for cannabinoids or CBD crystallization)
2. Anti-Solvent Crystallization (Not Covered)
3. Evaporative Crystallization (Not Covered)
4. Co-Crystal Crystallization (Not Covered)

In the cannabis industry, crystallization is the solidification of cannabinoids into a highly structured solid called a crystal or isolate. This purification is achieved by separating the solid from the liquid, where the cannabinoid in liquid solution forms a solid crystalline phase when cooled. This solid can then be filtered to remove the solvent, and then filtered and dried in a vacuum oven. If there are still impurities based on test results or color, then the crystallization process is repeated. Cannabinoid crystallization is based on their different solubility (solutes) in hot solvents versus in cold solvents. If a saturated hot solution is allowed to cool, the solute is no longer soluble in the solvent and forms crystals of pure compound. Impurities are excluded from the growing crystals and the pure solid crystals can be separated from the dissolved impurities by filtration.

CBD Crystallization

The CBD isolation and crystallization process begins after extraction and distillation. It begins with a supersaturation, where the distillate is suspended in pentane or hexane until it exceeds the solubility limits to force out the solids under cooling. The crystallization process is a multi-stage process but has two main techniques: static crystallization and stirred crystallization. In the static method, crystals form when the solution is cooled. Stirred crystallization uses movement of the solvent to increase the speed of the process. Static crystallization is used for small scale isolation, while the stirred crystallization method is for larger scale isolations.

The crystallization involves these steps:

1. Choose a proper solvent (CBD will be more soluble in Pentane at higher temperatures and will demonstrate limited solubility characteristics at lower temperatures, causing crystallization).
2. Always make sure to work in a fume hood and wear goggles, gloves and lab coats or scrubs.
3. Start heating the solvent until the entire distillate is dissolved.
4. Let the solution cool down in a freezer. Typically, these are deep freezers. May add a seed crystal to accelerate the process.
5. Once all crystals have formed, the solid is filtered and then dried.
6. Potency testing is required to determine the percentage of concentration of CBD which should be 99% or higher.

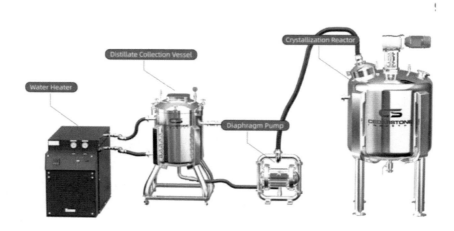

Figure: An entire set up for commercially available industrial scale CBD isolation, also referred to as a turn-key system. Only winterized product and distillate that tested above 80% for CBD can be used in this set up.Image Credit: https://www.cedarstoneindustry.com/product-category/extraction-equipment/crystallization-reactors

Principles of Chromatography, Isolation of Cannabinoids and Testing

All chromatographic methods are physical methods of separation. The principle of chromatography could be employed at both analytical, preparative and large scales.

1. **Adsorption chromatography**

   Adsorption refers to the physical process wherein a liquid or gas molecule is physically adhered to a solid substance. Adsorption is the result of an attractive chemical interaction between the surface functional groups in the solid support and the individual molecule. Solid substances, which are known as adsorbents, act like sponges and hold on to molecules (cannabinoids) at their surface, due to intermolecular forces, such as London dispersion forces, dipole or hydrogen bonding. This method is based on polar and nonpolar interactions between the cannabinoids and the adsorbent. This method is most often used in the cannabis industry. The different adsorption methods discussed are column chromatography (CC), thin layer chromatography (TLC) and high pressure liquid chromatography (HPLC).

2. **Partition Chromatography**

   This method is used to separate cannabinoids utilizing the **partition** of the solutes between two liquid phases. This method is sometimes used in the cannabis industry but is not readily available or yet widely used.

3. **Hydrophobic Interaction Chromatography**

   This separates molecules based on their *hydrophobicity (repulsion from water)*. This is useful for purifying proteins. This method is still only rarely used in the industry.

4. **Ion Exchange**

   This technique can isolate cannabinoids based on their respective charged groups and is based on coulombic and electrostatic (**ionic**) interactions. This method is also only rarely used in the cannabis industry.

5. **Affinity Chromatography**

   This method is based on highly specific binding between two molecules (like proteins, enzymes, antibodies, etc), such as key and a lock. This method is not used in the cannabis industry.

6. **Size Exclusion Chromatography**

   This method is also called molecular sieve *chromatography* and cannabinoids in solution are separated by their *size*, and in some cases molecular weight, or structural shape. This method is rarely used in the cannabis industry.

Detailed Description of Various Types of Chromatography

Adsorption Chromatography: Polarity and Hydrophobicity of Cannabinoids:

In the cannabis industry, the adsorption chromatography method is the most often used method, followed by partition chromatography. In some rare cases, the size exclusion chromatography technique has also been used. The full success of this method is still under investigation, however, and it is usually only used in a proprietary context. Thus, the focus will largely be on the adsorption method, as this is the most commonly used isolation method. It is based on intermolecular interactions between cannabinoids and the adsorbing matrix. Partition based chromatography is slowly emerging, but will not be covered in detail. A polar molecule has an electric dipole moment, with a partially negatively charged end and a partially positively charged end. There are differences in electronegativity between the atoms. A nonpolar molecule has a net zero dipole moment. For example, acetone is polar because it has a net dipole moment and carbon dioxide is nonpolar because it has a zero net-dipole.

The molecular geometry and shape contributes to whether the molecule is polar or nonpolar. Carbon dioxide (CO_2) is a linear molecule, and the two individual dipoles pointing from the C atom to each O atom cause the dipole to be zero, because they cancel each other out. Water is a bent molecule, and the dipoles point from the H atoms toward the O atom due to the higher electronegativity of oxygen. In this case, dipoles do not cancel each other out, and the molecule is therefore polar. Cannabinoids also have various degrees of polarities, but because their structures are all slightly similar, some cannabinoids have very similar polarities. To explain polarity differences in cannabinoids, in the Figure, THCA is more polar than THC. This is because THCA has the carboxylic acid that contributes to a greater dipole than THC. The separation and isolation of cannabinoids is based on the different polarities and the interactions of the polar or nonpolar adsorbent.

Polarity THCA and THC

THCA

Greater Net Dipole: More Polar

THC

Lesser Net Dipole: Less Polar

Figure: Chemical Scheme showing the decarboxylation of THCA to THC producing carbon dioxide demonstrating how the polarity of the molecule is changing. Image Credit: Modified from Shutterstock.

Thin Layer Chromatography and Column Chromatography in Cannabinoid Isolation

Column chromatography is separated into two categories. If the solvent is allowed to flow down the column by gravity, it is called **gravity column chromatography**. If the solvent is forced down the column by positive air pressure, it is called **flash chromatography**. Gravity column chromatography is used in small-scale isolation while flash chromatography is scalable for industrial purposes.

Polar Stationary Phase in Chromatography

Commonly used polar stationary phases are silica gel (SiO_2) and alumina (Al_2O_3) column chromatography. The mixture of cannabinoids is dissolved in less polar solvents, such as hexane and petroleum, with ether mixed with ethyl acetate. More polar cannabinoids stick to the polar silica phase, because of greater polar-polar interactions with the silica gel and less polar cannabinoids elute down the column faster due to the intermolecular interactions being not as strong.

Non-Polar Stationary Phase in Chromatography

For reverse phase column chromatography, reverse phase C18 or C8 is used for the stationary phase and polar solvents like methanol or water with 0.1% formic acid are used to elute the cannabinoids with different retention times.

Figure: An example of the chemical makeup of a C18 column that contains beads which have 18-carbon chains attached to silica beads. In the cannabis industry, the reverse phase column chromatography has been utilized more often than the normal phase because of better separation of cannabinoids, especially with respect to THC remediation. Image Credit: https://commons.wikimedia.org/wiki/File:Silica_gel_endcapping.png#filelinks

Column Chromatography to Isolate Cannabinoids

For column chromatography, a column is packed with a stationary phase. This stationary phase can either be polar (referred to as normal phase) or nonpolar (referred to as reverse phase). The cannabinoid mixture is dissolved in a mobile phase (solvent) and added to the column with the stationary phase. The cannabinoids in the mobile phase move down the column by gravity, but there are interactions between the stationary phase and the cannabinoids that separate the cannabinoids based on polarity.

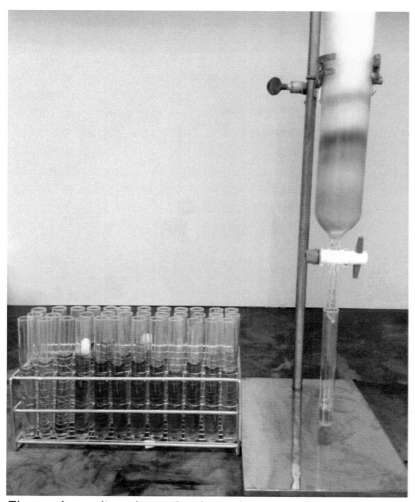

Figure: A gravity column that is packed with silica gel and the different compounds with different polarities are shown as colored bands. Fractions of the different bands are collected in test tubes and the like fractions are combined. Image Credit: Shutterstock.

In flash chromatography, the commercially available columns use pressure for upscaling and faster elution times. Flash Chromatography also helps with the efficacy of isolation, because conditions are constant, such as solvent flow per minute, throughout the purification. This automated software-controlled system consists of a pump to create the pressure, a column filled with the adsorbent, solvents and an ultraviolet detector to detect the cannabinoids as they exit the column. A fraction collector is used to collect the purified cannabinoids. The equipment uses normal-phase and reversed-phase adsorbents. Normal-phase uses a silica filled column and non-polar solvents such as hexane and ethyl acetate, while reversed-phases use C18 with water and ethanol and acids. Their separation mechanisms are based on polarity principles. While cannabinoids have differences in polarities, sometimes they are subtle; normal phase flash chromatography is thus not ideal. Therefore, reverse phase is often used, because it separates the components based on different hydrophobicity (negative reactions to water).

Figure: A commercially available flash chromatography unit is typically used to remediate THC from the cannabinoid mixture. The removal of THC is based on the fact that THC has a different retention time than the other cannabinoids (CBD, etc.). This difference of retention time is due to the different interactions between the cannabinoids and the stationary phase and the hydrophobic interaction with the aqueous solvent, because cannabinoids are very lipophilic (fat loving) and greasy. These instruments are expensive and the large column containing the reverse phase stationary phase needs to be replaced regularly to avoid contamination. These columns are also expensive, which drives the price point higher when THC-remediated products are prepared.
Image Credit: http://interchiminc.com/hemp/

Thin Layer Chromatography

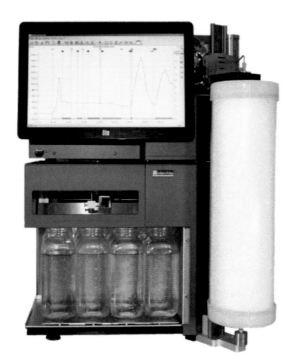

Thin-layer chromatography (TLC) is used for monitoring the progress of a column to purify cannabinoids or following an organic reaction that involves the conversion of one cannabinoid to another or precursors that form a cannabinoid. TLC visualizes the cannabinoids on a plate of glass, plastic, or aluminum foil, which is coated with a thin layer of adsorbent material, usually silica gel, aluminum oxide (alumina), or reverse phase C18. The same adhesion principles as in column chromatography apply. But this time, as seen in the Figure below, the TLC plate is placed in a developing chamber, and the solvent is moving upwards by capillary action, which is against gravity.

Figure: Typical set up of a thin layer chromatography set up. Image Credit: Shutterstock.

The retardation factor (Rf) is the factor that allows the differentiation of cannabinoids. To obtain the Rf, the following measurements are taken:

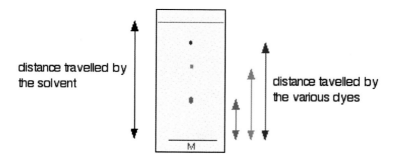

Image Credit: https://www.chemguide.co.uk/analysis/chromatography/thinlayer.html

The R_f value for each dye is worked out using the formula:

$$R_f = \frac{\text{distance travelled by component}}{\text{distance travelled by solvent}}$$

For example, if the red component travelled 1.7 cm from the baseline while the solvent had travelled 5.0 cm, then the R$_f$ value for the red dye is:

$$R_f = \frac{1.7}{5.0}$$
$$= 0.34$$

Credit to: https://www.chemguide.co.uk/analysis/chromatography/thinlayer.html

The Rf value is an indicator for polarity of cannabinoids. On a normal phase Silica TLC, the higher the Rf, the less polar the cannabinoid. Or, the lower the RF, the more polar the cannabinoid. This is due to the concept that the more polar molecules stay with the more polar stationary phase. THCA is the acidic cannabinoid, and after decarboxylation, the acid group gets removed and forms THC and CO_2 (Flaishman et al., 2019). This conversion changes the polarity of THCA and THC, because of the different dipole moments.

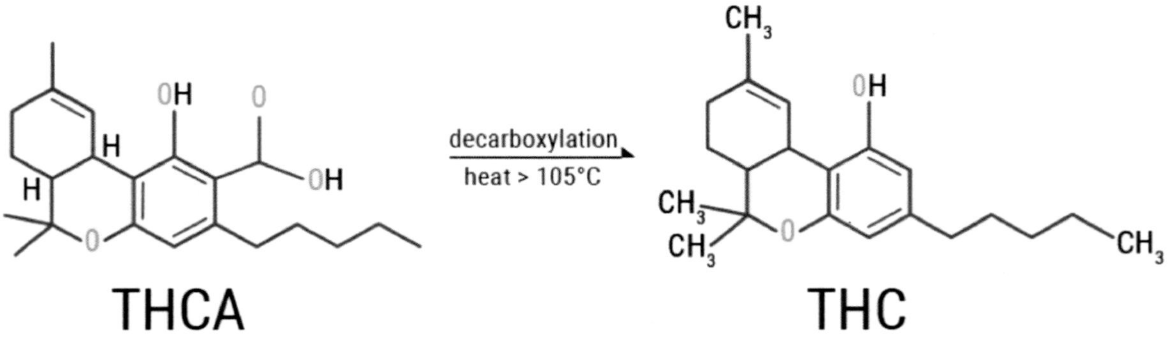

Figure: The polar carboxyl group on THCA is contributing to the molecule's stronger polarity than THC. Therefore, on a polar silica gel TLC, the Rf of THCA (more polar) would be lower than THC (less polar). Image Credit: Shutterstock

Chromatography Based Testing Instruments

The Figure below shows four of the most common examples on cannabinoid characterization A) Gas chromatography GC-FID B) HPLC-UV C) TLC chromatogram Fast Blue salt B as detection reagent D) 1H NMR spectrum.

The chromatography method in A is GC-FID. It clearly shows how all the cannabinoids are separated. This separation is based on boiling point and the different cannabinoids are separated based on different retention times due to their difference in volatility. The chromatography method in B is HPLC. This separation of these cannabinoids is based on different retention times of cannabinoids based on different polarities and hydrophobicity between the non-polar reverse phase stationary phase and the cannabinoids that are dissolved in polar solvents. The TLC in C shows the isolated cannabinoids CBD, THC and CBN on a polar Silica plate. CBD (least polar) has the highest Rf factor, followed by THC and then CBN (most polar). The crude extracts contain multiple cannabinoids. TLC plates are usually developed with TLC stains to visualize the cannabinoids. In this case, the stain Fast Blue was used, which is very popular to visualize cannabis constituents. The spectrum in D is a Nuclear Magnetic Resonance (NMR) Spectrum. This technique measures the different types of hydrogens present in cannabinoids. It is a great characterization technique to determine purity and quantity   of   cannabinoids.

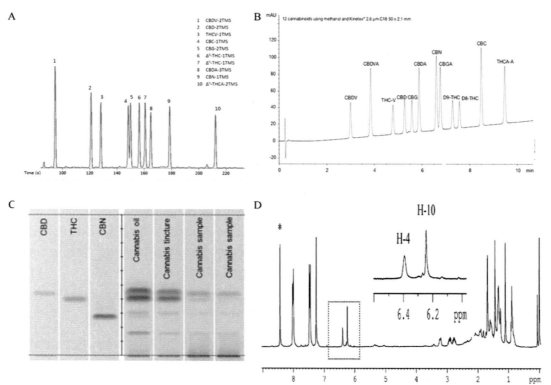

Figure: Examples of the 4 most common methods for the separation and analysis of cannabinoids Image Credit: https://analyticalscience.wiley.com/do/10.1002/gitlab.18169

Different Testing Analyses during Cannabis Processing

There are over 400 compounds in the cannabis plant. One accurate method to ensure the production of high quality and consistent cannabis products is to take samples during each processing step to test the potency. Most cannabis regulating programs require compliance and testing at many levels. If the cannabis biomass has any contaminants, such as pesticides, the contaminants can be concentrated during extraction and refinement processes and could have risky health effects when consumed.

Cannabis absorbs heavy metals from the soil, as well as fertilizers and water. Therefore, cadmium, arsenic, nickel, lead, mercury and other heavy metals accumulate in the plant and testing is necessary. Other contaminants found in hemp include highly toxic pesticides. Imported hemp and suspect or unverifiable growing practices domestically can introduce known carcinogens into the CBD product. Sloppy or poor processing methods can leave any number of residual solvents in a CBD tincture, soft gel or lotion. Harmful yeasts and molds, mycotoxins and other microbial pathogens are capable of causing disease and even death if contaminated cannabis is not rejected prior to processing.

There are many different types of analytical instruments on the market being used today to test cannabinoids, terpenes, microbial growth, heavy metals and pesticides in hemp biomass and processed hemp products. There is not just one method or instrument to test for everything and opinions vary on what is truly the best and most appropriate method or instrument.

Testing facilities should be state audited and ISO-certified. They should follow pharma-level QA/QC programs, use analytical testing with HPLC and GC-MS instruments used by professional lab technicians, employ bar-coded tracking systems for full traceability, enforce strict standard operating procedures and confirm final product quality with multiple levels of oversight. As with other aspects of the fast-moving cannabis industry, technologies and standards are improving and changing daily.

Gas Chromatography Mass Spectrometry (GCMS)

There are two commonly used techniques to determine the concentration of cannabinoids during each step of processing. Gas Chromatography Mass Spectrometry or GCMS is one instrument that can be used. GCMS characterizes the retention time and molecular mass of small and volatile molecules, including cannabinoids. GCMS can also be used to characterize residual solvents and terpenes, which are both getting more and more concentrated during processing and refinement.

High Performance Liquid Chromatography (HPLC) andLiquid Chromatography Mass Spectroscopy (LCMS)

HPLC is the standard method in the cannabis industry to determine the concentration of cannabinoids in any sample. In the Figure below, a sample such as cannabinoids are dissolved in a solvent like methanol and then injected into a port. The sample travels through an HPLC column and the cannabinoids are separated and eluted at different times through the detector. Often, the HPLC is coupled with a mass detector and this is called LCMS. A computer will display the spectrum.

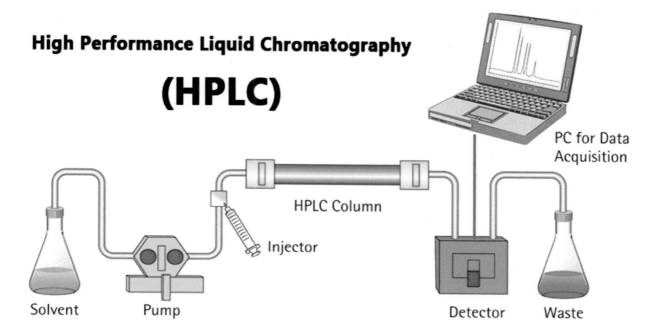

Figure: **Principle of High-Performance Liquid Chromatography (HPLC);** *Image Credit: Sartorius AG https://microbenotes.com/high-performance-liquid-chromatography-hplc/*

Below is a chart that lists some appropriate instruments to use for different categories:

Substance	Compounds	Application	Instrumentation Used
Cannabinoids	THCA, THC, CBDA, CBD, and all other minor cannabinoids	Determine the concentration of each cannabinoid. This is referred to as potency testing.	HPLCGC-FID (cannot distinguish between THCA and THC or CBDA and CBD as decarboxylation occurs in the instrument due to heat)

Terpenes	Alpha-pinene, *β-caryophyllene, limonene*	Determine concentration of terpenes which is important for flavor and aroma and medicinal benefits.	GC-FIDGC-MS
Residual Solvents	Butane, Pentane, hexane, Ethanol, Acetone, iso-propanol	Determine if any solvents remain in the product after solvent extraction of cannabis protecting the consumer.	GC-FIDGC-MS
Pesticides	Organophosphates, carbamates, etc.	Determine if any pesticides are present protecting the consumer.	HPLC-MS-MS GC-MS-MS
Heavy Metals	Arsenic, mercury, lead, cadmium	Determine if heavy metals are present protecting the consumer. Heavy metals are used in fertilizers for cannabis.	ICP-MS
Microbial pathogens	Yeast, Molds, Bacteria	To assure there are no harmful pathogens in the products such as E.coli, salmonella, candida Albicans, etc.	Agar PlatesAgar FilmsPCR

Table: Typical Testing Methodologies for Cannabis Products; Table Credit: Andrea Holmes.

Research on New and Emerging Processing and Cannabis Sourcing Methods:

Nature-Inspired Science

It is helpful to remember how many bioengineered products and medicines are used in our daily lives. Prior to 1978, all of the insulin that kept diabetics alive was derived from pig and cattle pancreases, until bioengineering made it possible to create insulin in a lab. Aspirin was originally derived from willow tree leaves, but today, there is no need to cultivate and chop down a forest of these farmed trees to extract this beneficial compound; scientists can now chemically produce it. Same with vitamins; virtually all Vitamin-C consumed is made in factories in Asia.

Personalized cannabinoid treatments may result from figuring out novel ways to "turn on" the human body's endocannabinoid system. A steppingstone to that reality may be prodrugs, which are biologically inactive compounds scientifically designed to transform themselves into naturally occurring bioactive cannabinoids using the acidic conditions in a person's stomach or the enzymes in the liver during metabolism. It is inevitable that these pathways to address deficiencies in body chemistry and homeostasis will be commercialized in the coming years.

Indeed, the ability to generate cannabinoids at scale using cutting-edge science and chemical synthesis is game changing. While traditionalists and makers of organic and craft products may continue sourcing cannabinoids derived from plants, regardless of scientific advances, alternatively sourced cannabinoids are opening up a whole new avenue of possibilities for the booming cannabis, hemp and CPG industries.

Nature inspires most of the all-time best-selling medicines. Caffeine derived from the coffee bean and those with beneficial but dangerous qualities like the poppy flower's natural opiates became lab-produced opioids. Science continues to look to the natural world for solutions to human problems, takes those solutions and advances them. This process provides multiple advantages as costs reduce, there is far less environmental impact and more people can benefit sooner from such nature-inspired innovations that drive high-tech science and ingenuity faster and in consumer quantities that Mother Nature cannot provide.

Now man is finally [globally] following Mother Nature's lead, propelling scientific understanding of the ways a cannabis plant makes its rich and complex mix of phytocompounds that have bioactivity in mammals; these changes are shifting the cannabis industry in a completely new direction.

How Science Advances Cannabinoid Sourcing Methods

Significant strides in the scientific understanding of complex bioactive phytocompounds in cannabis has increased demand for safe consumer health and wellness products. Such advances are catapulting the cannabis industry into a race to discover the most efficient, innovative, nature-inspired, environmentally friendly and cost-effective sourcing methods for cannabinoids.

Approaches range from traditional cannabis biomass extraction, to more advanced methods like biomimetic approaches, botanically derived synthesis, bioengineered fermentation and chemical synthesis. More unique ideas to obtain rare cannabinoids and their potentially bioactive metabolites are also emerging, including symbiotic fermentation, specific genome editing and algae-based technologies. This line up of existing and emerging innovative techniques requires a continuing closer examination to determine which methods are best suited and for which purposes.

Traditional cannabis plant oil extraction and downstream purification methods like distillation and even chromatography rely on crossbreeding and very soon, CRISPR-based gene editing to obtain desirable characteristics in plant biomass (Dolgin, 2019; Flaishman et al., 2019). For example, the goal might be the overexpression of the "minor" cannabinoid CBG, or removing the THC gene to obtain THC-free extracts, which would eliminate one of the most challenging and costly processing steps of THC remediation. Basic biomass extraction and refinement is the established method to extract cannabinoids. It is easy to upscale and low tech with fully integrated commercially available equipment. Disadvantages include environmental factors and processing-related issues like removing residual solvents, concentrating any pesticides or heavy metals in the biomass and microbial contamination, all of which require continuous analytical testing.

At the other end of the spectrum of traditional plant-based extraction, pharmaceutical companies are gaining access to single cannabinoid molecules by organic synthesis at the highest purity levels; all within a consistent supply chain untethered to the environmental conditions of a cannabis plant's growth cycle.

Biomimetics or semisynthesis applies the understanding of natural phenomena that occur in the plant to producing minor cannabinoids in pure oil, distillate and isolate form from plant grown cannabinoids. This technique enables researchers to derive rare cannabinoids that are not easily extracted from the cannabis plant itself due to their minute quantities. Similarly, botanically-derived synthesis uses botanical sources beyond cannabis plants to avoid the shifting legal issues and jurisdictional differences.

Host organisms like yeast can be genetically modified to express enzymes that are able to convert sugar or other compounds into cannabinoids which can be transformed into other cannabinoids using metabolic pathways. These natural bio-inspired machines are appealing. They use molecules that can be found in the plant and in living organisms, advantages of which include production consistency and the appearance and legitimacy of being environmentally benign and "organic". However, a cannabinoid molecule "factory" in a petri dish has not yet been successfully scaled to production quantities and smart bioengineering will have to overcome this obstacle.

Science continues to copy the natural world to find solutions to fight human disease and improve health. These advancements are poised to greatly influence the marketplace for growers, processors, product formulators and makers of pharmaceuticals and consumer goods in the United States and globally. The ability to generate cannabinoids at scale using cutting-edge nature-inspired science and chemical synthesis is opening up new possibilities for both the medical and health and wellness worlds as they continue to converge and evolve.

Chapter 13 - A New Revolution in Cannabinoids
(Dr. Andrea Holmes and Dr. Mahesh Pattabiramann)

Recent technological advances mean scientists can generate cannabinoid molecules identical to those produced by a cannabis plant. The vast majority of the cannabis product market primarily has been centered around THC and CBD, the two most plentiful compounds in the plant. But alternate methods for sourcing cannabinoids offer researchers the opportunity to produce and explore the potential health benefits of more than 100 of the "minor" cannabinoids, which until now have only been available in trace amounts in existing cannabis strains. These options would then become available to consumer health-and-wellness product companies to make more effective remedies that are often a compelling alternative to traditional pharmaceuticals.

At the other end of the spectrum from plant-based wellness products, pharmaceutical companies are gaining access to single cannabinoid molecules at the purity levels they require and in a consistent supply chain untethered to the environmental conditions of a cannabis plant's growth cycle.

Truly personalized cannabinoid profiles for each individual and each need, whether in the form of a clinically proven FDA-approved drug or a safe consumer product, are now possible. All of these advancements are poised to disrupt the marketplace for growers, processors, product formulators and makers of consumer packaged goods on both the hemp and licensed-THC sides of the regulatory divide, in the United States and globally.

Below are five approaches, ranging from the plant to the chemical reactor, for producing cannabinoid molecules that are reshaping the cannabis business landscape:

1. **Extraction and Purification from Cannabis Biomass:** Cross-breeding female and male plants with desirable characteristics and then extracting the plant's oil is an ancient practice, but technology is taking it to a whole new level. With <u>CRISPR</u>, (Dolgin, 2019) a powerful new genetic engineering tool, researchers can actually design plants with specific chemovars that could offer plentiful sources of formerly rare cannabinoids such as cannabigerol (CBG). A few scientists can now breed a cannabis plant that produces only CBD and no THC or edit its genes to produce different cannabinoids in large quantities and, in the future, approximate ratios.

2. **Biomimetics** is the study of nature and natural phenomena to obtain new ideas, then applying those concepts to science, engineering or medicine. Famously, the breakthrough antibiotic penicillin was discovered by accident after a scientist observed green mold in a petri dish that was curiously killing bacteria the scientist

was trying to grow. When applied with cannabinoids, biomimetics or as my colleagues and I like to call it, *cannabimimetics,* mimics bioprocesses like oxidation (UV, Temperature, Chemical Reactions) and enzymatic pathways that occur during a plant's life cycle. Utilizing nature's blueprint enables researchers to obtain rare cannabinoids from the more common ones produced by a naturally grown hemp or cannabis plant. This method of derivation starts with cannabis or hemp and can produce minor cannabinoids in pure oil, distillate and isolate form.

3. **Botanically Derived Synthesis:** Scientists can now make CBD from botanical sources beyond cannabis plants, such as <u>orange peels</u> and the <u>bark of certain species of pine trees</u>. Natural compounds are extracted from a source and combined with other molecules in order to produce cannabinoids. This method appeals to manufacturers who are reluctant to deal with the constantly shifting legalities of the cannabis plant.

4. **Bioengineered Fermentation:** <u>Biologists have engineered brewer's yeast</u>, algae and even E. coli to produce cannabinoids that are molecularly identical to ones produced by the plant. (Luo et al., 2019) Human insulin is <u>already produced in this manner</u>. Genetically programming a host organism like yeast to manufacture another molecule is the concept. Scaling the exacting conditions required to economically use such a molecule "factory" in a petri dish is the challenge these biochemists and bioengineers are working to overcome. They will do so in due course, just as with human insulin and other drugs now in the marketplace.

5. **Chemical Synthesis** is <u>the pharmaceutical industry's methodology</u> for producing pure, uniform single molecule compounds for incorporation into drugs. Pharmaceutical companies can harness hundreds of years of research, big data and cutting-edge innovation to produce the exact same molecules found in nature, as well as various isomers and derivatives of the naturally occurring cannabinoids for use in clinical trials and active pharmaceutical ingredients (APIs).

Nanoencapsulation for Improved Bioavailability and Water Solubility

Pharmacokinetic (PK) Curves

Pharmacokinetic curves are used by scientists to judge how fast, how much and how long a substance acts on our bodies. Bioactive molecules, whether cannabinoids or Advil™ or statins or blood pressure medicines, are intended to get into blood circulation and reach their site of therapeutic action to have an effect. The broad and somewhat nebulous concept of bioavailability is the crux of the matter. The pharmaceutical industry does not use the term because of its vagueness. Bioavailability, however, has been embraced by the cannabis industry for the time being.

Cannabinoids are "greasy" molecules. The human body is predominantly water, and water and fat do not mix. Think of the "oil-vinegar effect", i.e., what happens when your dressing looks like a chemistry experiment in your refrigerator with two layers of ingredients. Accordingly, only a surprisingly low percentage of the cannabinoids we consume are bioavailable to humans. This applies to the now ordinary cannabinoids like cannabidiol (CBD) or delta-9-tetrahydrocannabinol (THC), the increasingly common "minor cannabinoids" like cannabigerol (CBG) and cannabinol (CBN), and the exotic ones like cannabichromene (CBC), cannabidivarin (CBDV) or tetrahydrocannabivarin (THCV).

For various purposes, it is desired for these cannabinoids in our bloodstream speeding their way to the endocannabinoid system and its receptors. But, in reality, only a small percentage of cannabinoids (based on clinical studies), actually make it into our bloodstreams (maybe 30% via smoking and <10% for edibles). A syringe full of cannabinoids via an injection in a vein won't do anything until the blood gets processed through the liver. Remember, all cannabinoids are fat molecules and don't mix with aqueous blood. Even then not much will become bioavailable and it will be slow taking effect.

Therefore, in the world of pharmacology, PK and pharmacodynamic (PD) curves are important tools to determine dosing and serving sizes. They apply to whatever mode of delivery is chosen: transdermal, oral, edible, mucosal, inhalation and intravenous, as well as whether the molecules are enhanced with various technologies like nano-emulsions and liposomal treatments.

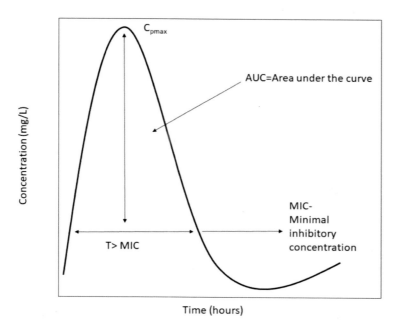

Figure: An example of what a pharmacokinetic curve looks like. Image Credit: Dr. Andrea Holmes

Setting aside potential malignancies and other issues, smoking is an efficient mode of sneaking cannabinoids into your bloodstream. With smoking or vaping, as well as intranasal, sublingual and other mucosal delivery modes, the liver is not initially involved and there is no metabolic first pass effect. However, once the inhaled cannabinoids are in the bloodstream, the blood will soon find its way to the liver. Obviously, inhaling does have serious health implications. There is a reason one coughs when one inhales.

The more knowledge one has and can quantify how molecules move through and interact with the body, the better. Moving from PK to another key branch of pharmacology known as pharmacodynamics, or PD, is defined as the study of the effects of a drug or compound in the body. To have the most complete understanding of what a molecule does and how it moves around, scientists and medical researchers employ PK/PD models to figure out dosing, benefit, timing, potential for side effects and adverse interactions. These curves and quantitative modeling are also critical in the design of controlled release capsules and pills that "meter out" a compound over time for long-lasting therapeutic effect.

A person's metabolism, a broad term encompassing a wide range of biochemical processes in one's body, can be considered a gatekeeper of molecules seeking admittance to their bloodstream. The stomach processes incoming molecules alone, or with other compounds arriving for processing at the same time, i.e., whatever else a person ate, drank or smoked recently.

A key system of the digestive tract is the liver, a super-smart organ, efficient, and always on the job, which continually processes a gallon of blood every two and half minutes. It is a filter, a detoxifier and an enzyme manufacturer. It is impressive at doing its job. The liver makes judgments about what immediately is excreted from the body and what is metabolized.

First pass metabolism is critical, as is second pass, i.e., the second time a substance passes through the liver in the bloodstream as it cycles. Notably, compounds are often routinely transformed, one into another, during these trips through the liver and gastrointestinal system. Some cannabinoids are converted into other bioactive or non-bioactive metabolites, including other non-naturally occurring cannabinoid family chemical compounds. Simply stated, regardless of the mode of ingestion, the liver determines what compounds and how many of them will gain access to a person's endocannabinoid system receptors.

The fact that cannabinoids appear to have high absorption variability adds to the complexity of determining "typical" pharmacokinetic (PK) and PD curves. For example, acidic forms of cannabinoids have been shown to have naturally higher bioavailability due to the pH dependence of lipophilicity meaning cannabidiolic acid (CBDA) will have a higher bioavailability compared to cannabidiol (CBD). All of these factors require further study.

Differences in PK and PD curves can vary greatly between a plain cannabinoid molecule and one that has been supercharged with an enhanced drug delivery system, which is a common technology in the pharma and functional food world as well as whatever else is in a person's system or on its way in. It is a complex equation with many variables, and each person is different. The tried and true maxims of "low and slow", "consult with the doctor", and "one size doesn't fit all" surely apply with anything a person added to their individual physiological equation at a particular time.

The current "hit or miss" or "self-dosing" situation with most cannabinoid consumer products is really not an optimal approach. More human studies will help in determining PK and PD curves for cannabinoids via the different form factors and delivery modes. In the near term, more detailed and quantitative product labeling will greatly help.
More effective and more personalized remedies and medicines are the goal. PK and PD curves, enhanced delivery technologies, and detailed, quantified cannabinoid product

labeling, together with more research, will allow cannabinoids to achieve their full potential.

Nanoencapsulation Processing Technology: Improved Bioavailability and Water Solubility

Cannabinoids have higher bioavailability when inhaled or used rectally in the form of a suppository because the first-pass metabolism through the liver is avoided. Such delivery modes may not be very appealing to many people and nanoencapsulation offers an alternative route for increase in oral-bioavailability. Nanoencapsulation is a common technique for drug delivery to improve the therapeutic efficacy and bioavailability of bioactive molecules, such as cannabinoids (Maran, 2019). Examples of nanoencapsulation methods include nanocarriers, such as nanoemulsions, dendrimers, micelles, liposomes, host guest complexes, surface modified nanoparticles (NP), nanocapsules and lipid nanoparticles (Chouinard & Conway, 2021; Rolle, 2020). For cannabinoid entrapment, liposomal NP and polymeric NP are most often used. Cannabinoids can also be non-covalently bonded with cyclized maltodextrins. This host-guest complex allows for increased water solubility (Conte et al., 2017). Through all these mechanisms, highly lipophilic cannabinoids get protected from harsh environments, such as the acidic gastrointestinal lining, and allow for more precise and time-released dosing.

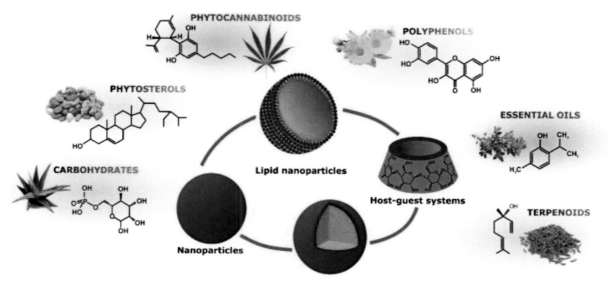

Figure: Nanoparticle-mediated delivery of natural products. Image Credit: Int J Mol Sci. 2017 Apr; 18(4): 709. Published online 2017 Mar 28. doi: 10.3390/ijms18040709.

Nanostructured Lipid Vectors or Lipid Nanoparticle (NP) for Cannabinoids (Liposomes and Micelles)

Liposomes are composed of a lipid bilayer but micelles have only one lipid layer. Their size ranges from 350 to 500 nm (sometimes smaller). In the micelle, the apolar section turns inward and surrounds the cannabinoids and the polar side interacts with the aqueous environment. The internal space of the micelle is much smaller than in the liposome and the liposome delivery system is still under development to improve optimal encapsulation and loading efficiency. Studies have demonstrated slow and prolonged release for more than five hours after administration. Liposomes are prepared by reverse-phase evaporation and their size ranges from small, medium or large. The reverse-phase evaporation is performed by adding the cannabinoid to the aqueous phase and the lipids to the organic solvent forming liposome bilayer. The cannabinoid then enters into the liposome and the organic solvent gets evaporated under reduced pressure. Any residual solvent can be removed by centrifugation, dialysis or running the liposomes through a column (Sepharose Gel). Sonication can also effectively encapsulate the **cannabinoids** into liposomes.

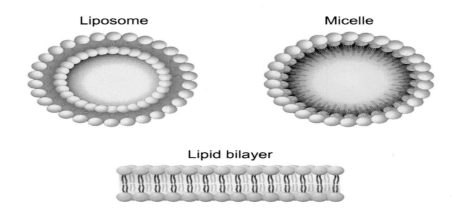

Figure: Image of various nano-particle delivery systems using lipids. Image Credit: Shutterstock.

Increased absorption of orally administered THC and CBD when co-administered via micelles achieve significantly higher bioavailability than in lipid-free formulations. It has been proposed that this increased bioavailability is due to the micelles containing the cannabinoids entering the intestinal lymphatic system instead of first passing through the liver. (Zgair et al., 2016).

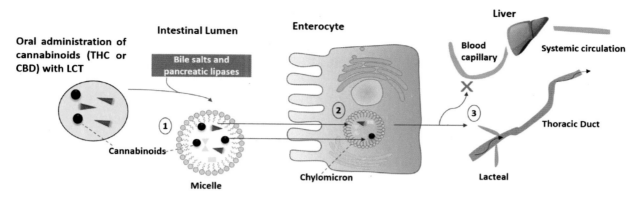

Figure: Fat-encapsulated cannabinoids bypassing the first pass liver metabolism increasing the bioavailability. Image Credit: Recreated by Mahesh Pattabiraman. Adapted from publication by Zgair A, Wong JC, Lee JB, et al. Dietary fats and pharmaceutical lipid excipients increase systemic exposure to orally administered cannabis and cannabis-based medicines. Am J Transl Res. 2016;8(8):3448-3459. Published 2016 Aug 15.

Polymeric Cannabinoid Carriers

Similar to liposomes and micelles, polymers have been used in drug delivery. For example, THC-loaded polymer nanoparticles were developed for use as an anticancer agent. The molecular structure, degradation and bioavailability profiles of the polymers can vary greatly depending on the application. One polymer called poly (lactic-co-glycolic acid) (PLGA) is hydrophobic, non-toxic and gets metabolized and excreted from the body. PLGA polymers are sometimes coated with other substances like Vitamin E or lecithin to further improve absorption into the bloodstream and bioavailability. Lecithin and vitamin E-modified particles also allow for higher release rates when compared to the other formulations. Another surface modification is done with poly (ethylene glycol) (**PEG**). PEG modification prevents protein adsorption, thereby increasing shelf life. PEGylation also protects the cannabinoid against immune processes. Poly-ε-caprolactone (PCL) is another biocompatible polymer that is biodegradable, FDA-approved, semi-crystalline and it degrades slowly. An example is that CBD was recently successfully loaded into PCL particles with a size range of 20 to 50 minimum and nearly 100% encapsulation efficiency.

Table 2

Nanosized delivery systems for anti-inflammatory phytocannabinoids.

Bioactive Principle	Nanovector	Type of Delivery System	Experimental Model	Reference
Δ-9-Tetrahydrocannabinol	Lipid nanoparticles	Nanostructured lipid carriers	In vitro	[110]
	Nanoparticles	Lipid NP containing lecithin	In vitro	[111]
		PLGA NP	In vitro/In vivo	[112]
		Cannabidiol loaded PCL NP	In vitro	[113]
		Δ9-THC-loaded PLGA NP	In vivo (immunocompetent C57BL/6 mice)	[114]

Table: A summary of synthesized nanosized delivery systems for phytocannabinoids. (Conte et al., 2017) Credit: Conte R, Marturano V, Peluso G, Calarco A, Cerruti P. Recent Advances in Nanoparticle-Mediated Delivery of Anti-Inflammatory Phytocompounds. Int J Mol Sci. 2017;18(4):709. Published 2017 Mar 28. doi:10.3390/ijms18040709

Water Soluble Cannabinoids

The lipid and polymer nano-emulsions discussed above are used for beverages, and sometimes carbonation is added to mimic the flavor of soda or beer. These water soluble delivery systems sometimes result in a hazy, non-transparent and oily look to the beverage. Therefore, other technologies have emerged to improve bioavailability and increase water solubility. For example, glycoside technology exists and adds sugar molecules to cannabinoids. This glycosylation, which happens in the plant naturally, can be mimicked by adding cannabinoids to enzymes. These enzymes can recognize cannabinoids and bond with them.

In the Table below, it is seen that this glycosylation can be done synthetically (Martin et al., 2006). In this sense, it is similar to other covalent derivatization, including carboxamido, imidazole, pyrazole, triazole and morpholine pentyl side chain analogs, as well as derivatization of phenolic alcohol. These processes operate to form substituted esters to increase water solubility. While the pathways have improved the solubility of cannabinoids in water, they release synthetic prodrug upon hydrolysis in the gastrointestinal system, which may or may not have been tested for any side effects.

Table:

Carboxamido	Imidazole, Pyrazole Triazole, Morpholine	Phenoxlic ester

Carboxamido

- O-2352 —CONH₂
- O-2490 —CONHCH₃
- O-2544 —CONH—N(morpholine)
- O-2489 -CONH—N(azepane)
- O-2543 -CONH—N(pyrrolidine)
- O-2372 —CO-N(morpholine)
- O-2373 —CO-N(piperidine)
- O-2381 —CO-N(piperazine)N—
- O-2399 —C(O)-N(pyrrolidine)
- O-2421 —C(O)-N(azepane)
- O-2589 —N(H)-C(O)-(methylthiazole)
- O-2590 —N(H)-C(O)-(phenyl methyloxazole)
- O-2619 —N(H)-C(O)-N(morpholine)
- O-2620 —N-(C(O)-N(morpholine))₂

Imidazole, Pyrazole Triazole, Morpholine

- O-2545 —N(imidazole) • HCl
- O-2651 —N(methylimidazole) • HCl
- O-2715 —N(pyrazole)
- O-2716 —N(triazole)
- O-2737 —(imidazoline NH) • HCl
- O-3226 —N(morpholine)

Phenoxlic ester

- O-1057 (morpholine) • HCl
- O-2365 (piperidine) • HCl
- O-2374 (piperidine) • HCl
- O-2426 (methylpiperidine) • HCl
- O-2486 (methylpiperidine) • HCl
- O-2383 (N-methylpiperazine) • HCl
- O-2427 (N-methylpiperazine) • HCl
- O-2484 (dimethylamino) • HCl
- O-2487 (dimethylamino) • HCl
- O-2548 (trimethylammonium) I⁻
- O-2650 (trimethylammonium) I⁻
- O-2382 (diisopropylamino) • HCl
- O-2485 (diisopropylamino) • HCl

Image Credit: Reproduced by Mahesh Pattabiraman; Adapted from Martin et al. Journal of Pharmacology and Experimental Therapeutics 2006, 318 (3) 1230-1239; DOI: https://doi.org/10.1124/jpet.106.104109

Organic Synthesis of Cannabinoids

Cannabis sativa flowers, like many other plants, contain numerous cannabinoids and terpenes. Whereas a few cannabinoids such as □9-THC (□9-Tetrahydrocannabinol), CBD (Cannabidiol) and CBG (Cannabigerol) can be obtained in appreciable quantities via extraction from the cannabis plant followed by refinement and purification, most other cannabinoids cannot. This is because they compose such small quantities in the current strains of hemp or marijuana in the marketplace. The THC content in marijuana is typically in the 25% to 28% range, and a couple strains of cannabis possess 19% to 21% CBD while most industrial hemp has 7% to 10% CBD. But other minor cannabinoids such as CBN (Cannabinol), CBC (Cannabichromene), CBT (Cannabicitran), CBL (Cannabicyclol), CBDV (Cannabidivarin) and THCV (Tetrahydrocannabivarin), exist in such minute quantities, in the 0.0% to 0.3% range, and therefore are not practical targets for extraction. In order to access these other biologically active minor cannabinoids organic synthesis is the alternate route to these important molecules.

There is currently growing commercial interest in the minor cannabinoids. The situation is predicted to change even more rapidly in the near future as knowledge of their academically established medicinal properties is explored for practical purposes. The industry is bound to emerge even more rapidly as academic research activity into the minor cannabinoids increases. So, in order to access these other biologically active minor cannabinoids, non-biological production is the alternate route to these important molecules. Two broad approaches exist for producing cannabinoids (major and minor) without involving cannabis: (a) chemical synthesis and (b) enzymatic or microbial production. The chemical synthesis route involves subjecting readily available inexpensive substances (chemical feedstock) to chemical reactions performed using chemical apparatus, often in series, to produce the target cannabinoid of interest. Enzymatic production refers to the process of using biological enzymes outside living organisms (especially plants) for the conversion of simple molecules, such as sugars, into cannabinoids.

In this context of producing cannabinoids through non-plant sources, two phrases and their meanings should be clearly defined: natural cannabinoids and unnatural cannabinoids. Natural cannabinoids are molecular structures of compounds found in the cannabis plant. If those exact structures are produced by chemists in the laboratory, through chemical transformations or through the use of engineered biological methods such as biochemical, cellular processes, they are still natural cannabinoids. Unnatural cannabinoids are compounds that are almost structurally similar to the natural cannabinoids but are still capable of eliciting a cannabinoid-like effect in a living organism by binding to the cannabinoid receptors. However, the unnatural cannabinoid is used loosely sometimes to refer to compounds that are just structurally similar but with no biological relevance.

Chemical Reactions and Organic Synthesis – A Crash Course

Chemicals are pure substances that are obtained from natural sources or produced in the lab starting from natural sources. A pure chemical is a substance that carries a specific elemental composition and structure at the molecular (smallest indivisible entity) level. When either the elemental composition or structure of the substance changes at the molecular level, it is said to have undergone a chemical change. A majority of these substances that laypersons, or even chemists, come across are stable compounds which do not change their identity within a noticeable timescale. They do, however, undergo rapid chemical change (a reaction), when there is enough energy to undergo such change and/or when they encounter another reactant that is a reactive match chemically to produce product(s). Chemists study such processes and have acquired the expertise to produce chemical change with desired product structure. More broadly, the ability to manipulate and control chemical change has been one of the greatest endeavors responsible for the material progress humans have made in the last two centuries.

While performing chemical reactions to produce a specific compound (of specific structure), especially small molecules (aka synthesis), chemists try to achieve two main goals: high reaction yield and high product selectivity. Reaction yield refers to the product amount obtained compared to the maximum obtainable mass (theoretical yield) if the reactant proceeded to completion. It is expressed as a percentage. Selectivity refers to the formation of desired product over unwanted products, as often in reactions, a reactant **R** could result in multiple products at expense of each other.

Components of Chemical Equations

Chemical equations represent the transformation of reactants to products along with important details such as co-reactants, temperature and pressure conditions, presence of catalysts, duration, etc. While it is possible to add as many types of information as possible, the basic components that a chemical equation must have are the reactants on the left hand side (LHS) of the arrow and products on the right hand side (RHS) of the arrow. Reagents (co-reactants that are not the primary focus), reaction conditions (heating, cooling, sonication, microwave, etc.), solvent used, duration, etc. are represented above or below the arrow. When reactions are performed and information about yield and selectivity is known, they are presented below the structure of each product on the RHS.

Chemical reactions usually are balanced, like mathematical equations, for the number of atoms representing the elements wherein the element count on the left and right should be equal. However, the same is not essential for organic reactions; as cannabinoids are organic molecules and the chemical equations are not balanced. All real and theoretical chemical transformations are balanced.

Organic Synthesis

Organic synthesis is the construction of organic compounds from smaller molecules, often referred to as building blocks, and can be divided into two types: total synthesis and semisynthesis. Total synthesis utilizes commercially available small molecule starting materials, which are usually simple in nature and often derived from petroleum products. Semisynthesis on the other hand, involves using more complex and unique starting materials that often come from natural resources like plants, animal materials or microbial materials such as cell cultures. The advantage of semisynthesis over total synthesis is that the starting material(s) from plant or animal natural resources used in semisynthesis have complex chemical structures that afford important chemical and/or unique medicinal properties.

With a typical orange having 50 mg of Vitamin C, most people know that citrus fruits are a good source of Vitamin C for their diet. However, many are unaware that the Vitamin C used to fortify foods like breakfast cereal or the Vitamin C added to nutraceuticals or vitamin and mineral supplements is synthesized, not isolated from fruits. 95% of the world supply of Vitamin C is produced in Asia via a *semisynthesis* route starting with glucose obtained from a starch, commonly potatoes.

Potatoes

Glucose

Reduction

Sorbitol

Fermentation

Vitamin-C

KGA (2-keto-gluconic acid)

Fermentation

Sorbose

Naturally occurring starch possesses the correct stereochemistry required for the chiral center on the lactone ring as well as the alcohol on the side chain. This semisynthesis route is efficient at 60% yield and is easy to scale up to industrial quantities which makes Vitamin C very inexpensive at $10.00/Kg. The first total synthesis of Vitamin C from a non-carbohydrate source was reported by an Australian group in the late 90's (Banwell et al., 1998).

Toluene from petroleum — Benzene — Chlorobenzene — Sevaral steps — Vitamin-C

Starting material used in 1998 synthesis of vitamin-C

Their synthesis started with Chlorobenzene, which is derived from the petroleum product Toluene. In order to generate the correct stereochemistry, the group utilized the microbial oxidation of Chlorobenzene as their first step. Their total synthesis, however, was operationally based on several steps using many expensive chemicals. It afforded an overall yield that was poor. Their method is thus impractical for large scale production applications. This example with Vitamin C exemplifies how semisynthesis can be much better than total synthesis in terms of production scale and consumer costs of the final product.

Several other examples exist where organic synthesis is used to generate compounds that are used to confer natural flavors, smells and other biological effects as it is commercially (more) viable to do so rather than isolate these substances from natural sources. Examples include isoamyl acetate for banana flavoring in foods, musk ketones in perfumery and cinnamaldehyde for cinnamon flavor.

Isoamyl acetate
Banana flavor

Musk ketone
Musk fragrance

Cinnamaldehyde
Cinnamon flavor

Vanillin
Vanilla flavor

Cannabinoids Can Be Synthesized

All cannabinoids can be synthesized. Whether using a semisynthetic route or a total synthesis route, if the starting materials are either prohibitively expensive or not readily available or if the overall yield of the synthesis is poor, then the scale up will not be practical.

There are three major cannabinoids of CBD, ☐9-THC, and CBG since, as of 2020, and there is enough cannabis biomass available for each of these (where the percentage to content in the plant is high enough) to make extraction, isolation and purification a practical method for obtaining them. CBD can be synthesized in a single step from (+)-p-mentha-2,8-dien-ol (a naturally occurring monoterpenoid found in spearmint and wild celery) and Olivetol (a naturally occurring compound found in various lichen) in the presence of an acid catalyst, but this transformation is prone to regioselectivity problems as a significant amount of "Irregular-CBD" forms as a byproduct and separation of the 2 isomers is problematic.

Monoterpenoid   Olivetol   Acid Catalyst   Natural-CBD **MAJOR**   Irregular-CBD **MINOR**

A better alternative is the indirect route where the (+)-p-mentha-2,8-dien-ol is coupled with Carboxymethyl Olivetol (CM-Olivetol); this is Olivetol possessing a methyl ester at the 4-position. The methyl ester moiety acts as a directing group to afford coupling only at the 2-position on the Olivetol ring. This results in cleaner conversion to Carboxymethyl-CBD (CM-CBD) and good yields at 85%. Base Hydrolysis at a 95% yield level then affords Natural-CBD with an 81% overall yield for the 2-step process.

CM-Olivetol   Acid Catalyst   Selectivity at C2   CM-CBD   Natural-CBD

☐9-THC can be synthesized in a similar fashion as CBD, but the acid catalyst in the coupling reaction must be a strong acid like BF$_3$-Etherate, the conditions must be anhydrous so no moisture is present and the formation of ☐9-THC is favored at cold temperatures.

Monoterpenoid   CM-Olivetol BF_3-OEt_2 $MgSO_4$ Cold   Natural-THC   Requires Chromatography

This route actually makes CBD *in-situ,* which subsequently cyclizes to make ☐9-THC as the major product. Varying amounts of other isomers can also, form so the crude reaction mixture must be chromatographed to achieve >95% pure ☐9-THC for even mediocre yields.

Because the price of CBD has dropped dramatically over the past 24 months, a more attractive synthetic route is to convert CBD to THC. Over the past 80 years, several articles have been published regarding the conversion of CBD to THC, (Tadayon & Ramazani, 2021) but the common pitfall is the formation of ☐8-THC as the major product, and in several cases the only product.

☐8-THC is the more thermodynamically stable form of THC, and hence it forms more readily than the desired ☐9-THC. The formation of ☐9-THC can once again be enhanced by using a strong acid catalyst, running the reaction under inert conditions to alleviate any moisture and then dropping the reaction temperature to sub-zero conditions. Utilizing this method, ☐9-THC is the major end product with only trace amounts of ☐8-THC forming. Such crude ☐9-THC can then be distilled for purification, obviating the need for tedious chromatography that usually is not economical to scale up for industrial production.

CBG gained much attention in 2019-2020, because a couple or few seed geneticists developed strains of hemp that are high in CBG, not CBD. Therefore, CBG can now be considered a "major" cannabinoid, the extraction of which is now practical. CBG can be synthesized in a single step, once again starting with Olivetol, but now coupling to a different monoterpene called Geraniol. Geraniol is a natural oil that is a component of rose oil and citronella oil.

Geraniol   CM-Olivetol   Acid Catalyst   Cannabigeraniol (CBG)

Solvent and catalyst are important in the CBG coupling as many byproducts are possible including Unnatural-CBG, di-addition adducts where two molecules of Geraniol add to the ring, O-alkylation byproducts where the phenolic oxygens of Olivetol attack the Geraniol, and even SN2' byproducts where Olivetol attacks C3 of Geraniol as opposed to the desired C1 position.

CBN is a cannabinoid that does not occur naturally in cannabis, rather it forms after the plant is harvested and results when THC is oxidized over time by exposure to air and light. Therefore, CBN is available only through synthesis from either CBD, ☐8-THC, or ☐9-THC and is formed by aromatization of the terpene ring in THC. CBN was actually first reported in the literature in the 1950s when THC was converted to CBN by heating with elemental Sulfur to 250 ∘C and then distilling from the pot.

Δ9-THC   Natural-CBD   Sulfur / DDQ or Chloranil / Iodine   CBN

Later, other oxidizers of the quinone series were used, such as Chloranil or DDQ (Dichloro Dicyano Quinone), and then as recently as 2018 in the *Journal of Natural Products*, elemental Iodine was shown to complete the transformation of CBD or THC to CBN at a 70% yield. (Pollastro et al., 2018)

CBC is synthesized in parallel fashion as CBG, but rather than coupling Olivetol with Geraniol, it is coupled with Geranial, the aldehyde oxidized terpenoid. Geranial is sold under the trade name Citral, and is very abundant in Lemon Grass and Lemon Myrtle.

Geranial   +   Olivetol   Acid Catalyst   Racemic mixture   Cannabichromene (CBC)

Unlike the synthesis of CBG that is plagued with many byproducts and varies widely depending on the solvent, the catalyst and the temperature, the CBC synthesis is clean and constitutes high purity CBC at >95%. It can also be obtained without chromatography or distillation. One interesting characteristic to point out about the CBC product is that it is a d/l mixture of the two stereoisomers, which is the same as what forms naturally in the cannabis plant.

CBT (Cannabicitran) is a "new" cannabinoid to hit the internet in 2020-2021, but it was discovered back in 1971. (Bercht et al.,.1974) Even though CBT is approaching 50 years old, very little is known about the medical benefits of CBT outside a study on rabbits that showed CBT reduces pressure in the eyes, making it a possible treatment for glaucoma. CBT can be made by heating CBC, in fact, performing a high vacuum distillation on CBC will afford only CBT as all of the CBC will cyclize during the distillation.

Another CBT-related point to note is that there is a second type of CBT product being marketed and sold on the internet, but this CBT = Cannabitriol(s), and is an oxidized form of □8-THC or □9-THC. In CBT = Cannabitriol, the alkene in the terpene ring of THC is oxidized to a dihydroxy, which gives 3 hydroxys due to the phenolic-OH on the aromatic ring.

CBT = Cannabitriol

CBT from Δ9-THC   CBT from Δ8-THC

Some websites are starting to distinguish between the two versions of CBT by adding a -C or a -T to give either CBT-C = Cannabicitran, or conversely, CBT-T = Cannabitriol. Cannabitriol is a natural oxidation product of THC. In fact, the synthesized THC drugs Dronabinol and Marinol all have traces of multiple Trihydroxy compounds that are detectable by HPLC. These Cannabitriols can be made in the lab by treating □8-THC or □9-THC with the traditional dihydroxylation reagents such as Potassium Permanganate, Osmium Tetroxide, or meta-Chloroperoxybenzoic acid.

CBT-T = Cannabitriol

Δ9-THC OR Δ8-THC → (OsO₄ / KMnO₄ / mCPBA) → CBT-T from Δ9-THC CBT-T from Δ8-THC

Switching now to the Varin-series of cannabinoids, the 5-carbon chain on the aromatic ring is cut to a 3-carbon chain, and although the change of losing 2 carbons does not seem like a big one, the human body disagrees as THCV does not have the same psychotropic effect as THC, and THCV and CBDV have different medicinal properties as well.

THCV and CBDV can be synthesized using the same reactions as those for THC and CBD, but the Olivetol in the THC/CBD reactions is exchanged for 5-Propylresorcinol which has the 3-carbon side chain. CBDV Route 1 gives a significant amount of Irregular-CBDV and separation is not feasible for scale-up.

CBDV Route 2 gives proper selectivity and although it requires a second step, the overall yield is >80%. One other consideration is the higher cost of the Carbomethoxy-5-Propylresorcinol compared to 5-Propylresorcinol, but this route is better than the one mentioned above.

THCV Route 1 is to use the stronger acid BF₃-Etherate, but other byproducts form so chromatography is required.

Monoterpenoid + 5-Propylresorcinol → (BF₃ - OEt₂, MgSO₄, COLD) Natural-THCV

MAJOR

Requires Chromatography

THCV Route 2 is to start with CBDV and cyclize using the strong Lewis Acid at sub-zero temperatures to minimize the formation of ☐8-THCV.

Natural-CBDV → (BF₃ - OEt₂, MgSO₄, -60 ºC) D9-THCV **MAJOR** + D8-THCV **Trace**

Advantages and Disadvantages of Synthesis versus Naturally Derived Cannabinoids

The age-old debate continues as to which is better, all natural from Mother Nature, or man-made. Although technically the choice is left to the individual, most often cost or affordability top the list of priorities that ultimately drive the direction of the relevant market.

Just as was the case with the Vitamin-C example, fruits and a few vegetables may be good sources of Vitamin-C for your diet, but almost all of the Vitamin-C fortified into foods, nutraceuticals, and vitamins and minerals come from a chemical reactor because isolation of Vitamin-C from oranges is not practical to meet the world's demand for this single key vitamin. Imagine trying to isolate only Vitamin-C from an orange, amid the myriad of other components: glucose, fructose, sucrose, protein, fiber, Vitamin-B1, potassium, calcium… just so you can add it to your breakfast bar.

Companies across the world are working every day to find the best/cheapest source for all of the cannabinoids to formulate into the multitude of cannabis products that are available in the marketplace. So let's look at two of the major cannas: CBD and CBG. Some people believe that CBD from hemp is better than synthesized CBD, because chemicals are used in the synthesis. They fail to recognize, however, that chemicals are used to extract the hemp, solvents are used to further refine and purify the product, and ultimately whether extracted or synthesized, both forms have to undergo the same stringent testing that is regulated by the government. Costwise, CBD from hemp is a far better deal than synthesized. The cost of CBD Isolate in the U.S. in 2018 dropped from $6,000.00 to $9,000.00/Kg, depending on purity, all the way down to $1000.00 to $1,200.00/Kg in 2020 because so many companies have invested $20 million - $100 million in extraction and processing facilities. Compare the current cost (as of early 2021) of >99% pure CBD Isolate at $1,000.00/Kg, but the cost of Carbomethoxy-Olivetol used to synthesize CBD is ~$4,000.00/Kg. So costwise, synthetic CBD cannot compete with the local farmers and processors.

In 2020, CBG Isolate was selling for $17,000.00 to $28,000.00/Kg depending on the vendor. But synthetic CBG can be purchased from multiple companies in Asia for $3,500.00 to $4000.00/Kg. And consider that hemp takes 90-100 days to grow, then harvest, dry, grind up or mill, extract, isolate, distill, and then crystallize to isolate; this constitutes at least a 4 month process. On the other hand, synthesis, workup, isolation, distillation, and crystallization to CBG isolate can be done in large vats in a matter of days using cheap starting materials that are readily available. So would you pay $17,000.00 for 1Kg of CBG because it came from the cannabis plant, or would you prefer to spend $4,000.00 for synthetic CBG because the HPLC and other modern analytical equipment says they are the same quality? To each their own, but the likely verdict of the market is obvious...

Functional Groups of Cannabinoids

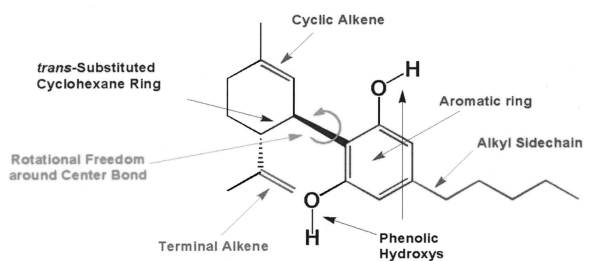

THC is a Tricyclic Molecule

Cyclic Alkene

trans-Substituted Cyclohexane Ring

Phenolic Hydroxy

Aromatic ring

Alkyl Sidechain

Third Ring Locks Molecule in a Cage Type Structure

Cyclic Ether

Enzymatic Synthesis of Cannabinoids

While chemists perform reactions in the labs in test-tubes where the only starting ingredients are organic reactant molecules, solvents, and heat, nature performs chemical transformations through enzymes. However, while nature does it in an entire biological setup that is governed by living organisms (from unicellular beings to humans), humans have tried to mimic nature by taming nature's bare minimum apparatus to perform the same chemical reaction: using enzymes. Enzymatic synthesis is still abiogenesis as this is still an unnatural method of synthesis and does not occur naturally and/or without human intervention. This process is akin to organic synthesis of cannabinoids, except that the operations are performed by enzymes, which are extraordinarily specific in their actions, and if engineered appropriately, they can produce large amounts of the desired product in relatively less time (aka catalysis).

Scientists have started looking into using enzymes to produce cannabinoids and currently such processes have been achieved on a small scale. The use of biologically engineered enzymes for producing cannabinoids such as CBG, THCA, CBDA, CBD and THC have all been performed successfully. However, these technologies are still at a rudimentary level; although it is very easy to predict that it is only a matter of time and market demand before they are optimized and scaled up for commercial level activity.

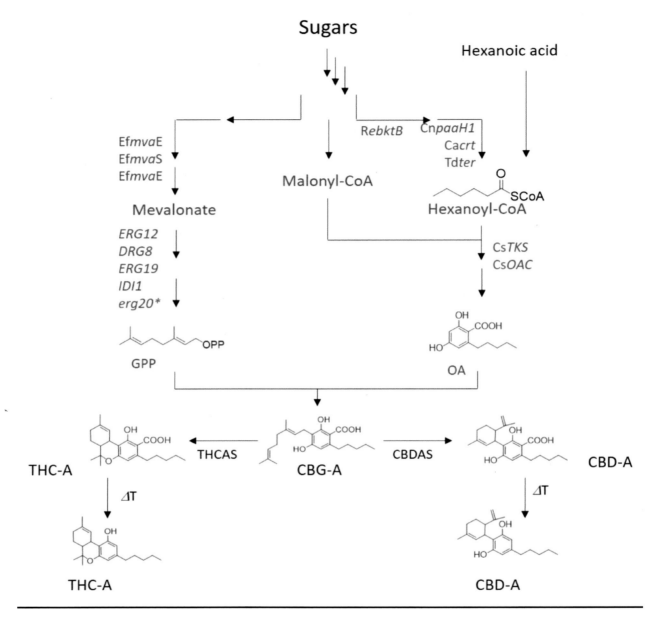

Figure. Enzymatic synthesis of cannabinoids starting from sugar. Text in purple are enzymes. Image Credit: Reproduced by Mahesh Pattabiraman from work published by Xiao Huo Lou et al., Nature 2019, 567, 123-126. (DOI: 10.1038/s41586-019-0978-9)

Synthesis of Unnatural Cannabinoids

The syntheses of cannabinoids shown above are that of naturally occurring compounds – the ones that are present in flowers of the cannabis plant. These cannabinoids, either obtained from natural sources or from the lab, have the same biological effect irrespective of origin, because they are the same substance: natural cannabinoids. They elicit such an effect in the body via their receptor chemistry as they bind to endo cannabinoid receptors.

Compounds with structures that possess the core pharmaco active scaffolding but differ slightly in other structural aspects (length, stereocenter, shape) might also be able to bind to the endocannabinoid receptors and elicit a different biological effect. These are called unnatural cannabinoids. Synthetic routes described above, through organic synthesis or enzymatic chemistry, could also be used to produce unnatural cannabinoids by using appropriate variants of the reactant used for natural cannabinoid synthesis. This is achieved by varying the involved reactant appropriately. For example, if instead of choosing n-pentyl side chain (5-carbon) in olivitol reactant, a chemists starts with n-heptyl olivitol (analogous reactant), then he/she will end up with the CBD structure with 7-carbon chain. This is a CBD analog and it may be now tested for potential biological activity based on its lead compound, which is CBD. The field of medicinal chemistry is dedicated to the understanding of structural variation and biological activity relationship. Most often, it is not possible to predict an analog's biological effect beforehand, though with experience, a medicinal chemist could employ principles of medicinal chemistry, empirical findings, and intuition, and be able to proceed in the right direction.

Figure. Structure of unnatural CBDs (analogs) produced through chemical synthesis. Image Credit: Reproduced by Mahesh Pattabiraman; adopted from review published by Jung et al, Chem. Asian Journal, 2019, 14, 3749 - 3762. (DOI: https://doi.org/10.1002/asia.201901179)

Several examples of synthesis of unnatural cannabinoids are known. For example Hanus et al (*Org Biomol. Chem. 2005, J. Med. Chem. 2006*) synthesized the 7-carbon chain (with 1,1-dimethyl) analog of CBD using the same reaction scheme as the synthesis of CBD (reference to image) by choosing the 7-carbon olivitol derivative. The newly synthesized product (DMH-Me) showed comparable biological activity in its ability to bind to the cannabinoid receptor as well as its being anti-inflammatory compared to CBD itself. In addition, they also changed the methyl group in CBD-C7 to -CH2OH and -COOH (DMH-OH and DMH-A), both of which showed improved biological activity.

Similarly, the CBD derivative (CBD-Cb) with four membered ring structure with -N(CO)CH3 was shown to be a better drug as a neuroprotective agent than natural CBD due to its higher permeability in hippocampal neurons in cell culture (*ACS Med Chem Lett., 2016*). The derivatives CBD-BuOH and CBD-PrA also showed improved biological effects.

Increasing chain length increases biological potency

Figure. Structure of unnatural THCs (analogs) produced through chemical synthesis. Dotted lines indicate variability in length of the side chain achieved through chemical synthesis. Image Credit: Reproduced by Mahesh Pattabiraman; adopted from review published by Jung et al, Chem. Asian Journal, 2019, 14, 3749 - 3762. (DOI: https://doi.org/10.1002/asia.201901179)

Several synthetic analogs of delta-9-THC (unnatural THC) and its biological effects have been studied by several researchers. Compilation of a broad collection of research published by various groups has enabled our understanding of structure activity relationship (SAR) of THC (Bow and Rimoldi, Perspect Medicin Chem., 2016). While natural THC has a 5-carbon chain on the aromatic ring, it is now deduced that for an analog to be psychoactive, it needs at least three carbons in the side-chain. SAR studies also indicate that as the chain length increases from three, up to eight carbons, the ability of THC to bind to CB1 and CB2 receptors (cannabinoid receptors) increases; stronger binding to CB receptors elicits a stronger psychoactive effect. This trend holds good for the delta-8-THC as well.

Unnatural analogs of other minor cannabinoids (in this context CBG included) have also been synthesized and their biological effects studied. However, they are not as well-studied as those of CBD and THC. As the biological effects of the minor cannabinoids become more clear, the effects of unnatural cannabinoids will also emerge more fully in time.

References:

Abu-Sawwa, R., & Stehling, C. (2020). Epidiolex (Cannabidiol) Primer: Frequently Asked Questions for Patients and Caregivers. *The Journal of Pediatric Pharmacology and Therapeutics, 25*(1), 75–77.
URL: https://doi.org/10.5863/1551-6776-25.1.75

Adair, C., Geiling, B., & Marynissen, Logan. (2021). *Separation of cannabinoids from mixtures thereof by distillation.*

Adesina, I., Bhowmik, A., Sharma, H., & Shahbazi, Abolghasem. (2020). A review on the current state of knowledge of growing conditions, agronomic soil health practices and utilities of hemp in the United States. *Agriculture (Basel, Switzerland), 10* (Copyright (C) 2021 American Chemical Society (ACS). All Rights Reserved.), 129.
URL: https://doi.org/10.3390/agriculture10040129

Aiello, A., Pizzolongo, F., Scognamiglio, G., Romano, A., Masi, P., & Romano, Raffaele. (2020). Effects of supercritical and liquid carbon dioxide extraction on hemp (Cannabis sativa L.) seed oil. *International Journal of Food Science and Technology, 55* (Copyright (C) 2021 American Chemical Society (ACS). All Rights Reserved.), 2472–2480.
URL: https://doi.org/10.1111/ijfs.14498

Akahoshi, Y., Endo, R., Kitani, O., Ikoga, Masanao., 2007. Comparative study of resource crops sugarcane and hemp in Miyako Island. Baiomasu Kagaku Kaigi Happyo Ronbunshu 2, 14–15.

Arrigoni, A., Pelosato, R., Melia, P., Ruggieri, G., Sabbadini, S., & Dotelli, Giovanni. (2017). Life cycle assessment of natural building materials: The role of carbonation, mixture components and transport in the environmental impacts of hempcrete blocks. *Journal of Cleaner Production, 149* (Copyright (C) 2021 American Chemical Society (ACS). All Rights Reserved.), 1051–1061.
URL: https://doi.org/10.1016/j.jclepro.2017.02.161

Banwell, M., Blakey, S., Harfoot, G., & Longmore, R. (1998). First synthesis of L-ascorbic acid (vitamin C) from a non-carbohydrate source. *J. Chem. Soc., Perkin Trans. 1, 19*, 3141–3142. https://doi.org/10.1039/A806062B

Baron, E. P. (2018). Medicinal Properties of Cannabinoids, Terpenes, and Flavonoids in Cannabis, and Benefits in Migraine, Headache, and Pain: An Update on Current Evidence and Cannabis Science. *Headache, 58*(7), 1139–1186.
URL: https://doi.org/10.1111/head.13345

Ben-Shabat, S.; Hanus, L. O.; Katzavian, G.; Gallily, R., New Cannabidiol Derivatives: Synthesis, Binding to Cannabinoid Receptor, and Evaluation of Their Antiinflammatory Activity. *J. Med. Chem.* 2006, *49* (3), 1113-1117.

Bercht, C. A. L., Lousberg, R. J. J. Ch., Küppers, F. J. E. M., & Salemink, C. A. (1974). Cannabicitran: A new naturally occurring tetracyclic diether from lebanese Cannabis sativa. *Phytochemistry, 13*(3), 619–621.
https://doi.org/10.1016/S0031-9422(00)91362-1

Carraher, J. M., & Baker, Z. Joseph. (2021). *Water-based extraction and purification processes for cannabinoid acids.*

Centola, Germano. (1954). The effect of retting on the chemical-physical properties of hemp fibers. *Teintex*, *19*(Copyright (C) 2021 American Chemical Society (ACS). All Rights Reserved.), 241–253.

Chouinard, F., & Conway, Justin. (2021). *Cannabinoid compositions, methods of making the same and uses thereof.*

Conte, R., Marturano, V., Peluso, G., Calarco, A., & Cerruti, P. (2017). Recent Advances in Nanoparticle-Mediated Delivery of Anti-Inflammatory Phytocompounds. *International Journal of Molecular Sciences*, *18*(4).
URL: https://doi.org/10.3390/ijms18040709

DeLong, G.T., Wolf, C.E., Poklis, A., Lichtman, A.H., 2010. Pharmacological evaluation of the natural constituent of Cannabis sativa, cannabichromene and its modulation by Δ(9)-tetrahydrocannabinol. Drug Alcohol Depend. 112, 126–133.
URL: https://doi.org/10.1016/j.drugalcdep.2010.05.019

Do Vale, T.G., Furtado, E.C., Santos, J.G., Jr., Viana, G.S.B., 2002. Central effects of citral, myrcene and limonene, constituents of essential oil chemotypes from Lippia alba (Mill.) N.E. Brown. Phytomedicine 9, 709–714.

Dolgin, E. (2019). Inner Workings: Genomics blazes a trail to improved cannabis cultivation. *Proceedings of the National Academy of Sciences*, *116*(18), 8638.
URL: https://doi.org/10.1073/pnas.1904094116

Flaishman, M. A., Cohen Peer, R., Cohen, O., & Bocobza, Samuel. (2019). *Methods of regenerating and transforming Cannabis.*

Grace, D.J., Roberts, W.J., 2020. Method of producing pathogen-free Cannabis plants and pathogen-free plants and clones produced therefrom.

Grace, D.J., Roberts, W.J., 2019. Culture methods for producing pathogen-free Cannabis plants and pathogen-free plants and clones produced therefrom.

Guan, H., Liu, L., Da, H., & Zhang, Y. (2020). Analysis of FDA assessment consideration on cannabidiol indicated for refractory epilepsy. *Zhongguo Xinyao Zazhi*, *29*(Copyright (C) 2021 American Chemical Society (ACS). All Rights Reserved.), 31–36.

Hanus, L. O.; Tchilibon, S.; Ponde, D. E.; Breuer, A.; Fride, E.; Mechoulam, R., Enantiomeric cannabidiol derivatives: synthesis and binding to cannabinoid receptors. *Org. Biomol. Chem.* 2005, *3* (6), 1116-1123.

Hemp Biofuel. (n.d.).
URL: https://nationalhempassociation.org/making-fuel-from-industrial-hemp/

Kamireddy, S. R., Li, J., Abbina, S., Berti, M., Tucker, M., & Ji, Yun. (2013). Converting forage sorghum and sunn hemp into biofuels through dilute acid pretreatment. *Industrial Crops and Products*, *49*(Copyright (C) 2021 American Chemical Society (ACS). All Rights Reserved.), 598–609.
URL: https://doi.org/10.1016/j.indcrop.2013.06.018

Kinney, W. A.; McDonnell, M. E.; Zhong, H. M.; Liu, C.; Yang, L.; Ling, W.; Qian, T.; Chen, Y.; Cai, Z.; Petkanas, D.; Brenneman, D. E., Discovery of KLS-13019, a Cannabidiol-Derived Neuroprotective Agent, with Improved Potency, Safety, and Permeability. *ACS Med. Chem. Lett.* 2016, *7* (4), 424-428

Luo, X., Reiter, M. A., d'Espaux, L., Wong, J., Denby, C. M., Lechner, A., Zhang, Y., Grzybowski, A. T., Harth, S., Lin, W., Lee, H., Yu, C., Shin, J., Deng, K., Benites, V. T., Wang, G., Baidoo, E. E. K., Chen, Y., Dev, I., … Keasling, J. D. (2019). Complete biosynthesis of cannabinoids and their unnatural analogues in yeast. *Nature*, *567*(7746), 123–126.
URL: https://doi.org/10.1038/s41586-019-0978-9

Maran, S. P. Mathi. (2019). *Method of extraction of phytocannabinoids and formulating the same into a water soluble nano cannabinoid.*

Martin, B. R., Wiley, J. L., Beletskaya, I., Sim-Selley, L. J., Smith, F. L., Dewey, W. L., Cottney, J., Adams, J., Baker, J., Hill, D., Saha, B., Zerkowski, J., Mahadevan, A., & Razdan, R. K. (2006). Pharmacological Characterization of Novel Water-Soluble Cannabinoids. *Journal of Pharmacology and Experimental Therapeutics*, *318*(3), 1230.
URL: https://doi.org/10.1124/jpet.106.104109

Moussa, M., El Hage, R., Sonnier, R., Chrusciel, L., Ziegler-Devin, I., & Brosse, Nicolas. (2020). Toward the cottonization of hemp fibers by steam explosion. Flame-retardant fibers. *Industrial Crops and Products*, *151*(Copyright (C) 2021 American Chemical Society (ACS). All Rights Reserved.), 112242.
URL: https://doi.org/10.1016/j.indcrop.2020.112242

Pollastro, F., Caprioglio, D., Marotta, P., Moriello, A. S., De Petrocellis, L., Taglialatela-Scafati, O., & Appendino, G. (2018). Iodine-Promoted Aromatization of p-Menthane-Type Phytocannabinoids. *Journal of Natural Products*, *81*(3), 630–633.
URL: https://doi.org/10.1021/acs.jnatprod.7b00946

Punja, Z.K., Holmes, J.E., 2020. Hermaphroditism in Marijuana (Cannabis sativa L.) Inflorescences - Impact on Floral Morphology, Seed Formation, Progeny Sex Ratios and Genetic Variation. Front. Plant Sci. 11, 718.

Rodriguez-Leyva, D., & Pierce, G. N. (2010). The cardiac and haemostatic effects of dietary hempseed. *Nutrition & Metabolism*, *7*(1), 32.
URL: https://doi.org/10.1186/1743-7075-7-32

Rolle, R. R. (2020). *Preparation of cannabinoid compositions with improved bioactivity.*

Rovetto, L. J., & Aieta, N. V. (2017). Supercritical carbon dioxide extraction of cannabinoids from Cannabis sativa L. *IV Iberoamerican Conference on Supercritical Fluids - ProSCiba 2016*, *129*, 16–27.
URL: https://doi.org/10.1016/j.supflu.2017.03.014

Russo, E. B. (2019). The Case for the Entourage Effect and Conventional Breeding of Clinical Cannabis: No "Strain," No Gain. *Frontiers in Plant Science*, *9*, 1969–1969. PubMed. URL: https://doi.org/10.3389/fpls.2018.01969

Sexton, M., Sexton, M., Shelton, K., Shelton, K., Haley, P., & West, M. (2018). Evaluation of Cannabinoid and Terpenoid Content: Cannabis Flower Compared to Supercritical CO2 Concentrate. *Planta Medica*, *84*(Copyright (C) 2021 U.S. National Library of Medicine.), 234–241.

Tadayon, N., & Ramazani, Ali. (2021). A review on the syntheses of Dronabinol and Epidiolex as classical cannabinoids with various biological activities including those

against SARS-COV2. *Journal of the Iranian Chemical Society, Copyright (C) 2021 American Chemical Society (ACS). All Rights Reserved.*, Ahead of Print.
URL: https://doi.org/10.1007/s13738-021-02212-0

Tian, H., Zheng, M., Zheng, Z., Luo, F., Ye, B., & Kang, Pu. (2020). *A method for extracting and purifying cannabidiol from Cannabis sativa.*

Vignon, M. R., Dupeyre, D., & Garcia-Jaldon, C. (1996). Morphological characterization of steam-exploded hemp fibers and their utilization in polypropylene-based composites. *Bioresource Technology, 58*(Copyright (C) 2021 American Chemical Society (ACS). All Rights Reserved.), 203–215.
URL: https://doi.org/10.1016/S0960-8524(96)00100-9

Yanchev, I., Zhalnov, I., & Terziev, Zhivko. (2000). Hemp's (Cannabis sativa L.) capacities for restricting heavy metal soil pollution. *Rastenie Vudni Nauki, 37*(Copyright (C) 2021 American Chemical Society (ACS). All Rights Reserved.), 532–537.

Wiseman, M.S., Bates, T., Garfinkel, A., Ocamb, C.M., Gent, D.H., 2021. First report of Powdery Mildew Caused by Golovinomyces ambrosiae on Cannabis sativa in Oregon. Plant Dis.

Wizenberg, S.B., Campbell, L.G., Weis, A.E., 2020. Comparing methods for controlled capture and quantification of pollen in Cannabis sativa. Appl. Plant Sci. 8, e11389.

Zgair, A., Wong, J. C., Lee, J. B., Mistry, J., Sivak, O., Wasan, K. M., Hennig, I. M., Barrett, D. A., Constantinescu, C. S., Fischer, P. M., & Gershkovich, P. (2016). Dietary fats and pharmaceutical lipid excipients increase systemic exposure to orally administered cannabis and cannabis-based medicines. *American Journal of Translational Research, 8*(8), 3448–3459. PubMed.

Chapter 14 - Cannabis: Business and Professions
(Dr. Andrea Holmes)

A. Professions in the Cannabis Industry

The cannabis industry is one of the fastest growing economic job sectors. With increased legalization, this growth shows no signs of slowing down. These jobs provide a critical momentum for Americans to support themselves, their families and their communities. With the 2018 Farm Bill, hemp was declassified as a controlled substance. Many states are quickly moving towards their own state plans to implement a cannabis infrastructure as an economic driver. In states with recent legalization, investors and entrepreneurs are securing and building facilities to prepare for harvest, processing and feeding into the vastly growing supply chain that is emerging worldwide.

Hot Jobs in Cannabis
These jobs have seen an sizeable jump in the amount of postings year over year

Cultivation Technicians

Trimmers/Packagers

Budtenders

Directors of Cultivation

Delivery Drivers and Logistics Coordinators

Sales Reps

Digital Marketing & e-Commerce

Administrative and Corporate Roles

Lab Managers

Directors of HR

Figure: 2020 Vangst Salary Guide

Academic institutions have responded to the growing job market in the cannabis industry and a number are now providing a relevant and modern curriculum. Most jobs in the cannabis industry require a workforce with qualifying credentials, experience, specific skills and competencies in cannabis. U.S. legal cannabis sales exceeded $12.4 billion in 2019 and are expected to reach $31.4 billion in 2024, rising at nearly 23% from $9.1 billion in 2018.

Leafly Jobs Report issued earlier in February 2021, reported 321,000 full-time equivalent (FTE) jobs supported by legal cannabis as of January 2021. That total ranges from entry level positions to upper level executive management. The report states that:

> "In the United States there are more legal cannabis workers than electrical engineers. There are more legal cannabis workers than EMTs and paramedics. There are more than twice as many legal cannabis workers as dentists."

One of the reasons why the cannabis industry and its workforce are growing so rapidly is because of the plant's multifunctionality and by creating jobs in many different market sectors. Hemp, for example, can make a variety of commercial and industrial products including rope, textiles, clothing, shoes, food, paper, bioplastics, insulation and biofuel. Hemp can be grown for its seeds, grain, roots and flowers that are extracted for oil and used in health foods, organic body care and other nutraceuticals. Multiple career pathways are emerging with workers needing education and training in areas such as cannabis-related Agriculture (Seed Production, Fertilizer, Pesticide and Weed Control), Marketing, Banking, Healthcare, Chemistry, Biology, Business. A Cannabis Science degree student would be well positioned to respond to an educational market gap; the need to educate a newly emerging workforce that must acquire qualifications and credentials to enter this rapidly growing industry.

There are many opportunities in the cannabis industry, but especially for science, technology, engineering and math (STEM) graduates. In 2019, over 210,000 jobs have been created in the cannabis industry and according to *Forbes*, that number is expected to grow to at least 300,000 in 2020. According to *Glassdoor*, a global job-recruiting website, cannabis industry jobs on average pay about 11% higher than the median U.S salary.

Some careers in the cannabis industry require very specific skill sets, knowledge and high-end degrees. Others can be started with little or no experience. There are many sectors in the industry where jobs can be found, including in growing, extraction, production, packaging, testing, delivery or sales. Alternatively, one can also find ancillary positions that support the industry. Training or experience in areas such as chemistry, biology, plant science, genetics, engineering, business, accounting, management, marketing, sales, law, technology, graphic design, IT and HVAC, can all help a person obtain a good job (inside or outside the industry).

Below are some additional Cannabis Industry jobs and a brief description of each:

B. Examples of Cannabis Professions at All Income Levels are:

1. Lower Income Tier (Hourly Pay): Planters, growers, cultivators, trimmers, harvest assistants, packaging, pre-processing, processing and post-processing.

2. Medium Income Tier ($40,000.00 to $100,000.00): Extractors, refiners, quality control, lab techs, analytical scientist, microbiologists, Research and

Development chemists, plant medicinal scientists, botanical specialists, engineers, geneticists, tissue culture experts, state auditors, regulations, compliance officers, state auditors, administration, marketing, sales, accounting, customer service, shipping receiving, formulators, chefs for edibles, product designers, retail, IT, banking, security, HR and administration.

3. Higher Income Tier (>$100,000.00): Harvest and processing equipment personnel, Master-level positions, C-level positions, consulting firms, lawyers, business developers and architects for processing facilities.

C. An Alternative to Academia's Crowded Job Market

There is no question that the cannabis industry needs scientists. Nevertheless, it looks as though scientists need the cannabis industry as well. U.S. Universities have been producing more research scientists than academia can accommodate. More scientists are entering the academic job market than retiring. Decreased funding and lack of tenure-track positions have contributed to a tight job market and a scarcity of STEM-related jobs in higher education. Opportunities created by the federal legalization of hemp are welcome news, not simply for STEM professionals facing an increasingly challenging job market, but also for those in the scientific community who are seeking new frontiers of discovery.

The rise of organizations such as the Institute of Cannabis Research and the International Cannabinoid Research Society, among others, signals the trend of scientists finding new opportunities and inspiration in the cannabis space.

Mainstream universities are creating programs dedicated to the study of cannabis and public health policy: UCLA's Cannabis Research Initiative, the University of Washington's Center for Cannabis Research, the University of Vermont's Medical Cannabis Center for Research and Education , and the University of Maryland School of Pharmacy's master's degree program in medical cannabis science and therapeutics, and of course the Certificate Programs at Nebraska's Doane University and Bellevue University to name just a few.

D. Qualifications Needed and Salary Ranges for some Popular Cannabis Jobs:

Many professionals in the Marijuana job sector require a special permit or registration and a background check by the FBI. Any previous drug possession charges would make it more difficult to enter the marijuana industry where THC is the major commodity. The hemp industry usually does not require this stringent qualification of licensure as a requisite of employment.

1. Cannabis Growers:

There are several categories of cannabis growers, and salaries start from $12.00 per hour for entry-level trimmers to $150,000.00 or more for master growers who have cannabis experience and PhDs. Master growers typically hold advanced college/university degrees or they have a lot of industry experience and knowledge in horticulture, botany, genetics, grow systems and effective harvests. Assistant growers should know about strains, lighting, irrigation, fertilizer, growing technologies and typical starting salaries are $30,000.00 per year and up.

Trimmers are employees who do not need a degree and they assist with harvest and trim the buds and are usually paid hourly. Trimmers are usually people's first job in the industry and then they work themselves up in the business hierarchy.

CULTIVATION SALARIES

	25th Percentile	50th Percentile	75th Percentile
Director of Cultivation	$90,000	$115,000 (+25% YoY)	$147,500
Grow Manager	$50,000	$65,000 (+3% YoY)	$75,000
Grower/Horticulturist	$16.00/hr	$18.00/hr (-9% YoY)	$22.00/hr
Trimmer/Post Harvester	$14.50/hr	$15.00/hr (+0% YoY)	$16.00/hr

Figure: *2020 Vangst Salary Guide*

2. Cannabis Extractors and Processors:

Organic extraction technicians or master extractors have varied educational backgrounds, from high school diplomas to PhD degrees, typically in chemistry. Extraction knowledge with organic solvents or carbon dioxide and general lab experience is a plus. Extraction techs or master extractors start with a base pay of $45,000.00 per year and highly skilled master extractors make over $100,000.00 per year depending on their experience and academic credentials.

	25th Percentile	50th Percentile	75th Percentile
Director of Extraction	$72,500	$105,000 (+14% YoY)	$145,000
Extraction Manager	$52,000	$65,000 (-3% YoY)	$80,000
Quality Manager	$42,750	$55,000 (-16% YoY)	$77,500
Compliance Manager	$50,000	$60,000 (-19% YoY)	$75,000
Chemist	$50,000	$75,000 (-5% YoY)	$85,000
Extraction Technician* *New data for 2020	$35,000	$37,440 (N/A)	$40,400

Figure: 2020 Vangst Salary Guide

3. Budtender

Budtenders are usually entry level positions and typically occupied by people wanting to get into the industry. Budtenders are knowledge experts, provide customer service and assist with sales in dispensaries. These workers must understand everything from how the plants are grown to extraction, smoking devices, other delivery systems like edibles and topicals, as well as the different types of marijuana that exist such as sativa versus indica. Budtenders must ensure compliance with their state's marijuana usage laws, such as the minimum age for customers and record all products sold through their dispensary's tracking system. The minimum educational requirement is a high school diploma. Budtenders are usually paid hourly and make between $12.00 to $20.00 hour or an average annual salary of $30,000.00 and above.

Average Budtender Salaries* in Select States

*Base salary, does not include gratuity

Alaska	$13.50/hr	Illinois	$16.00/hr	New Jersey	$15.50/hr
Arizona	$15.00/hr	Massachusetts	$16.00/hr	Oklahoma	$13.75/hr
California	$16.50/hr	Michigan	$14.00/hr	Oregon	$14.75/hr
Colorado	$14.50/hr	Missouri	$13.50/hr	Pennsylvania	$15.50/hr
Florida	$12.50/hr	Nevada	$14.50/hr	Washington	$14.50/hr

Figure: 2020 Vangst Salary Guide

4. Cannabis Testing Lab Manager

A lab manager must have a minimum of a bachelor's degree in biology, chemistry, environmental studie, or related sciences. Iso accredited or state approved testing labs often require several years of experience in managing an accredited lab. Lab managers must be able to implement training programs for employees, conduct quality and safety audits, know instrumentation, knowledge tracking and compliance, interpretation of test results and computer knowledge. They must be able to show detailed knowledge of testing of terpenes, cannabinoid levels, pesticides, heavy metals and microbial contaminants. The median salary for a lab manager in 2020 was $98,000.00 per year.

5. Marijuana Edibles Chef

This job requires experience in the food and beverage and an understanding of how to infuse marijuana into food and beverages in exact quantities. Educational requirements vary from high school diploma with experience or advanced degrees or certificates in food related science or professions. Marijuana Chefs earn between $40,000.00 to $50,000.00 a year or more depending on the size of the company.

MANUFACTURING SALARIES

	25th Percentile	50th Percentile	75th Percentile
Vice President of Manufacturing	$145,000	$150,000 (+10% YoY)	$177,500
Production Supervisor	$40,140	$50,000 (-14% YoY)	$62,200
Production Technician	$15.00/hr	$16.00/hr (-6% YoY)	$18.75/hr
Edibles Specialist	$35,750	$37,440 (-12% YoY)	$50,000
Packager	$14.50/hr	$16.00/hr (+8% YoY)	$18.50/hr

Figure: 2020 Vangst Salary Guide

6. Sales Professions in the Cannabis Industry

Sales professionals are responsible for visiting stores, clients, dispensaries and building business relationships. Sales associates are highly experienced and know all aspects of the industry including the products, regulations, the origin and manufacturing of the products, pricing and distribution. The income potential is pretty large, especially when working on commission.

SALES SALARIES

*New category for 2020, based on internal Vangst data
**Base salary before incentives

	25th Percentile	50th Percentile	75th Percentile
Vice President of Sales	$145,000	$160,000	$175,000
Director of Sales	$100,000	$120,000	$135,000
Sales Manager	$65,000	$82,500	$100,000
Account Executive	$45,000	$55,000	$65,000

Figure: 2020 Vangst Salary Guide

E. How Do You Find a Job in the Cannabis Industry?

1. The first step in finding a job is to figure out what a person will enjoy. The cannabis industry has so many job sectors, and a person has to refine and narrow the search that fits their character and qualifications.

2. Research potential employers. Once a person has narrowed down what type of profession they are pursuing, they should begin researching companies that are in this field by visiting their websites, calling them to ask questions, review Linked In pages and make connections with their staff.

3. Determine whether there is any license required for the job. If a person is not able to secure a license, there are many jobs in the industry that do not require one, such as in marketing, web design, consulting, accounting, legal and many more ancillary jobs.

4. Networking. The cannabis industry is tightly connected and everybody seems to know everybody. Attending industry events and expos is very important. Personal introduction, collecting business cards and follow up to emails are key to getting a job in this industry.

5. Work for free. If a person volunteers their time, secures an internship, offers to shadow someone, or helps during an event, then they will get the attention of the employees and that person will begin making connections...a small investment of time for a potentially big pay off.

6. Search job boards. Monster, Indeed, LinkedIn, Vangst, Flower Hire, Viridian Staffing, Ms. Mary Staffing, THC Staffing Group, HempStaf, Cannamed Talent Solutions and many more cannabis recruiters are more than willing to offer free talent matching.

7. Prepare a cutting edge resume, cover letter, and practice interviewing. The Cannabis industry is still rocky and it requires perseverance. It is important to not give up and continue to stay engaged with employers and their staff by emailing, visiting them at Expos, setting up appointments, sending articles that are relevant to the industry and the business and making new introductions.

How does the Cannabis Industry Work?

A. Supply Chain:

Cannabis is seeing a huge leap in market and the industry is growing at an exponential level. The demand for cannabis products in 2021 led to a $13.5 billion value and is projected to grow to USD $70.6 billion in 2028.

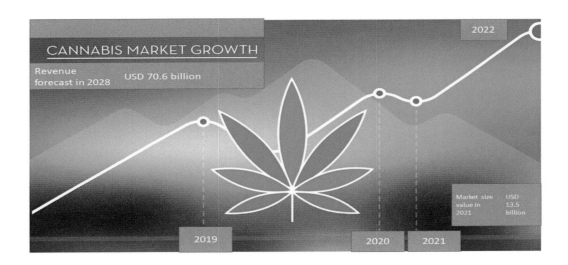

Figure: The rapidly expanding market in the cannabis industry. Image Credit: Andrea Holmes adapted from Shutterstock

Understanding the cannabis market supply chain is important for anybody who wants to enter into this industry as a professional. The supply chain of this industry is made up of several market sectors.

Figure: Cannabis Supply Chain Image Credit: Andrea Holmes

1. Seed Genetics

The cannabis seeds market is extremely varied and and can be categorized by

a. Seed type (Regular Seeds, Feminized Seeds and Autoflowering Seeds)
b. Strain (Indica, Hybrid and Sativa)
c. Cannabinoid (THC Dominant, CBD Dominant and Balanced THC & CBD)
d. Certifications (Inorganic and Organic)
e. Distribution (Store Based Retailing and Online/E-Commerce Retailing)
f. Type of vendors (Resellers, Breeders and Seeds Manufacturing Companies)
g. Country (U.S., Canada, Mexico, EU, Australia, Asia, Middle East and Africa)

This cannabis seeds market is expected to reach USD $723.77 million by 2027 and provides new research developments, emerging revenue possibilities, novel product development, niche market explorations, international expansions and technological innovations in science.

2. Cultivation

This sector in the supply chain is currently very saturated as more and more farmers and growers want to enter the marijuana and hemp space and the competition is growing. Furthermore, cultivation is also outsourced to other countries that offer cheaper labor, better weather for cannabis growth and a lesser regulations framework.

Cultivation operations are either stand-alone businesses or they can be part of a cohort of downstream cannabis licenses that also do extraction, distribution and retail. This business model is called vertically integrated from "seed to sale." It means they own and control the cultivation, lab and extraction, manufacturing and retail sectors of their business. <u>There are advantages and disadvantages to a vertically integrated business model.</u>

Some cultivating businesses grow their own flowers and pack them into pre-rolls and jars and directly deliver to dispensaries or wholesale distributors or brokers. Others sell their flowers to an extraction manufacturing facility for further processing.

3. Extraction

Extractors receive their biomass from cultivators. Extractors produce, crude extract, winterized extract, distillate or isolates. Sometimes extractors are also manufacturers and produce everything from tinctures, oils, vaporizers, edibles and concentrates.

4. Testing

After extraction, the next stage in the supply chain is testing. Before products made from cannabis can reach the retail market, they must undergo a series of analytical tests to ensure that the quality and safety are meeting the regulations and standards set by the government. The market for resting labs is expected to reach USD $1,806 million by 2025 from USD $962 million in 2020 and is mainly driven by increased legalization of medical cannabis and the growing adoption of regulatory Laboratory Information Management Systems (LIMS) to help manage every aspect of cannabis testing. This ranges from testing for/from potency, microbial contaminants, heavy metals, aflatoxin, residual solvents and pesticides, to self-service secure web reporting. However, a lack of uniformity in rules and regulations, high costs of instruments and operators, LIMS and stringent audits in ISO certifications are major factors expected to hamper market growth.

5. Distribution

The cannabis distribution market occurs worldwide via third-party distribution companies using freight trucks to deliver products across states and countries. Distribution involves shipping or transporting cannabis across state lines or international borders, requiring specialized distribution channels because of complicated legal, import, export and customs logistics.

6. Retail

Cannabis retail is the most visible market sector industry. Retail can occur via these channels:

    a. Dispensaries and CBD Stores
    b. Health and Grocery Stores (CBD Only)
    c. E-Commerce (Amazon, Facebook Etc, Hemp Only)
    d. Online Stores
    e. Hybrid Stores (Physical Stores and Online Stores)
    f. Ancillary Outlets (Boutiques, Spas, Coffee Shops and Cannabis Infusion Shops)

B. Hemp Specific Industry Consumer Market Sectors

It is quite an exciting time to be a part of the hemp industry. Its growth is exponential and expected to keep that pace for years to come. In 2010, the Hemp Industries Association estimated $419 million in U.S. retail sales of hemp products by 2016, but that number actually surpassed $688 million dollars. *The Hemp Business Journal* analyzed the market across seven primary product categories to obtain that number:

1. Food (Protein Bars, Edibles, Hemp Seed Oil)

2. Personal care (Lotions, Topical Ointments, Deodorants)

3. Textiles (Clothes, Bags)

4. Supplements (Pills, Tinctures, Tablets)

5. Hemp Derived Cannabidiol (CBD)

6. Industrial Applications (Car Parts, Hempcrete)

7. Other Products (Paper, Construction Materials)

C. The Impact of COVID-19 on the Cannabis Industry

Coronavirus affected the cannabis industry just like any other industry. The cannabis market declined because of closures of stores, labs, disrupted supply chains and restrictions on the import and export of cannabis testing products. Due to the economic uncertainties, business-to-business transaction sales have decreased and some employees lost their jobs. In 2019, many publicly traded cannabis companies lost more than 75% off their highs in the stock market due to the rapid decline in CBD pricing. Now, during this worldwide potential economic regression, cannabis companies may find it impossible to secure cash and expand their businesses. In addition, many growers and other employees could not do their job inside, and therefore, the workforce was laid off to keep people safe. In wealthier countries with effective vaccines, this latter problem is now being alleviated. Unless there is a bailout plan by the government for the cannabis industry, however, many companies will be forced to shut down. There is not any government bankruptcy protection for cannabis companies.

However, Cannabis retailers, like dispensaries, have also reported a sharp increase in earnings as medical and recreational cannabis users are trying to shop for supplies that will get them through potential extended quarantines and shut downs of businesses.

Covid-19 shut down all of the conferences and expos that many CBD and Hemp businesses rely so heavily on to:

1. Source Their Supply Chain
2. Meet New Clients to Sell Their Material
3. Deepen Existing Relationships
4. Locate Vendors to Help Them With White Labeling
5. Packaging
6. Formulations
7. Marketing
8. Sales
9. Merchant Processing

The cannabis industry was, however, comparatively robust during this challenging economic time, and cannabis is a supplement with extraordinary impacts on the health and wellbeing of humans and animals. As such, it will likely prevail and ultimately become stronger during these types of crises or economic recessions.

D. Building a Cannabis Business

If a person is considering opening a cannabis business, they have to first figure out what type of business to enter. There are many cannabis businesses, such as cultivation, extraction, processing, advertising, sales, marketing, testing, research, compliance, law and much more. A person has decided what business to open, they need to consider the following steps.

1. Research and understand all the rules including the supply chain. It is good to start a network and talk to people who have already opened a business.

2. Write a detailed business plan (investment costs, profit projections, location, employees, supply chain, customers and timelines).

3. Register the business and apply for a license.

4. Obtain permits.

5. Obtain a tax identification number.

6. Purchase accounting software and start keeping track of all financial transactions from the very first day.

7. Open a bank account.

8. Hire an accountant for taxes.

9. Hire an insurance company agent

10. Hire trustful partners with contracts in place to avoid future confusion of shares, etc.

11. Determine all aspects of getting funding, e.g. self-funded versus investors or partnerships, etc.

Tips to be Successful:

1. Hire a competent workforce who are willing to work hard.

2. Pay your qualified workforce well and treat them with respect.

3. Instill an atmosphere of support, appreciation, and allow for continuing education.

4. Be conscientious of employees' work-life balance.

5. Provide a safe workplace.

6. Follow OSHA rules and other pertinent regulations.

7. Be a strong leader with a vision that is shared with employees.

8. Be flexible.

9. Be consistent and fair.

10. Have a good attitude.

11. Design an organizational chart.

12. Appointment of proper management is crucial.

Most Marijuana Businesses (Especially Cultivation) Typically Fail for 3 Reasons:

1. Undercapitalized (...by contrast, always have access to 125% of budgeted expenses for construction and initial 2 years of operation).

2. Inadequate management team.

3. Inexperienced employees.

E. Safe Cannabis Production Practices

When it comes to producing a safe product for humans or animals to consume, it is important to comply with local, state and federal regulations pertaining to a person's specific business. Running a clean workspace requires daily effort. Sanitation of floors, tools, machines, etc. should be a daily practice.

There are several aspects to think about that may create challenges in terms of protecting the quality of the product. Crude hemp oil, distillate, isolate and other hemp products must be protected from contaminants, heat, humidity, light or oxygen post-processing. Therefore, special considerations should be taken when storing those items, such as using amber-colored food-safe containers.

There are several organizations and regulating bodies that can oversee hemp production and help guide new businesses with their standards of operation. Depending on if a person is growing, processing or distributing, there may be certain rules that they should uphold in their place of work. Consider appointing an advisory board qualified in the applicable areas of expertise. This looks good on the application and it is good for operational advice. Occupational Safety and Health Administration or OSHA sets standards for the workplace that involve biological, chemical or physical hazards. Below is a list of some regulation fields that OSHA applies to the cannabis industry at many levels:

1. Electrical Hazards
2. Flammable Gases and Liquids
3. Hazard Communication
4. Injury and Illness Prevention Programs
5. Personal Protective Equipment Requirements
6. Sanitation
7. Pest Control
8. Respiratory Protection

Good Manufacturing Practices or **GMP** relates to all food and drug companies and is related to the handling, cleaning, quality assurance and packaging processes in cannabis facilities. Many countries, including Canada, the United States, the European Union and Australia, have legislated that food and pharmaceutical manufacturers follow GMP procedures to ensure a food or drug product is safe for human consumption. It is very important that cannabis product manufacturers are GMP certified or follow the standard pharmaceutical companies use to assure safety, quality and consistency of the product. GMP certification is expensive and many start-up companies cannot afford this expense until the operation is cash-flow positive.

F. Suggested Policies and Procedures for Cannabis Businesses

It is very common for marijuana businesses to describe their anticipated policies and procedures in their application, but once a license is awarded, they never actually create policies and procedures. The lack of effective policies and procedures can be very troubling for businesses when trying to raise capital, trying to open bank accounts, trying to obtain insurance, trying to sell the business, trying to go public on a market (Toronto Exchange; Canadian Securities Exchange; NASDAQ) or being subjected to a regulatory investigation. **Do not** be the typical marijuana business that considers their application to be the practical end-point of their policies and procedures.

Practices and procedures that should be addressed are the following:

1. Cultivation Procedures
2. Manufacturing Procedures
3. Dispensing Procedures
4. Employee Recruitment, Hiring and Firing
5. Employee Training
6. Diversity and Inclusiveness
7. Community Relations

Local governments can play a very important role in the success of a marijuana businesses. In some states like Massachusetts, a community support letter is required; the state allows the local community to require charitable donations (sometimes up to $250,000.00 a year or a percentage of sales) in exchange for a community support letter.

Vendor Hiring and Firing

It is very important to vet vendors and ensure that they will operate in the same manner as a company's compliance policies and procedures.

Security

1. Building
2. Equipment
3. Personnel

Emergency Response Procedures

Customer Identification Procedures

The company should always be prepared in consideration of diversion concerns.

Visitors

Insurance

Recordkeeping

1. Confidentiality
2. Personnel Records
3. Financial Records - If someone has to explain the company's financials, then they are not transparent. Transparent financials are the key to compliance, especially given the Cole Memo priorities that focus on avoiding funds going to gangs, cartels or criminal enterprises.
4. HIPAA (Health Insurance Portability and Accountability Act) compliance.

Inventory Controls

1. Theft/Anti-Diversion is extremely important given diversion is a Cole Memo priority. Also, anti-diversion policies and procedures should be drastically different for cultivation/manufacturing (typical customers are other cultivation or manufacturing facilities or dispensaries) and dispensary operations (typical customers are the consumers).
2. Inventory Tracking
3. Seed to Sale
4. Supply Controls
5. Quality Controls
6. Storage
7. Labeling and Packaging
8. Testing
9. Testing Procedures
10. Requirements for Third-Party Testing Companies
11. Defective Product Handling and Disposal
12. Product Recall
13. Waste Management
14. Marijuana Waste Disposal
15. Non-Marijuana Waste Disposal

G. Who Else Do Cannabis Businesses Work With?

1. Third Party Vendors/Contractors It is very typical to work with 3rd party vendors and contractors in this business. Here are some of the most typical types of businesses you will work with in the cannabis industry.
2. General counsel or engagement of outside counsel experienced in marijuana law.
3. Security (Very important because security and anti-diversion work hand-in-hand, and prevention of diversion of marijuana to minors is one of the 2013 U.S. Department of Justice Cole Memo priorities).
4. Packaging and Labeling Companies.
5. Seed-to-sale tracking. Usually, the state mandates the use of specific seed-to-sale tracking software or even awards a license for all statewide marijuana businesses to use.
6. Compliance. Often a common way to get access to banking services, through a compliance company that has pre-established banking relationships.
7. Insurance:

   A. Errors & Omissions. Defends against general business negligence caused by errors and omissions of the company.

   B. Directors & Officers. Protects the company's officers and directors – usually an excess policy. Very often provides defense for regulatory investigations and enforcement actions.

   C. Property and Casualty. To monitor Marijuana and Non-marijuana losses.

8. Employment practices

   A. Payroll
   B. Benefits
   C. Training
   D. Compliance
   E. Insurance
   F. Taxes

9. Architects and Contractors

   Very important to engage architects and contractors with experience building cultivation facilities, because costs can get out of control and poorly constructed facilities can result in contaminants and defective products. In 2016, one third of all marijuana cultivated in Massachusetts was defective due to molds, pests and other contaminants. This was the result of poorly constructed cultivation facilities and lack of knowledgeable and experienced cultivators.

10. Accounting

Accounting is very important, because good accounting will result in financial transparency, which is a Cole Memo priority.

11. Sales, Marketing and Advertising

12. Delivery

13. Transportation

H. Blockchain: The Future of Cannabis Transactions

Blockchain is a shared cloud based platform that records transactions and enables tracking of all information in a business network from seed to sale. It is a standard technology used in many industries already, such as the crypto-currency Bitcoin, which records in real time **compliant banking** and credit card processing.

Blockchain is slowly emerging in the cannabis industry and it will most likely be a regulated requirement for federal compliance in the recreational and medical cannabis industry in the future. The information captured includes data like genetic strains, cultivator and processor information, soil conditions, weather conditions, certificates of analysis, hand off information from business to business, sensor and recording data on equipment used for processing, supply chain, bank transactions and virtually anything of value that can be tracked and traded to reduce risk and also cut costs for all involved. Fraud, cyberattacks and even simple mistakes can be prevented and therefore the system provides transparency and consistent information. Blockchain provides efficient movement of cannabis commodities making them fully traceable and creating cheaper, more effective regulatory oversight of businesses, and thus providing greater trust in all transactions.

I. Legal Considerations

Marijuana is currently illegal under the Federal **Controlled Substance Act**. It states:

> "It shall be unlawful for any person to distribute a controlled substance in Schedule I or II to another except in pursuance of a written order of the person to whom such substance is distributed, made on a form to be issued by the Attorney General [in blank] in accordance with subsection

(d) of this section and regulations prescribed by him pursuant to this section."

Controlled Substance Act §828(a) also applies. It states

"It shall be unlawful for any person knowingly and intentionally to manufacture, distribute or dispense, or possess with intent to manufacture, distribute or dispense, a controlled substance."

Controlled Substance Act §841(a)(1) also applies and delineates penalties. These penalties vary and depend on the volume of marijuana that one possesses. According to the Controlled Substance Act, the penalties are as follows:

Aiding and Abetting

"Whoever commits an offense against the United States or aids, abets, counsels, commands, induces or procures its commission, is punishable as a principal." 18 U.S.C. §2(a).

The legal amount to carry marijuana or cannabis concentrates is **one ounce of marijuana or 8 grams** of cannabis concentrates.

Internet Distribution

"It shall be unlawful for any person to knowingly and intentionally deliver, distribute or dispense a controlled substance by means of the Internet, except as authorized by this subchapter, or aid or abet (as such terms are used in section 2 of title 18) any activity described in subparagraph (A) that is not authorized by this subchapter."

Controlled Substance Act §841(h) (1) is also still officially in force. Consider the, at least potential, legal jeopardy of companies like *Weedmaps* and all dispensaries that advertise their products on websites.

Anti-Money Launder

It is illegal to conduct a financial transaction that involves the proceeds of specified unlawful activity under federal law, knowing that the property involved in the financial transaction represents the proceeds of that unlawful activity. 18 U.S.C. §1956(a)(1).

Punishments include up to $500,000 in fines and up to 20 years imprisonment. 18 U.S.C. §1956(a)(1)(B).

Financial institutions (including banks, bankers, credit unions, insurance companies and registered broker/dealer firms pursuant to 51 U.S.C. §5312(a)(2)) are required to file a suspicious activity report with federal regulators if they believe a financial transaction involves proceeds of unlawful activity. 53 U.S.C. §5318(g).

J. Cannabis Business Plan

Prerequisites:

1. Cannabis license application needs to be completed
2. Make convincing visuals and include charts, graphs, tables and images
3. Make realistic assessments of goals and objectives
4. When writing any business plan, ensure to instill trust and professionalism in readers of the plan

Essential Parts of a Cannabis Business Plan:

1. **Summary**

   A short summary (only a few pages) of your business motto that addresses the current market, the niche or problem, the solutions and the market outlook.

2. **Address the Problem and How the Business Solves It**

   Address an unmet need or problem that needs to be solved. Explain how extensive the problem is. For example, a particular state only has cultivation sites and no processors, then expand on this problem, as well as on how this problem will be solved by building a processing facility. Point out innovative ideas, services and why this business will be successful.

3. **Identity Opportunity**

   This section should be filled with data, market trends, laws, regulations and niche exploration. Identify the competitive landscape and how the business will be more competitive and why.

4. **Strategic Execution**

   This section includes timelines and metrics to measure success.

5. **Marketing Plan**

The marketing plan includes the branding, logo, website design, price points, promotions, target audience, etc.

6. **Operations**

This section covers the infrastructure needed, technology, equipment and staffing projections.

7. **Compliance**

This section describes how the business will operate legally and includes laws, processes, procedures, regulations, attorneys, standard operating procedures or examples of such, employee training and safety, inclusion and diversity and anti-discrimination plolices.

8. **Portfolio of Employees**

The portfolio of employees contains the resumes of executives, owners, investors, advisors and key personnel. This portfolio also includes an organizational chart. Every employee should be able to identify their immediate supervisor. The organizational chart should show all entry-level positions all the way up to the CEO or owner.

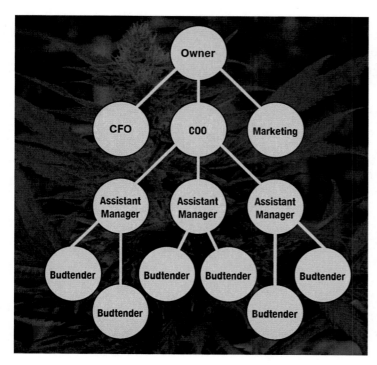

*Figure: Generic organizational chart of a Dispensary. Image Credit: Establishing a Hierarchy written by **Patrick Wagner***

9. Financial Plan

This part is often the most important part and requires the most thought and data. A detailed financial plan contains revenue forecasts, financing, sources of capital, operating costs, budgets, projected profit and loss statements, projected cash flow statements, projected balance sheets and a break-even analysis.

10. Appendices

The appendices provide the opportunity to add more data and charts to the company's plan. This may include existing contracts, personnel plans, bank statements and important publications or patents.

K. Cannabis Business Expenses and Budget

Every cannabis business is different, and the budget depends on the type of business, the size and the location. Below are some common expenditures that most businesses must account for in their budget.

1. General Business Set Up: Construction/Design, Architects, Blue Prints, Permits, Labor, Licensing, Taxes, Inspections and Distribution
2. Software, Computers, Phones, Furniture, Appliances (Refrigerator, Toaster, Coffee Maker, Washer/Dryer, Clocks), Office Supplies, Hardware (Scanners, RFID Tags, Printers),Track and Trace/Seed-to-Sale Software
3. Rent/Mortgage, Insurance (Building Liability, Surety Bonds, Product Liability, Equipment), Subscriptions, Professional Memberships, Utilities (Electricity, Water, Sewage, Gas, Telecom, Waste Disposal), Legal fees and Consulting
4. Infrastructure: Plumbing/Irrigation (Trench Drains and Discharge); Electrical (Lighting, Generator Backup, Transfer Switch, Panels, Outlets, Voltage Regulators); HVAC (Dehumidification, Air Conditioning, Heating, Venting and Ducting); Carpentry (Framing, Walls, Insulation, Paneling, Flooring, Sealing) and Painting (Finishing)
5. Compliance, Training and Waste Management (Containers, Scales, Pickup Service); Lab Testing (Cannabinoid, Microbial and Pesticide); Security (Internet, Cameras, Intercoms/Radios, Alarm System, Locks, Faults/Safes, Fencing); Health & Safety (Fire Extinguishers, First Aid, ADA, Signage, Protective Wear/Equipment and Sanitation/Custodial)

Chapter 15 - Cannabis Testing and Instrumentation - Part I
(Dr. Arin Sutlief)

Summary:

This chapter broadly covers analytical and microbial methods used to meet regulations of cannabis required by federal and/or state laws. This will include several analytical chemistry methods such as High Performance Liquid Chromatography (HPLC) for potency testing, Gas Chromatography (GC) for terpene profiling, various Mass Spectrometry (MS) instrumentation for pesticides, residual solvents and heavy metals analysis. Microbiology testing includes polymerase chain reactions (PCR) analysis for pathogens such as e coli, salmonella and total yeast and molds, as well as a comparison to the golden standard of plate counting. For each test required by regulations, the chapter will outline the Federal and State requirements for all states. Lastly, the chapter will introduce readers to ISO 17025 certification and some of the details included in this rigorous process commonly practiced in many analytical laboratories.

15.1 Cannabis Regulation

History of Cannabis Testing

For decades *Cannabis sativa*, both as hemp and marijuana, was illegal in the United States under the Controlled Substance Act of 1970, classified as a Schedule 1 Controlled Substance. Under the Compassionate Act of 1996, California was the first state to legalize medical cannabis for seriously ill Californians. This included the treatment for cancer, anorexia, AIDS, chronic pain, spasticity, glaucoma, arthritis, migraine or other illnesses for which marijuana provides relief. However, it would be almost two decades before any requirements for testing of cannabis products were set by a governing body.

In 2010, one of the first medical cannabis testing labs was opened in California, SC Labs. This lab helped pioneer cannabis testing for safety in a time when very little was known on how to test these products (Shaffer, 2019). In fact, during this time, it was illegal to test cannabis unless it was law enforcement doing forensic testing. The lab only began testing some cannabinoid levels including cannabidiol (CBD) and tetrahydrocannabinol (THC). Since then, the company has developed several tests for cannabis testing and started a third party certification company, Envirocann.

In November 2012, the Colorado ballet included Amendment 64 (Figure 15.1) for adult use of marijuana ("Amendment 64," 2012). This Amendment, when passed, included a time period for the development of a framework allowing commercial sales to begin in January 2014. In 2015, Colorado passed a bill to establish standards for marijuana testing making it the first government body to set any regulations for cannabis product safety (Wyatt, 2015).

In 2015, the United States Food and Drug Administration (FDA) also began to test cannabinoid-containing products for federal regulations (FDA, 2021). Many companies were found to sell products with incorrect cannabinoid levels and/or claims of diagnosis, cure, mitigation, treatment or prevention of any disease without any clinical trial evidence presented to the FDA false labeling, the FDA has issued several warning letters every year since testing began. Figure 15.2 shows a small clip of the FDA's testing results and warning letters submitted in 2015. Most products tested are reported to have cannabinoid levels that do not match the label claim.

Amendment 64
Use and Regulation of Marijuana

1   **Ballot Title:** Shall there be an amendment to the Colorado constitution
2   concerning marijuana, and, in connection therewith, providing for the regulation
3   of marijuana; permitting a person twenty-one years of age or older to consume or
4   possess limited amounts of marijuana; providing for the licensing of cultivation
5   facilities, product manufacturing facilities, testing facilities, and retail stores;
6   permitting local governments to regulate or prohibit such facilities; requiring the
7   general assembly to enact an excise tax to be levied upon wholesale sales of
8   marijuana; requiring that the first $40 million in revenue raised annually by such
9   tax be credited to the public school capital construction assistance fund; and
10   requiring the general assembly to enact legislation governing the cultivation,
11   processing, and sale of industrial hemp?

12   **Text of Measure:**

Figure 15.1: Colorado Amendment 64 passed in 2012. (Image Credit: Colorado Government) ("Amendment 64," 2012)

2015 Warning Letters

					Lab Results (mg/g)			Lab Results %(w/w)		
Firm	Product	State	Purchase Website	Product Size CBD Label Claim	CBD	Δ9-THC	Other Cannabinoids	CBD	Δ9-THC	Other Cannabinoids
Canna Companion, LLC	Canna Companion Capsule Size: 4	WA	cannaforpets.com	4 capsules N/A CBD	1	1	CBDA: 9 THCA: 3	0.1%	0.1%	CBDA: 0.9% THCA: 0.3%
Canna-Pet, LLC	CBD Wedges - Canna-Biscuits for Dogs	WA	canna-pet.com	2oz N/A CBD	None detected above 1 mg/g			None detected above 0.1% (w/w)		
Canna-Pet, LLC	Canna-Pet for Cats	WA	canna-pet.com	14 capsules N/A CBD	5	–	–	0.5%	–	–
Canna-Pet, LLC	Canna-Pet MaxCBD Capsules for Dogs	WA	canna-pet.com	10 capsules N/A CBD	26	1	CBC: 1	2.6%	0.1%	CBC: 0.1%
CBD Life Holdings LLC dba Ultra CBD	UltraCBD*	AZ	ultracbd.com	1oz 200mg Cannabinoids	None detected above 1 mg/g			None detected above 0.1% (w/w)		
CBD Life Holdings LLC dba Ultra CBD	UltraCBD*	AZ	ultracbd.com	1oz 200mg Cannabinoids	0.2	ID Only	CBDA: 0.2	0.02%	ID only	CBDA: 0.02%
Hemp Oil Care	Hemp Pure Vape E-Drops: Peached	CA	hempoilcare.com	10ml 50mg CBD	negative for cannabinoids			negative for cannabinoids		

***Figure 15.2**: List of some warning letters sent by the FDA in 2015 after lab testing. Product size CBD label claims are highlighted in red. (Image Credit: Food and Drug Administration) (FDA, 2021)*

As new products hit the market and the industry learns more about potential hazards of use, testing regulations are developed and modified to reduce these risks and protect customers. In early 2019, a mysterious lung injury started to appear in hospital patients (CDC, 2020a). After rising concerns and a number of deaths related to the illness, studies began to show a link to vaping, specifically THC-containing vaping products. It is now believed that vitamin E acetate, an additive to some vaping products, could be the underlying cause of this illness. As a result, regulations are now beginning to restrict the use of this additive and require analysis of vitamin E acetate concentrations, thus demonstrating why testing is important to human health.

Lastly, the 2018 Farm Bill that federally legalized hemp production in the U.S. required the establishment of a hemp regulating body. In 2019, the United States Department of Agriculture (USDA) started the national Hemp Program that began the building of hemp production and an accompanying testing-regulation framework. This was the first step the federal government has taken in regulating cannabis testing.

Federal and State Regulations

Under the Controlled Substance Act of 1970, all *Cannabis sativa L.* was made federally illegal and classified as a Schedule 1 Controlled Substance. This means that the Drug Enforcement Administration (DEA) regulates and enforces this law within the U.S. However, the 2018 Farm Bill descheduled hemp, which was defined as *Cannabis sativa L.* with tetrahydrocannabinol (THC) at or below 0.3% on a dry weight basis (Conaway, 2018). This made hemp legal for crop production for the first time in several decades and even longer for some states.

Because of the legalization of a crop that can easily grow to illegal content levels, the Farm Bill required the formation of a USDA Hemp Program that would establish a national regulatory framework. Currently, the program is controlled by the Interim Final Rule that passed on October 31, 2019 and will be in place until November 1, 2021 or until the Final Rule is published. Part of the USDA program directive in the Farm Bill was to develop a system where hemp production plans are developed and submitted by States and Tribal Territories. However, some states had started hemp pilot programs under the 2014 Farm Bill. States can choose to continue using their pilot program instead of creating a new program and submitting a state plan.

For *Cannabis sativa L.* with THC levels above 0.3%, a.k.a. marijuana, it is currently still a federal Schedule 1 Controlled Substance. However, in 1999, California was the first state to legalize medical marijuana. Since then, several states have legalized medical and recreational marijuana under state laws. Each state develops their own regulation system for marijuana but not all have. Figure 15.3 summarizes the current legalization of *Cannabis sativa* at federal and state levels. Set out throughout the chapter are the regulation requirements for all states with set laws for cannabis products.

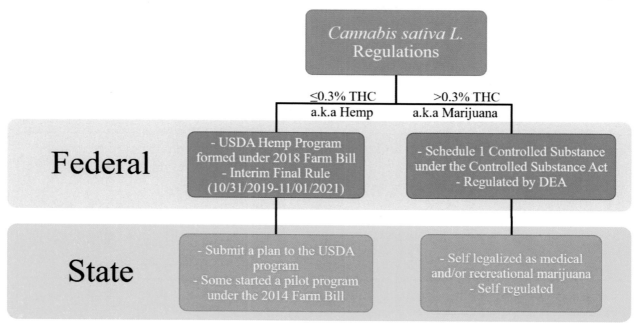

Figure 15.3: *Schematic of U.S Cannabis Regulations as of May 2021. (Photo Credit: Arin Sutlief)*

Interim Final Rule

The Interim Final Rule (IFR) was the USDA's first step in establishing a regulation framework for hemp production. Within the IFR, guidelines were outlined for the states in testing, noncompliant hemp disposal, licensing requirements and more. To have primary regulatory authority, states and Indian territories must submit a State Plan to the USDA for approval (Table 15.1). States without a USDA-approved plan will be monitored and regulated by the Federal Plan also outlined in the IFR. Currently, most states do plan or have already started a hemp program with state regulations. However, after the IFR was effective on Oct 31, 2019, any interested person was able to submit comments about the ruling until Dec 30, 2019 that were then made public. On February 27, 2020, a publication notified that enforcement of some requirements in IFR will be delayed until Oct 31, 2021 or until the publication of the Final Rule. These delays include:

1. the requirement of DEA registration for testing labs due to the limited number of registered labs and
2. the requirement of law enforcement or reverse distributor disposal for noncompliant plants. A producer is within the law if one or more of the following disposal methods are used for the disposal of noncompliant plants: plowing under, mulching/composting, dishing, bush mower/chopper, deep burial or

burning. ISO 17025 certification is not required in the IFR but is highly recommended ("Hemp Production | Agricultural Marketing Service," n.d.).

Table 15.1: *USDA State Hemp Plan Requirements* [‡]

Requirements	Details
Plan to maintain relevant producers and land information	• Keep information on all hemp producers up to date including name, address, telephone, email • Maintain status of licenses and licensed producers • Provide a legal description of the land • Report all information to the USDA
Plan for accurate and effective sampling and testing using post-decarboxylation or similarly reliable methods	• Procedure for sampling all lots at 95% confidence level • Procedure for performance-based sampling (if applicable) • Procedure on sampling agents including sampling practices at producer locations and training • Procedure for testing
Plan for disposal procedures	• Procedure for disposal or remediation of cannabis plants if testing above • Procedure for reporting non-compliant plants and disposal to USDA
Plan for remediation procedures	• Procedures that ensure the disposal or remediation of plants in violation of regulations
Plan for inspection procedures	• Procedure to annual inspections of random samples of licensed producers
Plan for collection of information	• Procedure for submitting information to the Secretary • Procedure for procedures to submit proper information to the USDA, Agricultural Marketing Service (AMS), and Farm Service Agency (FSA)
Plan to comply with enforcement procedures	• Procedure for the handling of negligent

	producers and corrective action plan
	• Procedure for producer violations greater than negligent
	• Procedure for addressing felonies
	• Procedure for any persons who materially falsify any information
Certification that the state or tribal government has resources and personnel to carry out required Farm Bill practices and procedures	
Plan may include other practices or procedures.	

(Table Credit: Arin Sutlief)

Current Demand for Cannabis Testing

With the increase in legalization of cannabis over the last few years, there have been changes in both agriculture and the cannabis market (Figure 15.4). In 2015, the first year of legal recreational use, the legal cannabis market reached $4.8 billion. Through 2014-2017, the market was observing over $1 billion growth per year. But in the last three years that growth has increased. In 2019, there was a 31.7% increase ($3.3 billion) in annual legal cannabis sales and a 52.6% increase ($7 billion) in 2020. This continued exponential growth has resulted in a projection for this industry to grow to a more than $30 billion industry by 2025 (Hudock, 2019a; Morrissey, 2021). Cannabis-related job growth has also increased with this growing market. With an increasing need for a range of employees including growers, bud tenders, scientists and more, the total U.S. legal-cannabis jobs increased by 81,900 in 2019. By 2025, it is projected that the total legal-cannabis jobs will reach 743,000 (Hudock, 2019b).

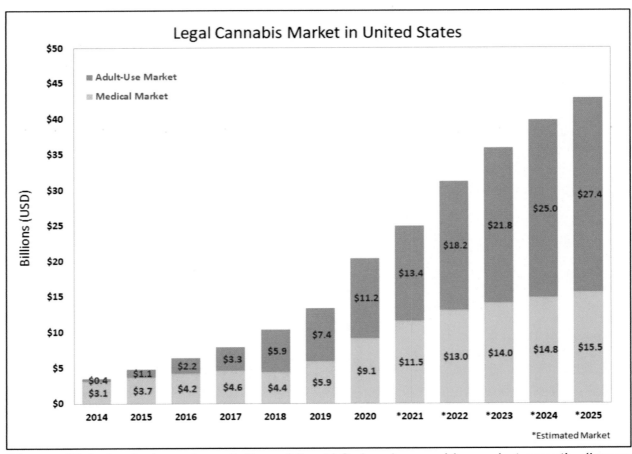

Figure 15.4: *Analysis and prediction of the U.S. legal cannabis market growth. (Image Credit: Arin Sutlief; Data from New Frontier Data) (Hudock, 2019a; Morrissey, 2021)*

As the acres of cannabis production increase and a growing number of products hit the market to meet consumer demands, a need for accessible testing is now recognized (Avins and Kopf, 2019). Federal regulations of hemp originally required a testing lab to be registered with the DEA to handle cannabis that may come in above federal regulations (THC > 0.3%) and ISO 17025 accreditation was highly recommended. As of May 2020, there were only 56 DEA-registered labs for hemp testing spread throughout the U.S. (Figure 15.5). But for the most part, these labs are not located in or around the states with major hemp production and more focused in states with legal marijuana use. This realization certainly played a part in the USDA's decision to delay enforcement of lab registration. ISO 17025 certification is also a determinant in the number of testing labs. Currently only recommended by the USDA, it can be a requirement in state plans for hemp testing and some states do require certification for marijuana testing labs. This ISO certification process will be discussed in fuller detail in section 5, but this process can be both expensive and time consuming.

But not only are products tested for regulatory purposes, they are often tested by developers more often for quality control purposes. In addition, much of this industry and our knowledge of everything from the growing to the sale of products continues to develop today; so, testing for monitoring compound levels and for research and development also increases the demand for quick and good quality testing.

Figure 15.5: DEA-Registered Hemp Testing Labs as of May 26th, 2020. (Image Credit: Doane University)

15.2 Chromatography

Liquid Chromatography Instrumentation

In previous chapters, chromatography and the technique high performance liquid chromatography (HPLC) were presented. The major components of modern HPLC instrumentation using cannabinoid analysis will serve as an example. These components will be presented in the order that solution moves through the instrument (Figure 15.6). This begins with what is known as the mobile phase. Depending on the instrument's capabilities, instruments can be set up with 1-4 different solvents to make up the mobile phase that is pumped throughout the instrument. But often, only one to two solvents are used in a single method to avoid complexity. These solvents must be made with highly pure, HPLC grade reagents to avoid signal interference from impurities. These solvents must also be degassed to avoid air bubbles in the instrument that has micrometer diameter tubing throughout.

In the case of cannabinoid analysis, a set percentage of an aqueous (water-based) solvent and organic solvent (e.g. acetonitrile or methanol) typically make up the mobile phase for efficient peak separation. The mobile phase is commonly a high percentage of organic solvent making it a more nonpolar mobile phase. A gradient can be used that increases the organic solvent percentage or the solvent can be left at one setting making it an isocratic method. By using a gradient, the chemical properties of the mobile phase will change over time which will cause different interactions of the compounds with the mobile phase and stationary phase. This could potentially decrease the analysis time while still achieving efficient peak separation but can also be difficult to develop and modify over time compared to isocratic methods. The mobile phase can also include acidic modifiers that act as a buffer to maintain a constant pH. If pH is not controlled, ionizable compounds such as acids like CBDA and THCA could easily lose protons which would affect their retention time. Acidic modifiers are typically added to each solvent of the mobile phase at the same concentration for a consistent pH throughout analysis especially in gradient methods.

Most modern HPLC systems come with an autosampler that is capable of being programmed to run a number of samples without manual injection of each sample into the instrument. This has significant advantages for a laboratory, especially when high throughput testing is needed. However, manual injection is also an option. When a sample is injected into the HPLC, a needle is plunged into the sample vial to withdraw sample solution into the sample loop. The needle is used to then inject the appropriate amount of sample into the injection port for analysis. The injection volume can vary, but typically methods require less than 50 µL to be used.

As the sample passes through the instrument in very thin tubing, it is led to the other key component in chromatography techniques that effect compound separation. The column of HPLC is essential to its function and has great versatility. Column selection can come with a lot of trial and error. Searching for the column with ideal chemical properties that allows for the interaction of targeted analytes, which result in good separation, can be a difficult process. In the case of cannabinoid analysis, C18 columns have been most commonly used. This column is modified with an eighteen carbon alkyl group resulting in a more nonpolar stationary phase for efficient separation of the nonpolar cannabinoids. A guard column can also be attached before the separation column to help prevent matrix material that can cause contamination of the stationary phase or the instrument. This column is usually much shorter with an identical stationary phase to the column. Using a guard column can help prolong the lifetime of the column and reduce expenses.

After compound separation in the column, theoretically each compound is in an isolated group continuing through the HPLC tubing to the detector. All detectors are designed to produce a signal that is proportional to the amount of isolated compound present but each has a limited functioning range. While there are several types of detectors, this chapter will focus photodiode arrays.

In photodiode arrays (PDA), a light source such as a deuterium lamp is directed into a sample. The ultraviolet/visible light passes through a sample and some wavelengths are absorbed by certain molecules, functional groups, ions or complexes of the sample. Sometimes samples can consist of molecules, ions or complexes that emit certain wavelengths of light when exposed to these light sources. However, this is a more uncommon situation. After the light passes through the sample, the wavelengths not absorbed will continue to a holographic grating that separates the wavelengths, before they reach the diode array detector. The light intensity that reaches the diode array produces a directly proportional charging current, which is converted to a signal. This type of detector allows for simultaneous detection of wavelengths 190 - 1100 nm, giving the instrument flexibility in analysis and data collection.

Once a signal is produced by the detector, the data can be analyzed. The signal (in arbitrary units, AU) is plotted as a function of time creating what is called a chromatogram. In the chromatogram, each target analyte can be identified based on the retention time.

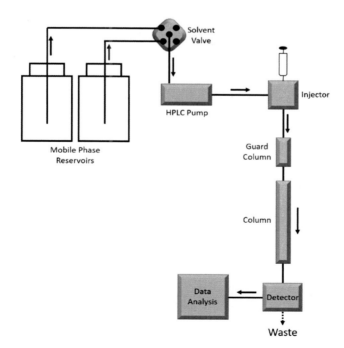

Gas Chromatography Instrumentation

Gas chromatography (GC) is very similar to HPLC and is also essential in cannabis testing. Using similar techniques, gas chromatography is able to separate compounds in a mixture and detect each. But it is only applicable to a limited number of sample types, specifically those that are able to easily go into the gas phase. With more sophisticated technology, the application of GC has expanded in the last few decades. Let's briefly go over the main components of GC and the key differences this method has from HPLC.

GC does not have a traditional mobile phase. Instead, it uses an inert gas such as helium or hydrogen called a carrier gas to move the sample/compounds through the instrument. It has no interaction with the sample other than to transport it and does not effect the separation of compounds. So, when a sample is injected into the instrument at the injection port, it must be in the gas phase or converted into a gas phase. For liquids, this would mean that the injection port is set on a high temperature for evaporation. This requirement can eliminate some classes of compounds from GC analysis. For example, cannabinoids with leaving groups of low temperatures like the carboxylic group in CBDA and THCA will have some degradation occur due to the required temperatures. CBDA and THCA are converted to CBD and THC, respectively, in GC analysis and will only allow for the evaluation of total CBD and THC. This limits the analysis and must be considered when selecting instrumentation and methods for analysis. As a result, this is a major reason why HPLC has become the golden standard for cannabinoid analysis.

As the injected sample passes through the instrument, it will need to remain in the gas phase. The column is in a column oven that can also be held at one temperature throughout analysis (isothermic) or a temperature program can be used. Like HPLC gradient methods, temperature programs can be used to decrease analysis time and increase peak resolution. GC columns are also much longer than LC columns, typically reaching 1-2 m lengths. Because of this, columns are typically coiled to reduce the oven size. GC column materials and stationary phase must also maintain stability at temperatures required for the sample to stay in the gas phase, which can be a challenge in column and method development.

GC detectors are also different from HPLC detectors due to the different phases being analyzed. The most common detector used in GC is a flame ionization detector (FID). As an almost universal detector, it is compatible for detecting all carbon-containing compounds with very few expectations. Hydrogen and oxygen or air are required to fuel the flame in the detector cell. When an analyte containing carbon atoms is introduced in the detector cell, the flame breaks up the molecule into fragments that can be positively charged ions. These ions result in a current being produced that is proportional to the amount of analyte prevent. Chromatograms are then plotted for analysis.

Quantitation

The concentration of an analyte of interest within a sample can be determined by quantitative analysis. The signal of an instrument can be correlated to the concentration of an analyte through the development of a calibration curve. In the case of chromatography, the area under the peak, versus peak height, is the more reliable response proportional to concentration.The peak area is considered the signal produced by the instrument when the analyte is present.

Calibrations of instrumentation must be performed regularly to ensure accurate quantitative results. The process for calibration begins with the preparation of external standards for a calibration curve. Typically, certified reference standards (CRM) with known concentrations of analyte(s) are used to prepare at least five calibration standards ranging in concentrations (Figure 15.7). These calibration standards are often within the linear range of the instrument response to ensure the most consistent quantitative analysis. The lowest point of the calibration curve would be the limit of quantitation (LOQ) which is the lowest concentration that can be reliably measured for quantification. The most common method for the preparation of calibration standards is using serial dilution. First, the highest concentration of the calibration curve is prepared, and the solution serially diluted to the required concentrations to complete the calibration curve.

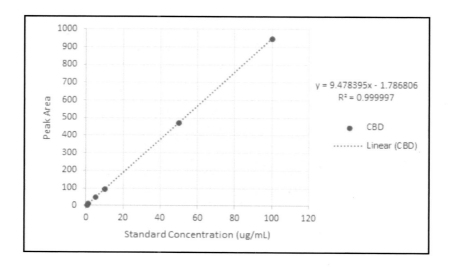

Figure 15.7: Calibration curve for CBD using six external calibration standards with linear regression. (Image Credit: Arin Sutlief)

Since the calibration curve is typically made in the linear range of the instrument signal, the concentration of analyte is directly proportional to the instrument signal and linear regression is used to determine the relationship. The square of the correlation coefficient (r^2) is one method to determine the linearity of the calibration curve. It is commonly used to determine the qualification of a calibration where the closer to 1.00 (a straight line) the better. Typically, r^2 greater than 0.99 is considered acceptable within the cannabis industry. After the slope and y-intercept of the line are determined, the equation $y = mx + b$ is used to determine the concentration of analyte in a sample based on the area under the analyte peak.

Internal standards can be used in a method to enhance result reliability. Internal standards are typically a compound similar to the analyte(s) of interest but elutes from the column at a different retention time. Therefore, a known concentration of an internal standard can be added to the sample during analysis. Internal standards have been used in two ways in the cannabinoid analysis. To check for consistent instrument performance, an internal standard can be added to the sample during sample preparation. This process would include a study of the internal standards response where technicians and analysts of the lab prepare blank samples (no sample matrix present) that include the internal standard at the known concentration. These should be prepared the exact same way the samples are prepared. Typically, a study of 10-20 samples would be appropriate for analysis to achieve an average response for the internal standard. An appropriate range for acceptable values can be determined so that any internal standard responses outside the range will result in the conclusion of *error* and the sample re-prepped or instrument maintenance performed.

Internal standards can also be used to adjust results to account for any random error that may occur during sample analysis. Any random error that occurred after the addition of the internal standard would effect both the analyte(s) and the internal standard. To eliminate random error in results using an internal standard, a calibration curve should be made with calibration standards that include the internal standard. The instrument response for the analyte is then expressed as the ratio of the response to analyte and the response to the internal standard. This use of internal standards is very useful when inconsistency is more likely. For example, sample injection could be a source of error if the same exact amount of sample isn't injected every time. The internal standard would be affected in the same way and the response ratio will be consistent.

Cannabinoid Regulations

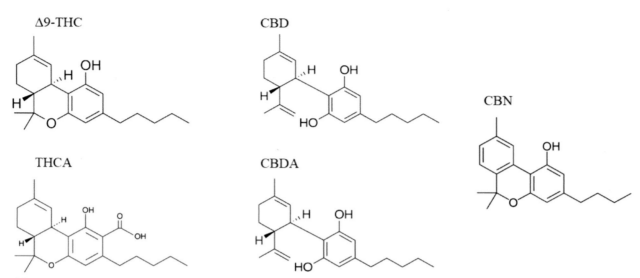

Figure 15.8: Top five cannabinoids found in cannabis regulations in the U.S. (Image Credit: Arin Sutlief)

Cannabinoids are compounds in cannabis that are highly regulated, maybe even the most regulated (Figure 15.8). Δ9-tetrahydrocannabinol (Δ9-THC) is the cannabinoid responsible for the psychotropic effects of cannabis. Because tetrahydrocannabinolic acid (THCA) can easily be decarboxylated by heat, it is both Δ9-THC and THCA levels that are regulated for total THC present in cannabis products (Eqn 15.1). Total THC levels are important in legalization, especially where set limits are required such as medical marijuana and hemp. In fact, total THC is the only test legally required for hemp production in all 50 states.

$$Total\ THC\ = [Δ9THC] + 0.877 * [THCA] \qquad \text{Eqn 15.1}$$

Cannabidiol (CBD) is a non-psychotropic cannabinoid but of great interest to producers. It is starting to appear in many products including tinctures, lotions and even shampoos. Because CBD also has an acidic form (CBDA) that can be decarboxylated with heat, total CBD levels are reported with both concentrations (Eqn 15.2).

$$Total\ CBD = [CBD] + 0.877 * [CBDA] \qquad \text{Eqn 15.2}$$

Δ9-THC, THCA, CBD and CBDA are the four major cannabinoids and regulated the most by states, but there are other minor cannabinoids that some states do regulate (Table 15.2). The fifth most regulated cannabinoid is Cannabinol (CBN), a non psychotropic compound seen at higher concentration in older plants. Regulation of CBN has been required because of its ability to increase euphoric effects of ☐9-THC giving users a bigger high (Earlenbaugh, 2015). Other minor cannabinoids like CBG, ☐8-THC, THCV, CBC and CBDV are only regulated by a few states.

Table 15.2: Cannabinoids Required in State Testing (Table Credit: Arin Sutlief) [‡]

Δ9-THC	THCA	CBD	CBDA	CBN	CBG	Δ8-THC	THCV	CBC	CBDV
AK	AK	AK	AK	AK					
AR	AR	AR	AR						
CA	CA	CA	CA						
CO	CO	CO	CO	CO					
CT	CT	CT	CT						
DE	DE	DE	DE	DE	DE				
HI	HI	HI	HI	HI	HI				
LA	LA	LA	LA						
ME	ME	ME	ME				ME		
MD	MD								
MA	MA	MA	MA						
MI	MI	MI	MI						
MO									
MT	MT	MT	MT						
NV	NV	NV	NV	NV					
NH	NH	NH	NH	NH	NH		NH	NH	
NY	NY	NY	NY	NY	NY		NY	NY	NY
ND	ND	ND	ND						
OH	OH	OH	OH	OH					
OK	OK								
OR	OR	OR	OR						
PA	PA								
UT	UT								
VT	VT	VT	VT						
WA	WA	WA	WA						
WV	WV	WV	WV	WV	WV		WV	WV	WV
26	25	21	21	9	5	1	3	3	2

Terpene Regulations

Terpenes are a class of molecules that people are probably very familiar with and don't even realize it. Bringing fragrance to everyday life, these molecules are aromatic oils that are naturally found in many plants including cannabis. For thousands of years, these terpenes, also familiarly known as essential oils, have been used in religious ceremonies, aromatherapy and even in medicinal practices. Over the centuries, continued discovery of new terpenes expanded their uses into perfumes and food additives and led to advancements like synthetic production and understanding the molecule interactions in the body.

One of the most important ways terpenes play a key role in the body is through the "Entourage Effect." Through years of research, it was discovered that terpenes are molecules that can also bind to the receptors of the Endocannabinoid System, the system determined to interact with cannabinoids in the body. Terpenes present with cannabinoids can enhance the effects of the cannabinoids, magnifying their effect beyond how they would act alone and creating the Entourage Effect. A different way to picture this, instead of 2+2 = 4 the Entourage Effect makes 2+2 = 10 (Potter, 2019).

Like all testing, the structure and properties of the molecules in question are key to method development. Terpenes are made up of at least one isoprene unit (C_5H_8; Figure 15.9) and are classified by the number of isoprene units within the molecule. Molecules that contain two isoprene units are classified as monoterpenes, diterpenes for four units, triterpenes for six, etc. Other molecules with an odd number of isoprene units are named differently. For example, a terpene with three isoprene units is called a sesquiterpene. Terpenes can also be modified by heat, oxygen or time either naturally or for artificial production. These modified molecules are often classified as terpenoids.

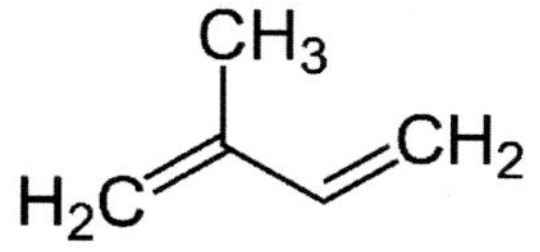

Figure 15.9: *Structure of isoprene unit found in terpenes and terpenoids. (Image Credit: Arin Sutlief)*

Terpene analysis in cannabis is still in the development phase. The industry lacks the supplies needed for high quality results like standards for many compounds found in cannabis. There is also a deficiency in molecule identification where not all molecules have been properly identified. Despite the slow evolution of terpene analysis, many methods have been developed for the analysis of several terpenes via a single method. But there are still improvements to be made to get to a level of thorough terpene evaluation in cannabis.

Terpene analysis in cannabis can be referred to as a recreational test. Regulations for all cannabis for the most part do not include terpenes with the exception of Nevada, which does have a list of ten terpenes required for testing but with no set limitations. Therefore, they are a part of cannabis testing because of consumer demand. Terpene profiles are becoming increasingly important to consumers as a profile for flavoring and beneficial effects. But as research continues to expand, terpene profiles could play a major part in medical cannabis development.

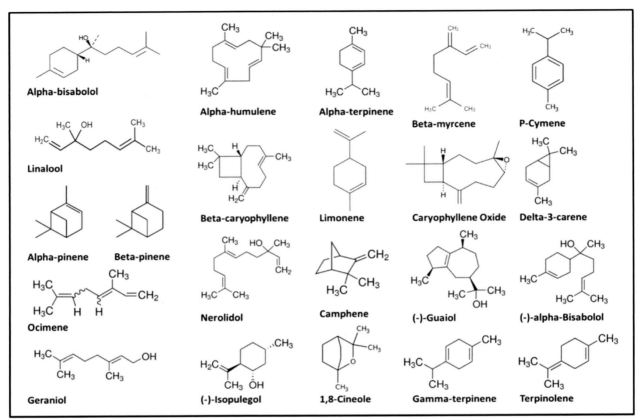

Figure 15.10: *Molecular structures of 21 common Cannabis terpenes. (Image Credit: Arin Sutlief)*

Cannabinoid Sample Preparation

Guidelines for hemp testing have been published by the USDA in the Hemp Program (U.S. Domestic Hemp Production Program, 2021). However, this sample preparation can be applied to all cannabis flower material. This sample should include flower material from a single lot in preparation for a single sample analysis.

Dry and Mill the Sample

Samples submitted can either be dried prior or still wet. But for sample preparation, materials must be dry. Samples can be dried in a low temperature oven, dehydrator or freeze dryer until a consistent sample weight is achieved or 5% to12% moisture content. This improves grinding and homogenization of the sample. This also allows the analysis to be performed on a dry weight basis or adjusted for moisture content (a test discussed in section 16.1).

After the sample is dry, the flower material is brittle and easy to mill and manicure. Sample must consist of only plant material that can pass through a wire screen no larger than 1.5 x 1.5 mm (Mesh 14). So seeds, larger twigs and stems can be filtered from the plant material to be tested. Figure 15.11 shows an example of a dried flower and one milling process. Once all of the plant material for a sample is milled, the sample should be gently homogenized so if the sample consists of multiple plants, a sample will represent an average of those plants. From the homogenized sample, a sample is weighed out to create a "Test Specimen." The rest of the milled sample is packed, labeled as "Retain Specimen" and stored in a secure place for any future sampling such as retesting.

Figure 15.11: Left - Dried Cannabis plant material. Right - Sifting plant material with a wire screen. (Image Credit: Arin Sutlief)

Extraction of Cannabinoids

At this point, the USDA guidelines leave chemical analysis up to the laboratory and what testing method is being used. For all methods, cannabinoids are extracted from the flower material by an organic solvent such as methanol. Organic solvent is added to the sample and mixed to allow for cannabinoid extraction (Figure 15.12). Because of the chlorophyll in plant material, the solvent will go from a colorless solution to green with the plant material settling at the bottom of the tube.

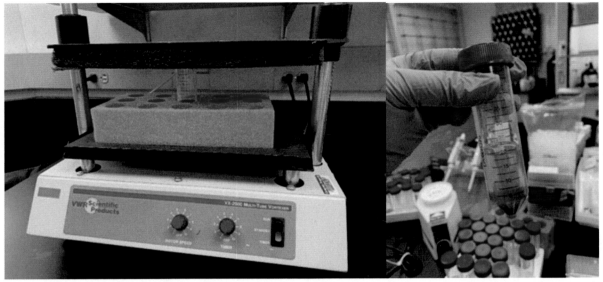

Figure 15.12: *Left - Multi-vial shaker used for liquid extraction of cannabinoids from plant material. Right - Post extraction with a top layer of liquid that contains the cannabinoids, chlorophyll, and other molecules from the plant and a bottom layer of plant material. (Image Credit: Arin Sutlief)*

Filter and Dilution

Because of the small tubing used in many analysis methods such as HPLC, flower material in the sample could cause damage to the instrumentation. To avoid this, samples are filtered. The sample is added to a syringe with a filter that has pore sizes of at least 0.45 µm or less to remove large material from the solution (Figure 15.13). As the sample is pressed through the filter, the sample can be placed into a sample vial. *Note*: it is important to make sure sample preparation steps such as the syringe filter step do not affect the concentration of the analyte being quantified. This is an important part of method development, to be discussed further in Section 16.2.

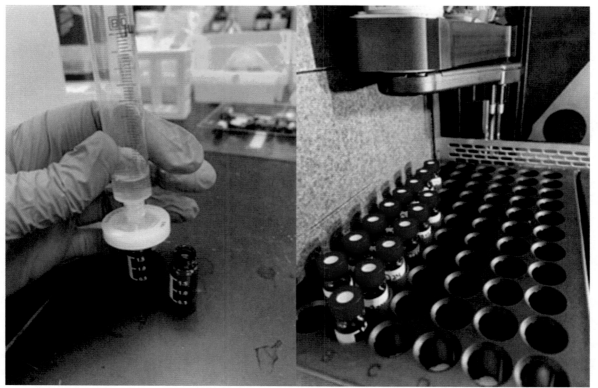

Figure 15.13: Left - Syringe filtering of extract solution into an HPLC vial. Right - Vial autosampler of an HPLC. (Image Credit: Arin Sutlief)

Terpene Sample Preparation and Analysis

Terpenes are volatile molecules and evaporate quickly. This is why when a person walks outside in the morning, they smell the "fresh morning air" when the terpenes are evaporating from the surrounding plants as the sun is rising. This easy conversion to the gas phase makes gas chromatography a great candidate for terpene analysis but requires some unique sample preparation/instrumentation to complete this analysis.

Sample Grinding

Samples should be grounded prior to analysis to help create a homogeneous test sample. But because of terpenes' low boiling points, the samples cannot be dried with heat prior to grinding. One method to use is freezing the sample prior to grinding. This both helps prevent the loss of terpenes and also to simplify the grinding process. Samples can also be ground under liquid nitrogen to make the material brittle and easier to grind.

Headspace Autosampler

A homogeneous sample of ground cannabis material is weighed and placed in headspace vials (Figure 15.14). Samples were analyzed using the full expiration technique (FET) during which the vials are incubated at temperatures that result in all or most of the analyte to evaporate from the sample into the headspace of the vial. After a set amount of time (15 to 20 minutes) to reach equilibrium, the autosampler is used to sample the headspace and inject the analytes of interest into instrumentation for analysis.

GC Analysis

Once the analysts are in the vapor state in the headspace, it is injected into the instrument. GC is commonly used for analysis of terpenes since analysis is performed on the gas phase of the analyte. The stationary phase used for terpene analysis can vary within published methods, but all are of low to mid polarity. For example, WAX columns with silica-based stationary phase lined with polyethylene glycol (PEG) have been used and are very nonpolar. These columns are regularly used in the food and fragrance industries. Instrumentation acronym for analysis can be summarized as FET-GC-FID with the detector sometimes being included.

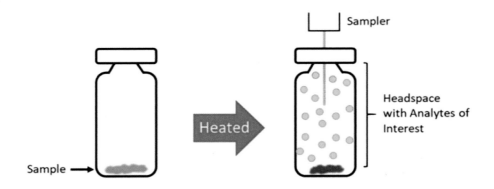

Figure 15.14: *Full evaporation technique used for headspace analysis of a sample by GC (FET-GC). (Image Credit: Arin Sutlief)*

15.30 Mass Spectrometry

Instrumentation

Mass spectrometry (MS) is a technique that allows for the ionization of molecules, the separation of these ions and the measurement of the abundance of the ions present. A mass spectrometer has components that are able to complete all of this in one instrument. When a sample is injected into MS, the molecules present must be ionized. There are a variety of ionization sources with some that are able to also accomplish fragmentation of molecules where the molecule breaks down into smaller pieces called fragments. Both ionization and fragmentation can be advantageous in MS. The most common ionization source is electron ionization (EI). In EI, a beam of electrons is emitted from a heated metal filament (e.g. tungsten) that crosses paths with the sample molecules. The high-energy electrons (e⁻) cause the sample molecule (M) to ionize (M·⁺) and fragment: $M + e^- \rightarrow M^{\cdot +} + 2e^-$. When ions form, MS is able to separate the ions for detection based on their mass-to-charge ratio (m/z), where m is the mass of the ion and z is the charge of the ion.

EI is categorized as a hard ionization source because of the high energy that can result in significant fragmentation. Fragmentation can be useful in determining molecular structure when the molecule is fragmented into smaller ions. But in hard ionization, fragmentation can be extreme resulting in no ions present of the original structure that would have an *m/z* close to the molecular weight of the molecule. While this can be useful in some analyzes, it is not ideal for identifying unknown molecules. Collisions between ions and molecules can also result in other ions. For example, a common interaction between protons (H⁺) and molecules can result in protonated ions, (M+H)⁺. But since most MS operates under vacuum, these interactions are able to be limited.

While there are a number of different ionization sources with a variety of applications, the other most common ionization source is electrospray ionization (ESI). As a liquid containing the sample molecule passes through a metal capillary, a strong electric field is applied causing the liquid to ionize into positive or negative ions and disperse into a spray. This type of ionization source does not produce a lot of fragmentation and is categorized as a soft ionization source. ESI is especially useful when analyzing large molecules like biomolecules, because it produces ions of multiple charges but has little fragmentation. This renders the results easier for interpretation. ESI also operates at atmospheric pressure, which will be advantageous in some instrumentation; to be discussed later in the section.

Once ions are formed, mass analyzers are used to separate ions by their *m/z*. In this textbook, focus will be on the most common, quadrupole mass analyzers. A quadrupole is made up of four rods that make an electric field (Figure 15.15). Opposite pairs of rods are connected to the opposite ends of a direct current (DC) source. At any given time, one pair is negatively charged while the other is positively charged and they are alternated. These rods are also connected to an electrical source oscillating at radio frequency (RF). This results in an AC potential superimposed on the DC potential. So as an ion passes through the quadrupole, it will be attracted to the rod of the opposite charge. Then, when the charge of the rod is oscillated, it is repelled from the rod resulting in a "corkscrew" path through the quadrupole of the ion. The ratio of DC to RF allows for a single *m/z* value to pass through for detection, while all other ions collide with rods or are lost in the vacuum system. To scan a sample for multiple ions, different methods have been developed; including holding the frequency of the RF oscillation while varying the potentials of DC and RF.

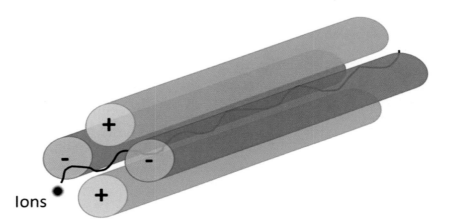

Figure 15.15: *Transmission of ions in a quadrupole mass analyzer by oscillating RF voltage and DC voltage. (Image Credit: Arin Sutlief)*

As individual ions reach the end of the mass analyzer, the number of ions of each *m/z* must be detected. The most common detector used in MS is the electron multiplier (EM). A discrete-dynode EM is made up of 12 to 24 dynodes that each have a surface which produces several electrons when electrons, ions or neutrals collide with the surface. This results in an amplified current that arrives at the collector producing a signal.

After a signal is produced, it is plotted at a function of *m/z* into a mass spectrum (Figure 15.16). The most abundant peak is called the base peak. Mass spectrums are commonly scaled to 100; they are plotted as relative abundance versus *m/z* with the base peak set as 100. The nominal mass of a molecule is determined by the nominal mass of the atomic isotopes present. For example, Figure 15.16 is the mass spectrum of limonene ($C_{10}H_{16}$). The nominal mass of limonene is calculated as the sum of carbon and hydrogen nominal masses, 10(12) + 16(1) = 136. The peak with the m/z equal to the molecular nominal mass is the molecular ion peak or the peak corresponding to the original molecule and its molecular weight. Peaks of lower m/z are then fragment ion peaks that correspond to the fragment ions formed from the original molecule. These peaks can be used to identify compounds of a mixture of analytes or help determine the structure of unknown molecules. For further help in analyzing mass spectra, refer to organic chemistry, instrumental analysis or mass spectroscopy specific textbooks.

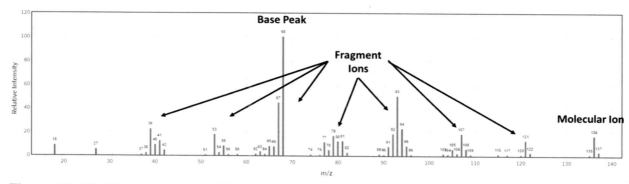

Figure 15.16: *Mass spectrum of limonene. (Image Credit: Arin Sutlief)*

Tandem MS and Hybridization

As seen in MS, this technique offers information that is unique for each compound analyzed by the presentation of fragment ions. To obtain even more information from MS, tandem MS has been developed. In tandem MS instrumentation, also referred to as MS-MS or MS^n, ions produced by an ionization source are passed through a mass analyzer. Ions, called precursor ions, can be selected to go through an additional process that results in more fragmentation or other ions. These new ions (product ions) pass through a second mass analyzer for detection. In MS^n, this process can be continued with more fragmentation or ionization and additional mass analyzers. Discussion of pesticide analysis in cannabis products will be discussed later with a review of an example of MS-MS testing and analysis.

Alone, both chromatography and mass spectrometry are techniques that provide a lot of information about molecules and samples which help in many laboratory aspects. But over the years, instrumentation has been developed to combine these two techniques presenting even more advantages. There are some challenges when coupling these two concepts. The largest challenge is GC and LC both operate at atmospheric pressure with a significant amount of carrier gas or solvent present, while MS operates under vacuum. The carrier gas or solvent must be removed during the introduction of the sample into the MS.

When GC and MS are hybridized, the instrumentation acronym is GC-MS. When interfacing these two instruments, the column end can be directly coupled to the ionization source if MS vacuum pumps are able to remove the large amount of carrier gas present in the sample. Quadrupole mass analyzers are also the most common mass analyzer used, because of their capability of fast scanning speeds required with GC. Similarly, LC-MS is the acronym for LC coupled with MS and presents the same challenges. The use of ESI, discussed previously, as an ionization source has greatly helped in interfacing these two techniques.

The concept of quantification is slightly more complex with hybridization, but this instrumentation presents huge benefits. As separated compounds elute from chromatography into the MS, information about the ions produced over time can be either fully scanned or select ions detected. When full-scan mode is used, a total ion chromatogram (TIC) is plotted as the total counts from ions of all masses versus scan number/time. Then at any given time point, a complete mass spectrum can be plotted and analyzed. From full-scan mode, certain ions can be extracted to plot an extracted ion chromatogram (XIC) that will display a chromatogram of peaks which have these ions present. This makes the analysis of complex mixtures much easier. If two compounds have similar retention times that result in unresolved peaks, select ions can be used to distinguish one compound from the other. In a similar way, MS can also use selected ion monitoring (SIM), where only select ions are monitored throughout analysis instead of all ions. While it also allows for easier identification of compounds in complex mixtures similar to XIC, it also improves the sensitivity of detection and the quantitative precision.

Mass Spectrometry for Cannabinoids and Terpenes

Exploring mass spectrometry instrumentation, MS is a pretty universal instrument that can be filled with information about a molecule. Cannabinoids and terpenes analysis using chromatography methods can be used for analysis, but MS can also be used for analysis.

In cannabinoid analysis, MS can be used in hybridization with liquid chromatography. When mixtures are introduced to LC-MS, separation of targeted analytes will occur for identification. Unknown peaks/molecules which can consist of new cannabinoids, terpenes or other compounds/contaminants can be further identified with MS structural analysis. MS is also a way to confirm the known molecules/peaks. However, MS can also introduce more complexity and higher instrumentation costs when it doesn't really add a lot of advantages in most situations. Especially in the case of cannabinoids, their structures are very similar, including the molecular weights, making MS even less practical to identify individual cannabinoids. Notice the example of the two spectra in Figure 15.17. The spectrum for Δ9-THC (MW=314.469 g/mol) and CBD (MW=314.469 g/mol) have similar peaks, including the same base peak and molecular ion peak, making the cannabinoids only identifiable by fragment peaks. Cannabinoid structure analysis typically requires the use of nuclear magnetic resonance (NMR). Many HPLC methods have been developed that result in efficient quantification of current cannabinoids of interest.

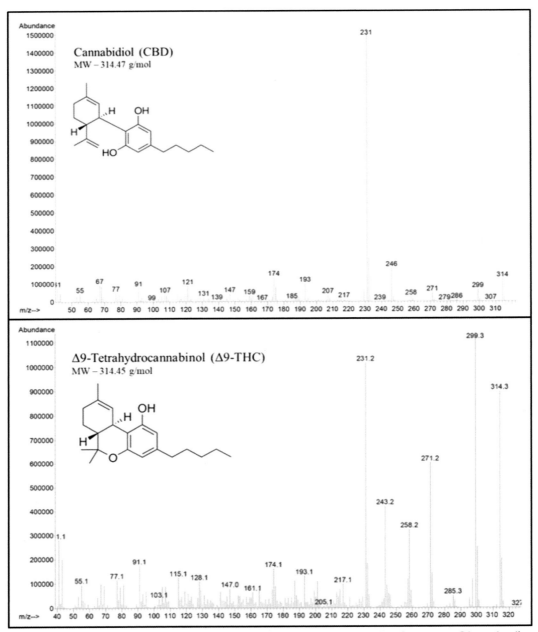

Figure 15.17: Mass Spectrum of CBD and Δ9-THC. (Image Credit: Cayman Chemical)

Hybridization with MS also can be advantageous when there are complex mixtures to analyze, like numerous terpenes of interest that must be identified in a single run. More molecules in a mixture can make it difficult to develop a method for a quick analysis while providing enough separation between peaks. MS can make method development easier by being able to detect and identify multiple molecules within a single peak or overlapping peaks. For terpene analysis, the most common instrumentation is GC-MS to help with the complexity of analyzing multiple molecules at once.

Pesticide Regulations

Pesticides are compounds that have been used in agriculture for many years and are continually being developed and utilized. Different classes of pesticides exist to help increase crop yields including insecticides, herbicides, fungicides and more. Pesticides can be also classified into chemical classes: organophosphorus (OP) compounds, carbamates, chlorinated hydrocarbons, pyrethroids and heterocyclic compounds. While these compounds are useful in agriculture, they are increasingly becoming a concern in environmental and human health. This has resulted in a number of pesticides being banned or being closely regulated in some food industries (Taylor and Birkett, 2020).

In the cannabis industry, a limited number of pesticides have been allowed for use by both federal regulations for hemp and state regulations. Pesticides become particularly harmful when the common method for cannabis use is smoking, the rawest form customers can consume. But there are real advantages of smoking including increased bioavailability, so it is important that products are closely regulated for pesticides. State regulations vary across the U.S. and some have separate regulations for inhalables versus other cannabis products. A number of states use the Code of Federal Regulations (CFR), 40 CFR 180, as a guide for pesticide regulations (EPA, 2014). This CFR published by the EPA lists the tolerances and exemptions for pesticide chemical residues in food.

Residual Solvent Regulations

Solvents are organic solutions typically utilized in the extraction of compounds and some product formulations. Solvents can be removed after extraction, but many still exist at low concentrations. Solvents that are used can be harmful for consumption if they exist at a high enough concentration in the final product. Therefore, residual solvent testing has been included in many regulations of cannabis products (Table 15.4). Note that residual solvent testing would only need to be required in products following extraction; so, plant material testing is not required. Regulations typically follow guidelines established by the U.S. Pharmacopeial Convention (USP), which has a list of 59 solvents used in manufacturing herbal medicines and other drug products with set limitations. However, this list does not include butane and propane, which have been used in the cannabis industry. State regulations vary, making it vital for processors to pay close attention to their state regulations.

Heavy Metal Regulations

Because of cannabis remediation capabilities, common water and soil contaminants can become an issue in the use of cannabis products. Heavy metals, a growing concern in water and soil contamination, are part of regulations to avoid the consumption of large concentrations that could be harmful. Heavy metals in most industries are regulated by the FDA with set limitations often based on the delivery mechanism of the product. For example, in cosmetics, FDA guidance includes mercury, lead, arsenic and chromium limits allowed in the product and color additives (Nutrition, 2020a). Arsenic, cadmium and chromium VI are three of five transition metals that are classified as human carcinogens and are highly regulated. This is not only to ensure that products are safe for consumption, but also in disposal, so as to prevent environmental contamination such as water systems (Goyer, 2004). The cannabis industry has developed similar guidance regarding arsenic (As), mercury (Hg), cadmium (Cd) and lead (Pb); these being the most common heavy metals found in regulations. The limitations set by the regulations also follow this guidance with some states even setting limitations for different products that differ in pathways of exposure.

Limitations and reporting of heavy metal contamination often uses units of ppm or ppb to present these very dilute concentrations in solution. Parts-per-million (ppm) is equal to one part per 10^6 parts (10^{-6}). As mass fractions, this means that 1 ppm is equal to 1 µg of analyte per 1 g of sample. However, in the case of liquid samples, 1 ppm is equal to 1 mg of analyte per 1 L of sample. Ppb (parts-per-billion) is also commonly seen in units with even more dilute concentrations (10^{-9}).

Pesticide ple Preparation and Analysis

The method for sample preparation for pesticide analysis has been developed and used in many industries; for example. Including the food industry analyzing products like fruits, vegetables, grains and more. The cannabis industry has been able to adopt a similar technique. This sample preparation process is more complex with more steps than any test discussed thus far. First, a sample size of around 1 g is used and 5 mL of water is added. This is followed by 5 mL of acetonitrile added. QuEChERS salts, 3 g of $MgSO_4$ and 0.75 g sodium acetate, are added and the contents shaken for extraction of pesticides into solution. After thoroughly mixing, the sample is centrifuged and the supernatant used for analysis. Some samples might require further clean-up using dispersive solid phase extraction (dSPE) that uses a C18-E column to extract unwanted molecules. This hydrophobic column uses a 18 carbon chain to extract nonpolar molecules as the sample solution is passed through the column. Commonly, the solution can be passed through using gravity or a pump, but it can require some time to complete this step. Then, some samples may require even more steps to completely clean the sample prior to analysis (Armstrong et al., 2017; Moulins et al., 2018; "What is QuEChERS?," 2019).

Some of this sample preparation process has been able to be simplified for higher throughput of samples. For example, the QuEChERS salts can be purchased in packets so each salt is pre-weighed and one packet added to each sample eliminating the need for two tedious measurements. C18-E columns are also manufactured in convenient sizes and made with material that makes it a one-time use disposable consumable.

LC-MS/MS is the most common method for the analysis of pesticides. As previously discussed, the hybridization of LC with MS adds a huge advantage to analyzing complex mixtures where many analytes must be identified if present. LC is able to first separate compounds based on retention times and MS used to identify the compounds. The use of tandem MS (MS-MS) allows for product ion detection, which aids in the identification of compounds that may have overlapping peaks that are not resolved. Figure 15.18 goes through one pesticide example. When a sample containing the pesticide imazalil is analyzed by LC-MS/MS, the compound is fragmented into the first mass spectrum that has the molecular ion peak present, $m/z = 297$. That ion is selected and further dissociated for more fragmentation that produces the second mass spectrum. Ions 255.1 and 159.0 m/z are found to be specific for imazalil in a mixture of pesticides often required in regulations. These ions can be used to extrapolate chromatograms for quantification. Method development for this kind of complex instrumentation and mixture of target analytes can be very difficult to develop and operate consistently. It is one of the more challenging tests in cannabis regulation that often requires skilled analysts and time for precise development.

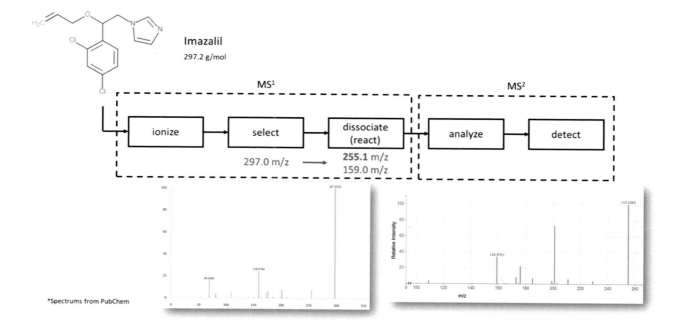

Imazalil
297.2 g/mol

*Spectrums from PubChem

Figure 15.18: *Schematic of LC-MS/MS and Imazalil detection. (Image Credit: Complied by Arin Sutlief with spectra from PubChem)*

Residual Solvent Sample Preparation and Analysis

Sample preparation for residual solvents is, by contrast, fairly simple. After the collection of a representative sample, commonly taken at multiple sampling points, a 0.5 g sample is weighed into a vial. The sample is then diluted with dimethylacetamide (DMA) to a final volume of 10 mL. Headspace autosamplers were used to analyze terpenes where a sample is heated to evaporate all analytes of interest and the headspace above sampled for analysis. For residual solvent analysis, headspace sampling is also used since solvents remaining in cannabis products from manufacturing have low boiling points. With the target analytes being in the gas phase, GC is the logical method for analysis coupled with MS (HS-GC-MS) for accurate identification of solvents that commonly have similar retention times. This method of solvent analysis has already been regularly used in many industries including pharmaceutical and food, making the transition to the cannabis industry easier than some other tests (Marotta et al., 2018).

The column used for solvent separation is what will make this method different from terpene analysis. Like other tests, there are a number of different methods that have been published with a variety of columns used. Typically, these columns range from low-polarity to mid-polarity. For example, the Agilent VF-35 column is of medium polarity and is shown to have high stability even at high temperatures. It is commonly used for trace environmental and chemical analyses.

Heavy Metal Sample Preparation and Analysis

Sample preparation for heavy metal analysis is slightly more complex. After a sample is weighed, 2 mL of concentrated acid (e.g. 9:1 nitric and hydrochloric acid) is added. This sample is placed in a microwave digestion vessel or tube that is used, with a specialized laboratory microwave, to aid in the breakdown of the sample. After the solution is centrifuged and filtered, it is diluted with dilute acid before analysis.

Heavy metal analysis is performed on a slightly different MS than what has previously been discussed. The ionization source used is called inductively coupled plasma (ICP) that uses an argon plasma to efficiently ionize most elements of the periodic table and produces mainly singly charged positive ions. The ICP is typically interfaced with a quadrupole MS (ICP-MS). The mass spectra of heavy metals are simple and easy to interpret. Because of the isotopes of elements, heavy metals are able to be identified by their isotope patterns (Figure 15.19). Since there are only a few isotopes that overlap in elements, there is typically at least one that can be used to quantitatively determine the concentration of the element by the isotope abundance. ICP-MS is calibrated with standards, like all instruments, to determine a calibration curve. ICP-MS is very sensitive with the ability to establish very linear calibration curves. It also has a wide linear range and is able to detect very low concentrations.

See image below…

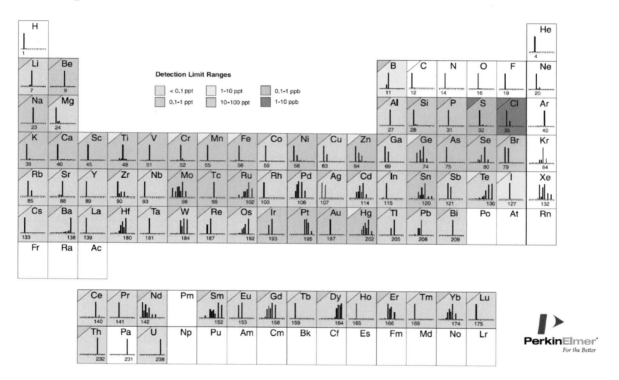

Figure 15.19: *Isotopic pattern and detection limit range for elements in ICP-MS analysis. (Image Credit: Used with permission from Perkin Elmer)*

Chapter 16 - Cannabis Testing and Instrumentation - Part II
(Dr. Arin Sutlief)

16.1 Other Regulation Tests: Microbial, Mycotoxin and Foreign Matter Regulations

Microbial

Microbial are microscopic organisms that exist in many parts of life. These organisms include archaea, bacteria and some eukaryotes like fungi. There are both beneficial and harmful microbial and they can be present in cannabis products. Because of their harmful effects to consumers, a number of microbial have been included in cannabis regulations. Regulations are commonly based on the number of colony forming units (CFUs) per gram of product. A CFU is a colony that theoretically forms from one viable cell from the original sample, and therefore, represents the quantitative presence of the organism. Methods are developed for either CFU growth or, with more recent technology, quantifying DNA of organisms present.

Measures can be taken to prevent microbial development in cannabis products. Water availability is a major contributor to microbial growth. Water activity is one parameter evaluated in many industries for safe consumer products including in the food industry. Water activity is best described as the amount of free water available to the environment, which would include any organisms. It is evaluated on a scale from 0.00-1.00 where 1.00 is pure water and 0.00 is completely dry. All microbial have an ideal water activity at which they will grow (Table 16.1). If they are in an environment that is lower than their ideal water activity, (through osmosis) cells will lose water to the environment making it more difficult for growth. (Carter, 2019) For cannabis, the ideal water activity to minimize microbial growth is 0.55 to 0.65 aw (Aroya, n.d.).

Table 16.1: Water activity lower limits for growth for some common spoilage organisms (Table Credit: Arin Sutlief; Data from Carter, 2019)

Microorganism	A_w Limit	Microorganism	A_w Limit
Escherichia coli	0.95	Aspergillus fumigatus	0.82
Salmonella	0.95	Aspergillus niger	0.77
Staphylococcus aureus (anaerobic)	0.90	Aspergillus ochraceous	0.77
Candida	0.88	Aspergillus restrictus	0.75
Staphylococcus aureus (aerobic)	0.86	Aspergillus candidus	0.75

Moisture content is also used as a regulation with limits to help prevent microbial contamination, especially in product storage. Expressed in the unit percent (%), it is the measure of the mass of water present in the sample or, put more simply, how much water is present. This analysis is particularly useful in processing to ensure compensating for the water that is already present (Aroya, n.d.). Both water activity and moisture content are regulations that will be discussed further later in this section.

The following list is of microbes that are currently found in state regulations across the United States (Table 16.2). With the exception of Utah, states specifically list the microbial that are required for testing with limits set for a product safety. Some states have regulations based on the product being tested. Utah's regulations are based on Section 1111 of U.S. pharmacopeia, which includes microbes that are described below (U.S. Pharmacopeia, 2016).

1. ***Escherichia Coli (E. coli):*** Bacteria commonly found in the gut that consists mostly of harmless strains but there are six pathogenic strains. The most common pathogenic strain is Shiga toxin-producing *E. coli* (STEC). ("Questions and Answers | E. coli | CDC," 2019) Ingestion of this bacteria can cause extreme discomfort. Symptoms include severe stomach cramps, diarrhea possibly with blood and vomiting. This infection can lead to a life threatening complication Hemolytic Uremic Syndrome (HUS) that could cause kidney failure or other serious problems. ("Symptoms | E. coli | CDC," 2021) Some states require only the testing for STEC, while others require testing for all six pathogenic strains.

2. ***Salmonella:*** Bacteria that causes the common illness "food poisoning". It is a foodborne illness infecting an estimated 1 million people every year in the United States. Symptoms include diarrhea, feve, and stomach cramps but could be serious and dangerous for some people. Children, older adults and immune compromised people can become seriously ill. (CDC, 2020b) Most states with cannabis regulations require testing for *Salmonella*.

3. ***Total Enterobacteriaceae:*** A large family of bacteria that contains pathogens that are part of the human intestinal tract but also cause complications. This family of bacteria include *E. coli*, *Salmonella*, *Enterobacter*, *Shigella* and more. (Kobedi, 2019) This family of bacteria is also known as Bile-tolerant gram-negative bacteria. ("Testing Enterobacteriaceae on Cannabis," n.d.) Many states require the analysis of total Enterobacteriaceae or Bile-tolerant gram negative bacteria.

4. ***Coliforms:*** A group of bacteria typically used as an indicator for unsanitary conditions in many food and beverage industries. This sub-family of Enterobacteriaceae includes *Citrobacter*, *Enterobacter*, *Escherichia*, *E. coli* and more.("Coliform | 3M-US," n.d.; "Testing Enterobacteriaceae on Cannabis," n.d.)

5. ***Staphylococcus Aureus:*** A Gram-positive bacteria that commonly causes infections in humans. On healthy skin, infection will not normally take place, but if it enters the bloodstream or internal tissues it could cause very serious infections. (Ta and Cg, 2017) Currently only three states, Delaware, Oklahoma and certain products in Colorado, include regulations for the analysis of *S. aureus*.

6. ***Pseudomonas Aeruginosa***: A Gram-negative bacteria that causes lung infections and is acquired both in the community and in hospitals. These infections can be life-threatening, especially to immunocompromised patients like those with cystic fibrosis. Lung infections are a major contributor to the morbidity and mortality of these patients (LaBauve and Wargo, 2012).

7. ***Aerobic Microbial:*** Aerobic microbial are organisms that require oxygen to grow. This includes all of the microbial species or families already discussed (Nutrition, 2020b). Many states require the analysis of products for total aerobic microbial count to indicate the level of microbial present.

8. ***Aspergillus Fumigatus:*** A fungus species of genus *Aspergillus* prevalent in the soil that has become one of the most common airborne fungal pathogens in immune compromised people. It is the most common pathogen in this genus and now is a major cause of death, especially in leukemia treatment centers and transplantation units (Latgé, 1999).

9. ***Aspergillus Flavus, Aspergillus Niger, Aspergillus Terreus:*** Three Aspergillus species that, while less common, also cause infections referred to as aspergillosis like *A. fumigatus*.(Person et al., 2010) Testing for any of this species is not required by many legal cannabis states.

10. ***Candida Albicans:*** One of the most common fungal pathogens found in humans. Considered a yeast, it can result in a number of yeast infections called candidiasis in many places including in the mouth, throat and vagina. While not commonly a serious infection, it is most prevalent in those with weakened immune systems and young children. ("Candida infections of the mouth, throat, and esophagus | Fungal Diseases | CDC," 2021) Only Colorado, in certain products, requires the analysis of isolated *C. albicans*.

11. ***Total Yeast and Mold:*** Many states require the analysis of a broad spectrum of yeast and molds with set limits to protect customers from contaminated products. This would include the already discussed *C. albicans*. This can also be considered as the analysis of culturable mold required by Montana regulations

Mycotoxins

Mycotoxins are toxins produced by microfungi contaminants that affect many products in agriculture. These toxins are suspected of being carcinogenic and can be harmful to both animals and humans if consumed. Aflatoxins are a subset of mycotoxins produced by some fungus species including *A. flavus* and *Aspergillus parasiticus* (CESCON et al., 2008; Nie et al., 2019). There are four major aflatoxins called B_1, B_2, G_1 and G_2. Aflatoxin B_1 is the most common aflatoxin and is the most potent natural carcinogen known. (Bennett and Klich, 2003) Ochratoxin A is also a subset of mycotoxins produced by different fungus species including *Aspergillus ochraceus*, *Aspergillus carbonarius*, *A. niger* and *Penicillium verrucosum*. (Bui-Klimke and Wu, 2015) Therefore, many states regulate the presence of these toxins in cannabis products (Table 16.3).

Table 16.3: U.S. Mycotoxin Regulations as of May 2020 (Table Credit: Arin Sutlief) ‡

Mycotoxin	Mycotoxin Limitations (ppb)																		
	CA	CO	CT	DE	HI	IL	LA	MD	MA	MI	MT	NV	NM	ND	OH	OK	PA	UT	WA
Total aflatoxin B1, B2, G1, G2	<20	<20			<20 mg/kg					<20	<20	<20	required	<20	<20			<20	<20
Ochratoxin A	<20	<20	<20	required			<20	<20	<20	<20	<20	<20	required	<20	<20			<20	<20
Alfatoxin B1			<20	required			<20	<20	<20								<5		
Alfatoxin B2			<20	required			<20	<20	<20										
Alfatoxin G1			<20	required			<20	<20	<20										
Alfatoxin G2			<20	required			<20	<20	<20										
Total									<20							<20	<20		

Foreign Matter

Currently, eight states require the inspection of cannabis products for foreign matter that can be introduced during harvest, processing or storage (Table 16.4). Foreign matter can include a visual inspection for dirt, sand, insect fragments, hair, etc. To complete this, a laboratory should have a microscope with a camera for photographic evidence and tweezers. In the state of California, regulations require the inspection of the exterior and interior of flower samples and the inspections of exterior of cannabis product samples ("California Code of Regulations," 2019).

Table 16.4: U.S. Foreign Matter Regulations as of May 2020 (Table Credit: Arin Sutlief) ‡

Foreign Matter Limitations								
Foreign Matter	**CA**	**DE**	**HI**	**ME**	**MT**	**NV**	**OK**	**WA**
Sand	<1/4 Total area			Required				
Soil	<1/4 Total area			Required				
Cinders	<1/4 Total area			Required				
Dirt	<1/4 Total area			Required				
Mold	<1/4 Total area		Required	Required				
Insect fragment	<1 per 3.0 g	Required	Required	Required	Required		Required	
Hair	< 1 per 3.0 g	Required	Required	Required	Required			
Mammalian excreta	<1 per 3.0 g			Required	Required		Required	
Imbedded foreign material	1/4 Total area							
Metal			Required					
Plastic			Required					
Packaging contaminants					Required			
None detected						Required		
5% of stems 3mm or more D								Required
2% of seeds or other foreign matter								Required

Microbial Sample Preparation and Analysis

Microbial analysis is a comprehensive process and most likely very different from any other test performed within the laboratory. It requires highly trained personnel in microbiology to develop and execute methods and a number of safety measures and equipment to complete. Because of the concerns of contamination of other samples and processes, microbial testing calls for an isolated space, ideally an enclosed room separate from the rest of the laboratory. The equipment needed is very specific to microbiology analysis, and therefore, results in a large budget expenditure. This process also includes the handling and disposal of pathogenic bacteria such as *P. aeruginosa* and *S. aureus* categorized as Biosafety Level 2 bio material. This level demands safety measures in place to ensure employee and environmental safety.

There are three common methods for quantification of microbial: conventional plating, petrifilms and polymerase chain reaction (PCR). Conventional plating is the oldest method used for analyzing the quantity of bacteria and is still the golden standard for most testing. If any other method is used for analysis, plating is often used as the confirmation or comparative test. For this method, certain items must be prepared before any analysis can take place. Agar plates are used as the surface to grow the bacteria on. The agar must be heated and sterilized in an autoclave to be poured into petri dishes. The agar is then allowed to cool and solidify. All supplies used to prepare the samples must also be sterilized prior to use. This includes pipette tips, centrifuge tubes, growth media, etc. This kind of preparation can be very time consuming, but any contamination of equipment or supplies could lead to false results.

When all equipment and supplies are ready, samples are prepared in a sterile environment. This may require a specialized hood or an open flame to prevent any cross contamination. A sample of cannabis flower or product is agitated in a buffer solution to extract any present microbial into the solution. The solution is serial diluted up to approximately 10^{-6} (some procedures may require more or less dilutions). At least three dilutions are then plated onto agar plates by pipetting 1 mL of the solution onto a plate and spreading it so that theoretically each cell is isolated on the surface. A separate plate is used for each dilution. The plate is incubated at the ideal temperature for the appropriate time dependent on the microbial. This procedure typically requires a 24 to 72 hour time period. Individual bacterial cells that are present will grow into a colony called a colony forming unit (CFU) that can be visually seen and counted. Plates with a CFU count between 25 and 250 are considered to be the most accurate plates to use for quantification. Plates above 250 are considered too numerous to count (TNTC). The CFU count in the original sample is then calculated to CFU/g.(Nutrition, 2020b; Stolze et al., 2019) This whole process is both time consuming and costly. Therefore, over the years, different methods have been developed to improve this process.

3M™ Petrifilms™ are an alternative to plate counting. Similar to agar plates, petrifilms can be used as the surface that bacteria cultures grow on, so CFUs can form for counting. But petrifilms are paper thin and come pre-made with the appropriate nutrients for detection of the targeted microbial. After a sample is extracted, the solution is pipetted onto the petrifilm and the sample pressed down with a spreader to have the sample cover the entire area. The petrifilm is then incubated and a present indicator dye helps highlight CFUs for easier counting. Several petrifilms have been developed for a number of types of microbial analysis including total yeast and molds, aerobic count, *E. coli*/Coliform, *Enterobacteriaceae*, *Salmonella*, *E. coli*, *S. aureus* and more. By using petrifilms, laboratories are able to avoid the hassle of analysis preparation, reducing labor costs by around 45%, and decreasing the space required for plates by 85%. In addition, petrifilms are able to produce results in half of the time as conventional plating while reducing waste by 66%. (3M, 2020)

Counting either plates or petrifilms is a tedious task that, while not requiring a lot of skill, does require consistency. One of the biggest concerns with manual counting is user bias, where the interpretation of a spot on a surface is categorized. This is made more difficult with samples that introduce a matrix that could be present, like plant material. Figure 16.1 gives an example of a sample where plant material is present that should not be counted. This figure also highlights areas that might cause more user bias because of aggregation of cells into a single area. Thus, making it hard to distinguish one colony from another. As technology improves, automated methods for counting plates/petrifilms are being developed, but many still rely on manual counting to reduce expenses and personnel training (Stolze et al., 2019).

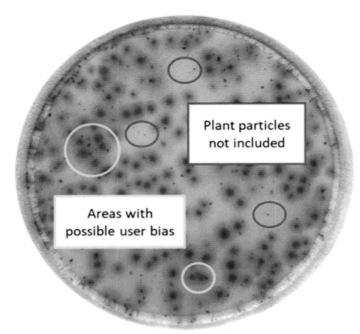

Figure 16.1: *Challenges of counting CFUs on plates or petrifilms. (Image Credit: Arin Sutlief)*

The third method that is becoming more predominant as a quick, first test in microbial analysis is polymerase chain reaction (PCR). This method targets DNA and quantifies the presence of microbial cells based on the amount of DNA present. Similar to plating, bacterial cells are agitated into a solution. A small amount of that solution is transferred to centrifuge tubes to isolate the matrix from the microbial cells. Once the cells are isolated, a lysis buffer is added to destroy the cell membranes so that cell DNA becomes free flowing. PCR solution is added to the sample that contains primers and polymerase. A primer is a sequence of DNA that is designed to identify a unique DNA sequence which corresponds to a target microbial. When the sample is placed into a thermal cycler the sample will be heated. This causes the DNA double helix to split; then, cooling will result in the primer binding to the DNA sequence. The polymerase in the solution will extend the DNA sequence replicating the original DNA double helix. This process is cycled several times to amplify the target DNA sequence for detection (Figure 16.2). There are multiple forms of detecting the DNA, including UV detection or tagging the DNA for colorimetric detection (PathogenDx, 2020). This process can be quicker than the conventional plate counting and some groups have shown how PCR methods can display uncertainty levels that are equal or better than plate counting (Ricchi et al., 2017).However, well trained personnel are required to complete PCR analysis, along with expensive equipment and a high consumables budget.

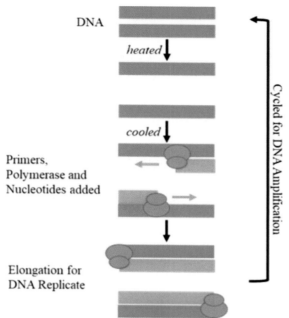

Figure 16.2: Polymerase Chain Reaction (PCR) process at the DNA level. (Image Credit: Arin Sutlief)

Mycotoxin Sample Preparation and Analysis

Sample preparation for mycotoxin analysis is very similar to sample preparation for other tests like cannabinoids and microbials. Analysis is performed on ground cannabis material or products to increase the efficiency of extraction. A test specimen is weighed out (approximately one gram) and placed into a 50 mL centrifuge tube. An organic solvent such as acetonitrile is added to extract the target analytes into the solution and is vigorously mixed with a vortex. The matrix material must be separated from the solution for analysis to avoid matrix interference in instrument detection. Lastly, the sample is diluted to the appropriate levels for the most reliable results (Dalmia et al., 2018). What makes mycotoxin analysis different from other analyses is the instrument and instrument setup. Mycotoxin analysis is completed by LC-MS/MS and can actually be performed in tandem with pesticide analysis.

Water Activity & Moisture Content

Many states include regulations that require the evaluation of the water available and/or moisture of the plant material as a measure to prevent microbial growth over time. Commonly, water activity and moisture content are measured, both being a way to determine how much water is present in products. Some states require both water activity and moisture content to be analyzed, while others require one or the other (Table 16.5). As discussed previously, water activity and moisture can be used to prevent or determine the probability of spoilage. After gaining an understanding of microbial and how water plays a part in microbial contamination, the reader should have a good understanding of the reasoning behind state limitations on the amount of water that can be present in cannabis products. Commonly, water activity is found to be regulated to values less than 0.65, with the exception of California and Maine that have separation limits for solid/semi-solid edibles at water activities below 0.85. However, at water activity levels below 0.55, terpenes can dry up, decreasing the quality of the product (Aroya, n.d.). Therefore, the ideal water activity for cannabis in general is between 0.55--0.65. Some states also require testing for moisture content, with limits found to be between 5%--15%.

Table 16.5: U.S. Moisture Content and Water Activity Regulations of May 2020 (Table Credit: Arin Sutlief) ‡

	Water Limitations												
	AR	CA	CA*	HI	ME†	ME*	MD	MT	NV	ND	OR	PA	WA
Moisture Content (%)	<15			<15				<12	<15	<15	<15	5-15	<15
Water Activity (Aw)	<0.65	<0.65	<0.85		<0.65	<0.85	<0.65			<0.65	<0.65	<0.65	<0.65

* solid/semi-solid edibles
† dried flowers

Water activity is determined by a meter that measures the amount of free water available. A sample is placed into a meter with an enclosed container and a consistent temperature applied. The equilibrium relative humidity is measured to determine the water activity or amount of free water available.

Moisture content can also be determined using a moisture analyzer. This is a balance with an enclosed container on top that contains a heating element. A sample of approximately 2.000 g is placed on a sample pan and the sample weight recorded while heat is applied. The method includes setting a temperature that is used to heat the sample as well as the selection of what should be the lowest acceptable change in sample weight effectively denoting the sample as dry. The moisture content or percentage of the sample weight composed of water is determined by equation 16.1, where w_{wet} is the sample weight when wet and w_{dry} is the sample weight after dried.

$$moisture\ content\ (\%) = \frac{(w_{wet} - w_{dry})}{w_{wet}} \times 100\%$$

Eqn 16.1

Moisture content can also be determined with equipment probably already in the laboratory. Plant material can be weighed for an initial wet weight and then dried at low temperatures using equipment like a dehydrated freeze dryer or oven until a constant weight is observed. This process can be time consuming with constant drying, cooling and weighing of samples.

Because each sample to be analyzed can contain a different amount of water, all analyses and regulations are based on a dry weight standard. However, it is possible to avoid waiting for long drying times before analysis. Moisture content can be used to correct for the weight of water contributed in the sample (Eqn 16.2), where w_{wet} is the wet weight of the sample, w_{dry} is the dry weight of the sample, and MC% is the determined moisture content (%) for the sample. However, the sample size received must be large enough to determine moisture content along with any required additional analysis.

$$w_{dry} = \frac{w_{wet}}{\left(1 - \frac{MC\%}{100}\right)}$$

Eqn 16.2

16.2 Quality Testing

ISO 17025 Certification

ISO 17025 is one of the most stringent accreditations a laboratory can get to be certified in competent analytical testing. This standard is established and regulated by the International Organization for Standardization (ISO), a worldwide federation of national standards bodies. In the United States, there are currently seven accreditation bodies including the American Association for Laboratory Accreditation (A2LA) and Perry Johnson Laboratory Accreditation (PJLA). These bodies and other international accreditation bodies require businesses seeking accreditation to these ISO standards to achieve a uniform operation of laboratories worldwide. ISO 17025 is the "gold standard" that applies to analytical testing and calibration laboratories to ensure competent testing and calibration.

During this process, a laboratory can spend weeks to months getting all documentations together that are required for ISO 17025 certification. This includes diligent policy building and putting procedures in place for all processes carried out throughout the laboratory. It is both a timely and a costly task to undertake, but in the end, the accreditation not only brings value to laboratory testing, but a high standard is also built to help protect the business. When a laboratory is readying for assessment and accreditation, an on-site audit is scheduled, where the assessor will evaluate all documentation and ensure the laboratory has all data necessary to meet the standard. When accreditation is awarded to a laboratory, the laboratory is continually re-evaluated with annual audits. The following sections will go into more detail about some major parts of the accreditation process.

Quality Manual

While there are a number of documents that are prepared and kept for ISO 17025 accreditation, one of the most important is the quality manual. The quality manual is basically the bible of the lab. It is the guide to how the laboratory plans to uphold all requirements of the standard. It contains the policies that should be in place, refers to forms and documents that should be used throughout the process in the laboratory; outlines the organization authority, responsibilities and more. It is the document that every employee should have training on and access to at all times. Any policies or processes outlined in the quality manual must be followed or the manual modified to update the policies.

Quality Control

Quality Control (QC) is a key part of validating results in ISO 17025 certification. All aspects included in the testing of samples must continually function in ways to meet the high ISO expectations. Records must also be kept that prove daily reliable testing. Balances are checked daily before samples are weighed with certified weights. Pipettes are regularly verified, so that the pipetting volume is consistent by weighing a volume of solution pipetted into a weigh boat. Solvent pumps used for dispensing sample prep volumes are verified daily with the most accurate graduated cylinders available (Type A). In addition, this kind of laboratory equipment is annually calibrated onsite by a certified third party and calibration is verified by the laboratory. To meet that ISO 17025 standard for instrumentation like HPLC, there are a number of checks that should be used including blind sample testing, QC samples, etc. (International Standard, 2017).

Proficiency tests are a key requirement in validating results. Accredited laboratories are required to perform, at minimum, one proficiency test a year by purchasing a blind sample from a certified supplier like Emerald Scientific. The results are reported to the supplier and after validation, the laboratory will receive a report of pass or fail based on the accuracy of their results. Some suppliers also offer programs that organize the participation of interlaboratory comparisons in biannual proficiency testing. It is also important to validate the QC samples, thus ensuring the accurate functioning of instrumentation. There are several different QC samples that can be used and are described in Table 16.6. Each QC sample has a function in validating the precision, accuracy and reproducibility of testing and should be used to detect and correct any errors that could occur (Modern Canna, 2020). When QC samples are analyzed, they should meet certain criteria. California has set requirements that should be calculated to ensure the quality of testing and are used as an example in the table below. For most samples, percent recovery is calculated using Eqn 16.3, where the reported value is divided by the expected value. For laboratory replicate samples, relative percent difference (RPD) is calculated using Eqn 16.4 and must be less than or equal to 30% for that QC sample to pass.

$$Recovery\ (\%) = \frac{reported\ value}{expected\ value} * 100$$

Eqn 16.3

$$RPD\ (\%) = \frac{|(representative\ sample\ measure\ -\ replicate\ sample\ measurement)|}{(representative\ sample\ measurement + replicate\ sample\ measurement)/2} \times 100$$

Eqn 16.4

Table 16.6: *Quality Control Samples and Requirements based on California Regulations ("California Code of Regulations," 2019) (Table Credit: Arin Sutlief)*

QC Sample	Description	Requirements
Initial Calibration Verification (ICV)	□ At least one standard prepared at a mid-range calibration concentration. □ Prepared with standards that are of a different lot than those used for calibration. □ Analyzed immediately following a new calibration. □ Validates the calibration.	Percentage Recovery: 70% - 130%
Continuous Calibration Verification (CCV)	□ At least one standard prepared at a mid-range calibration concentration. □ Analyzed at the beginning and end of a batch of	Percentage Recovery: 70% - 130%

	samples. ☐ Daily validates the calibration.	
Method Blank (MB)	☐ A sample prepared without any sample or material. ☐ Follows the sample prep procedure step-by-step. ☐ Ensures there are no analytes or other interfering chemicals introduced during sample preparation or contaminating the instrument.	There should be no reported cannabinoid peaks.
Laboratory Control Sample (LCS)	☐ Typically a matrix blank - a blank sample prepared from reference material with no analytes present. Does not exist in the cannabis industry. ☐ One alternative is a sample prepared without any sample or material with a known concentration of analyte standard spiked into the final HPLC vial. ☐ Another alternative is a collection of plant material that has detectable cannabinoids of interest like CBD, CBDA, THC, and THCA. After the analysis of 10-20 samples of this plant material, an average can be established and an acceptable value range determined.	Percentage Recovery: 70% - 130%

Laboratory Replicate Sample (LRS)	☐ A random test sample is prepared twice. ☐ Ensures repeatability of the method from homogeneous sampling to analysis.	Relative Percentage Difference: ≤30%
Matrix Spike Sample (MSS)	☐ A random test sample spiked with a known concentration of analytes. ☐ Evaluates the effects of sample matrices on method performance (Modern Canna, 2020)	Percentage Recovery: 70% - 130%

How often QC samples are prepared and run is dependent on the policies of the laboratory which must be upheld. Additionally, maintenance of records reflects compliance with the policy put into place. Table 16.7 is one example of a batch of samples prepared for a run that includes QC checks throughout the batch to ensure instrument operations were consistent for all samples and results are reliable. In this example, a maximum of 40 samples can be prepared for a single batch. The sample batch begins with an injection blank where nothing is injected into the instrument but runs the method to show no interference from contaminants and that the instrument is operating correctly. Second, a methanol blank is injected to also show no interference from contaminates. Then, the batch is opened with a CCV QC sample to validate the calibration of the instrument followed by the other QC samples including MB, LCS and LRS. In this laboratory's policy, a maximum of 20 customer samples can then be injected consecutively before another CCV is required (CCVmid). This ensures that the instrumentation is still operating at the highest efficiency. Another 20 customer samples can then be analyzed before the batch is closed with the final CCV. If there are more than 40 customer samples to be analyzed, this would require the preparation of two batches and therefore two sets of QC samples.

Table 16.7: An example of a sample batch including quality controls (Table Credit: Arin Sutlief)

Injection #	Sample	Injection #	Sample	Injection #	Sample
1	Injection Blank	19	Customer 13	37	Customer 28
2	Methanol Blank	20	Customer 14	38	Customer 29
3	CCVstart	21	Customer 15	39	Customer 30
4	MB	22	Customer 16	40	Customer 31
5	LCS	23	Customer 17	41	Customer 32
6	LRS	24	Customer 18	42	Customer 33
7	Customer 1	25	Customer 19	43	Customer 34
8	Customer 2	26	Customer 20	44	Customer 35
9	Customer 3	27	Methanol Blank	45	Customer 36
10	Customer 4	28	CCVmid	46	Customer 37
11	Customer 5	29	Methanol Blank	47	Customer 38
12	Customer 6	30	Customer 21	48	Customer 39
13	Customer 7	31	Customer 22	49	Customer 40
14	Customer 8	32	Customer 23	50	Methanol Blank
15	Customer 9	33	Customer 24	51	CCVend
16	Customer 10	34	Customer 25	52	Methanol Blank
17	Customer 11	35	Customer 26		
18	Customer 12	36	Customer 27		

All of these QC parameters are recorded and monitored in control charts (Fig. 16.3). These charts allow for the organization of data and are used to show the proficiency of testing on any questioned results. If, at any time, samples fall outside the required parameters which can be dependent on federal and/or state regulations, all or some of the batch may require retesting.

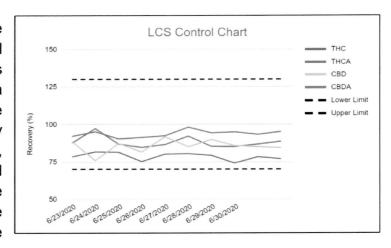

Figure 16.3: *Example of a control chart for a QC sample with failing parameters (dashed line) included. (Image Credits: Arin Sutlief)*

For example, if a QC sample fails at the beginning of the batch like the LCS, the LCS would be reprepped and the entire batch reanalyzed by the instrument. If the final CCV were to fail but the mid CCV passes. Only samples 21 to 40 would require reanalysis with the corresponding QC samples included in the reanalysis.

Uncertainty

Uncertainty is not only a requirement of ISO accreditation, but it has also been a factor in regulations. In February 2020, a USDA public announcement included the modification to the interim final rule to include the uncertainty range in federal hemp regulations. So if a sample is tested, for example, as 0.31% with an uncertainty of 0.01% or greater, it is considered compliant with the interim final ruling. This makes uncertainty a huge factor in cannabis testing. Uncertainty is the estimated range of values where the measured quantity is likely to be. It can be determined annually or as a continuous policy put in place for uncertainty to be determined in a set frame of time. Several methods have been developed for calculating uncertainty with varying degrees of acceptance by accrediting bodies, but all methods should include sources of constant uncertainty and random error that can occur (BIPM, 2008; Birch, 2003; Fillinger, 2018).

This textbook will present one example of calculating percent uncertainty in an analytical testing laboratory (Birch, 2003). Using the example of cannabinoid analysis by HPLC to calculate the uncertainty of a given cannabinoid, the reader must consider (1) the purity uncertainty of the certified reference material used for calibration of the HPLC, (2) any uncertainty in instruments used during sample preparation like a balance and micropipettes and (3) calculated uncertainty from the HPLC determined during calibration. This requires the purchase of certified reference material from an ISO 17034 accredited supplier, the calibration of sample prep equipment by an ISO 17025 accredited calibration laboratory and calibration standards of a method analyzed in triplicate. Eqn 16.5 is used to calculate the percent uncertainty for a single cannabinoid in a single validated method:

$$Uncertainty\ (\%) = 2\sqrt{(u_{ref})^2 + (u_{pip})^2 + (u_{bal})^2 + (u_{cal})^2}$$

Eqn 16.5

where u_{ref} is the CRM purity uncertainty, u_{pip} is the uncertainty of micropipettes, u_{bal} is the uncertainty of the balance and u_{cal} is the uncertainty determined for the calibration. When the percent uncertainty is calculated, the uncertainty range is determined by multiplying the measured value by the decimal of the uncertainty. For example, the percent weight of CBD in a product is determined to be 9.845% and the percent uncertainty is 1.673%. To determine the uncertainty range, 9.845 is multiplied by 0.01673 which is equal to 0.165 so the range is 9.845% ± 0.165%.

Method Validation

Section 7.2.2 of the ISO 17025 standard outlines the requirements for validation of methods used within the laboratory. A method that is not a standard method or is used as a modified standard method must be validated to meet this standard.(International Standard, 2017) The validation process involves a number of tests and can be time consuming. After all, data is collected and analyzed, a report is written and filed by the authorized personnel outlining the experimental process and significant parameters. So, what parameters should be considered?

The linearity of calibration curves must be assessed to ensure the accurate quantification of analyte concentrations. To determine the linearity, the calibration standards are injected in triplicate and the relative standard deviation (RSD) is calculated for each analyte at every calibration point. The concentration of the analyte is determined from each injection based on the calibration curve and Eqn 16.6 is used to determine RSD where $\underline{x}$ is the mean and S is the standard deviation of the three injection concentrations. Recovery efficiency is also determined by calculating percent recovery. RSD should be low at higher concentrations and recovery close to 100%. Then, as the concentration approaches the limit of quantification (LOQ), RSD will increase and recovery will increasingly deviate from 100%.

$$RSD\ (\%) = \frac{S}{\underline{x}} \times 100$$

Eqn 16.6

Quantification of target analytes is also dependent on the limit of detection (LOD) and the limit of quantification (LOQ). LOD is the lowest concentration at which an instrument can reliably detect an analyte. For low analyte concentrations, the signal for the analyte must be distinguishable from the baseline. However, both the signal and baseline are not smooth, because random signals called noise are present. Therefore, the signal to noise ratio (S/N) must be great enough for the analyte signal to be distinguishable. Typically for LOD, S/N must be between 2 or 3. (Şengül, 2016) To determine LOD for a method for each analyte, multiple low concentration standards might need to be prepared. S/N can also be used to define LOQ. LOQ is the lowest concentration that can be reliably quantified. This concentration is typically the lowest point in the calibration curve and has a S/N close to 10 or above. There are also other accepted ways of determining LOD and LOQ, such as methods published by the United States Food and Drug Administration and United States Environmental Protection Agency.

Accuracy and precision of a method must also be assessed. Accuracy will evaluate how well the method is able to get the correct value, while precision will evaluate how reproducible the method is. Samples of known concentrations are prepared and analyzed in triplicate. Percent recovery and relative standard deviation are calculated and reported to evaluate accuracy. To evaluate precision, five LCS samples are prepared and analyzed on the same day for intra-day reproducibility. This is repeated for three days. RSD is calculated for each day to establish inter-day precision.

The last section of method validation establishes the specificity that a particular usage of an instrument has for detecting each analyte individually from other analytes or compounds that might be present in the sample matrix. Specificity is demonstrated through the use of sample blanks and reference standards. For example, in HPLC, retention time windows are set for the best detection of each analyte. By using reference standards, it is demonstrated that the retention time windows are at the ideal settings to allow for the most reliable detection of analytes of interest, while doing the best to exclude any other analytes that may be present in samples such as terpenes. Then, the instrument software is able to correctly identify the analyte of each peak.

Standard Operating Procedure (SOP)

A standard operating procedure (SOP) is a step by step manual relevant to a single method performed within a laboratory. It should include key details to achieve reliable, accurate results from that method. Each user should have sufficient training in the SOP and follow it precisely for the greatest reproducibility. The following is the basic outline of the sections of an SOP.

1. **Header:** All documents have a header that includes the title of the testing method, authorization signature by the appropriate laboratory official, laboratory designation like a logo or company name, the current version number, the approval date and running page numbers (Figure 16.4).

	HPLC analysis of cannabinoid potency	SOP Number: SOP-055 v-1.1
	Standard Operating Procedure	Date Approved: 11/20/20
HP Labs	Authorized by signatory below for use at 1014 Boswell Ave. Crete, NE 68333 *John Smith*	Page 1 of 16

Figure 16.4: Example of a SOP header. (Image Credit: Arin Sutlief)

2. **Purpose:** Describes the goal(s) of the SOP.
3. List of acronyms, abbreviations and definitions.

4. **Scope:** A description of who is authorized to use the SOP and when it should be used.

5. **Procedure:** Step by step instructions detailing how to perform each task to achieve the purpose of the SOP with the greatest accuracy and reproducibility.

6. **Corrective Actions:** A list of actions that should be taken if something goes wrong at any point within the procedure. For example, if a QC sample like the CCV were to fail, the user should first reprep the sample and reanalyze the batch. If the CCV fails again, more stringent measures are required to identify the problem, like instrument maintenance or the purchase of new reference material. Notification to an authorized person like a laboratory manager or director may also be required.

7. **References:** Any material used to develop concepts or methods within the SOP should be clearly referenced. This helps track how methods are developed and if they are the most relevant methods. Any outdated references could lead to SOP revision. This is especially important in a growing industry like that of cannabis.

8. **Revision History:** A history of development and modifications should be recorded with new version numbers given with each revision. A description of amendments is also included, along with the date the revision was made and the name of the authorized reviewer.

It is important that all laboratory personnel know what they are doing in the laboratory or have the most up to date resources to double check any steps that may need clarification.

Records

Documentation is a key element in ISO certification. Sample tracing is one requirement that entails a lot of recordkeeping. Anything that happens within the laboratory must have some sort of documentation; tracing the sample from the time it enters the lab to how it was used and handled, until the time it leaves the laboratory or at the time of disposal. A laboratory information management system (LIMS) is a requirement of ISO 17025 for such recordkeeping and the control of data. If the customer information is submitted prior to sample drop off or shipping, this system can start tracking information before the sample even reaches the laboratory. Upon entering the laboratory, the sample is given a unique ID and the location of the sample known at all times. All sample preparation information is recorded in LIMS, including the weight of the sample used for analysis, which balance was used, the pipettes used, the solvent volumes and their lot numbers, date(s) prepared, SOP used, identified user and more. Any QC samples or solvents prepared for instrument analysis are also required to be traced and should include the SOP, solvents' lot numbers, date (s) prepared and more. This amount of tracing continues for sample analysis, sample storage and sample disposal so that a user can find a sample at any time and know exactly what happened to it while in the laboratory.

Records should also include any error that occurs in the laboratory or customer service. Unusual behavior should be reported with a nonconforming report (NCR). If the behavior persists and a number of nonconforming reports gather with the same reported behavior, a corrective action report (CAR) may be needed that will lead to an investigation of the behavior by the appropriate party, evaluation of action that should be taken for correction of the problem and a follow up of the situation to ensure the correction of the problem. This constant improvement system also requires that all feedback/negative customer interactions be documented and the appropriate management member following up with CARs as needed.

Record keeping also includes a number of other laboratory aspects. An inventory of all equipment must be kept in an updated equipment list requiring the labeling of any equipment used with unique IDs. An inventory of all supplies must also be kept up to date and a record maintained to show the purchase of products from reputable sources. All equipment and aspects of the laboratory must be kept in good working order and maintenance records kept. This includes regular hood inspections and maintenance, eyewash and show station inspections, balances and micropipette calibrations and verifications and all instrumentation calibrations, errors and maintenance. In addition, the laboratory, refrigerators, freezers, ovens, incubators and autoclaves must be kept at temperatures and humidity for optimal operation, sample preparation and sample and supplies storage. This requires the continual monitoring of temperature and humidity in each area with properly certified measuring devices. *And all of this is just a quick snapshot of ISO 17025!* There are a number of other documents and continuous record keeping tasks that makes meeting and maintaining this standard quite arduous. It is necessary to understand that regardless of its immense benefits, ISO certification is both time consuming and costly. But in the end, it brings great credit and reliability to the laboratory and business.

Suggested Reading

Envirocann, Cannabis Certification Company
https://www.envirocann.com/

Cannabis Science and Technology
https://www.cannabissciencetech.com/

U.S. Department of Agriculture | Hemp Production
https://www.ams.usda.gov/rules-regulations/hemp#

Terpenes: The Magic within Cannabis
By Beverly A. Potter, Ph.D.

Undergraduate Instrumental Analysis
By James W. Robinson, Eileen M. Skelly Frame, and George M. Frame II

ISO/IEC 17025:2017 General Requirements for the Competence of Testing and Calibration Laboratories by International Standard

References

3M, 2020. 3M Petrifilm Plates and Plate Reader.

Amendment 64, 2012.

Armstrong, B., Carnagey, C., Wu, J., Reddy, S., Ye, J., Qin, F., Wichems, D., Schmidt, C., 2017. Analysis of Pesticide Residues in Cannabis Regulated by Oregon State Using LC/MS/MS.

Aroya, n.d. Drying cannabis - The cannabis processor's complete guide to moisture and water activity. URL: https://aroya.io/resources/drying-cannabis-the-complete-guide/ (accessed 3.30.21).

Avins, J., Kopf, D., 2019. The number of U.S. acres devoted to hemp is 100 times greater than five years ago. Quartz.

Bennett, J.W., Klich, M., 2003. Mycotoxins. Clin. Microbiol. Rev. 16, 497–516. URL: https://doi.org/10.1128/CMR.16.3.497-516.2003

BIPM, 2008. JCGM 100:2008 Evaluation of Measurement Data - Guide to the Expression of Uncertainty in Measurement.

Birch, K., 2003. Measurement Good Practice Guide No. 36: Estimating Uncertainties in Testing. Crown. Bui-Klimke, T.R., Wu, F., 2015. Ochratoxin A and human health risk: A review of the evidence. Crit. Rev. Food Sci. Nutr. 55, 1860–1869. URL: https://doi.org/10.1080/10408398.2012.724480

California Code of Regulations, 2019.

Candida infections of the mouth, throat, and esophagus | Fungal Diseases | CDC [WWW Document], 2021. URL: https://www.cdc.gov/fungal/diseases/candidiasis/thrush/index.html (accessed 4.25.21).

Carter, B.P., 2019. The What, How, and Why of Water Activity in Cannabis. Cannabis Sci. Tech 2, 30–35.

CDC, 2020a. Outbreak of Lung Injury Associated with E-cigarette Use or Vaping [WWW Document]. Cent. Dis. Control Prev. URL: https://www.cdc.gov/tobacco/basic_information/e-cigarettes/severe-lung-disease/ (accessed 3.29.21).

CDC, 2020b. Salmonella and Food [WWW Document]. Cent. Dis. Control Prev. URL https://www.cdc.gov/foodsafety/communication/salmonella-food.html (accessed 4.21.21).

CESCON, D.W., PAGE, A.V., RICHARDSON, S., MOORE, M.J., BOERNER, S., GOLD, W.L., 2008. Invasive Pulmonary Aspergillosis Associated With Marijuana Use in a Man With Colorectal Cancer. Invasive Pulm. Aspergillosis Assoc. Marijuana Use Man Colorectal Cancer 26, 2214–2215.

Coliform | 3M-US [WWW Document], n.d. URL: https://www.3m.com/3M/en_US/food-safety-us/resources/microorganisms/coliform/ (accessed 4.22.21).

Conaway, K.M., 2018. H.R.2 - Agriculture Improvement Act of 2018.

Dalmia, A., Cudjoe, E., Astill, T., Jalali, J., Weisenseel, J.P., Qin, F., Murphy, M., Ruthenberg, T., 2018. A Single Cannabis LC/MS/MS Method to Meet California Pesticide and Mycotoxin Residues Regulatory Requirements.

Earlenbaugh, E., 2015. What is CBN (cannabinol) and what are the benefits of this cannabinoid? Leafly. URL: https://www.leafly.com/news/science-tech/what-is-cbn-and-what-are-the-benefits-of-

this-cannabinoid
(accessed 5.1.21).

EPA, 2014. 40 CFR 180 - Tolerances and Exemptions for Pesticide Chemical Residues in Food.

FDA, 2021. Warning Letters and Test Results for Cannabidiol-Related Products [WWW Document]. Warn. Lett. Test Results Cannabidiol-Relat. Prod. URL: https://www.fda.gov/news-events/public-health-focus/warning-letters-and-test-results-cannabidiol-related-products (accessed 3.29.21).

Fillinger, N., 2018. TX-PM 1.11 Measurement Uncertainty.

Goyer, R., 2004. Issue Paper on the Human Health Effects of Metals.

Hemp Production | Agricultural Marketing Service [WWW Document], n.d. . Hemp Prod. URL: https://www.ams.usda.gov/rules-regulations/hemp (accessed 5.1.21).

Hudock, C., 2019a. U.S. Legal Cannabis Market Growth. New Front. Data. URL: https://newfrontierdata.com/cannabis-insights/u-s-legal-cannabis-market-growth/ (accessed 5.1.21).

Hudock, C., 2019b. Potential Cannabis Market Job Growth. New Front. Data. URL: https://newfrontierdata.com/cannabis-insights/potential-cannabis-market-job-growth/ (accessed 5.1.21).

International Standard, 2017. ISO/IEC 17025:2017 General Requirements for the Competence of Testing and Calibration Laboratories.

Kobedi, P., 2019. Enterobacteriaceae. NICD. URL: https://www.nicd.ac.za/diseases-a-z-index/enterobacteriaceae/ (accessed 4.22.21).

LaBauve, A.E., Wargo, M.J., 2012. Growth and Laboratory Maintenance of Pseudomonas aeruginosa. Curr. Protoc. Microbiol. 25, 6E.1.1-6E.1.8. URL: https://doi.org/10.1002/9780471729259.mc06e01s25

Latgé, J.-P., 1999. Aspergillus fumigatus and Aspergillosis. Clin. Microbiol. Rev. 12, 310–350.

Marotta, L., Kwoka, T., Scott, D., Snow, M., Astill, T., 2018. Fast, Quantitative Analysis of Residual Solvents in Cannabis Concentrates.

Modern Canna, 2020. The importance of quality control when building a sustainable cannabis company [WWW Document]. Leafly. URL: https://www.leafly.com/news/industry/quality-control-building-sustainable-cannabis-company (accessed 4.9.21).

Morrissey, K., 2021. Cannabis in the U.S. 2021 Mid-Year Market Update. New Frontier Data.

Moulins, J.R., Blais, M., Montsion, K., Tully, J., Mohan, W., Gagnon, M., McRitchie, T., Kwong, K., Snider, N., Blais, D.R., 2018. Multiresidue Method of Analysis of Pesticides in Medical Cannabis. J. AOAC Int. 101, 1948–1960. URL: https://doi.org/10.5740/jaoacint.17-0495

Nie, B., Henion, J., Ryona, I., 2019. The Role of Mass Spectrometry in the Cannabis Industry. J Am Soc Mass Spectrom 30, 719–730.

Nutrition, C. for F.S. and A., 2020a. FDA's Testing of Cosmetics for Arsenic, Cadmium, Chromium, Cobalt, Lead, Mercury, and Nickel Content. FDA.

Nutrition, C. for F.S. and A., 2020b. BAM Chapter 3: Aerobic Plate Count. FDA.

PathogenDx, 2020. PathogenDx Product Insert QuantX.

Person, A.K., Chudgar, S.M., Norton, B.L., Tong, B.C., Stout, J.E., 2010. Aspergillus niger: an unusual cause of invasive pulmonary aspergillosis. J. Med. Microbiol. 59, 834–838.

URL: https://doi.org/10.1099/jmm.0.018309-0

Potter, B.A., 2019. Terpenes: The Magic Within Cannabis. Ronin Publishing Inc.

Questions and Answers | E. coli | CDC [WWW Document], 2019.

URL: https://www.cdc.gov/ecoli/general/index.html

(accessed 4.21.21).

Ricchi, M., Bertasio, C., Boniotti, M.B., Vicari, N., Russo, S., Tilola, M., Bellotti, M.A., Bertasi, B., 2017. Comparison among the Quantification of Bacterial Pathogens by qPCR, dPCR, and Cultural Methods. Front. Microbiol. 8.

URL: https://doi.org/10.3389/fmicb.2017.01174

Rigdon, A., Hilliard, C., Cochran, J., n.d. A Preliminary FET Headspace GC-FID Method for Comprehensive Terpene Profiling in Cannabis | SelectScience.

Robinson, J.W., Skelly Frame, E.M., Frame II, G.M., 2014. Undergraduate Instrumental Analysis, 7th ed. CRC Press.

Şengül, Ü., 2016. Comparing determination methods of detection and quantification limits for aflatoxin analysis in hazelnut. J. Food Drug Anal. 24, 56–6.

URL: https://doi.org/10.1016/j.jfda.2015.04.009

Shaffer, C., 2019. Medical Cannabis Poses Unique Testing Challenges. Genet. Eng. Biotechnol. News 39, 23–26.

Shapira, A., Berman, P., Futoran, K., Guberman, O., Meiri, D., 2019. Tandem Mass Spectrometric Quantification of 93 Terpenoids in Cannabis Using Static Headspace Injections. Anal. Chem. 91, 11425–11432.

URL: https://doi.org/10.1021/acs.analchem.9b02844

Stolze, N., Bader, C., Henning, C., Mastin, J., Holmes, A.E., Sutlief, A.L., 2019. Automated image analysis with ImageJ of yeast colony forming units from cannabis flowers. J. Microbiol. Methods 164, 105681. https://doi.org/10.1016/j.mimet.2019.105681

Symptoms | E. coli | CDC, 2021.

URL: https://www.cdc.gov/ecoli/ecoli-symptoms.html

(accessed 4.21.21).

Ta, T., Cg, U., 2017. Staphylococcus Aureus.

Taylor, A., Birkett, J.W., 2020. Pesticides in cannabis: A review of analytical and toxicological considerations. Drug Test. Anal. 12, 180–190. https://doi.org/10.1002/dta.2747

Testing Enterobacteriaceae on Cannabis, n.d. . Med. Genomics.

URL: https://www.medicinalgenomics.com/enterobacteriaceae/

(accessed 4.22.21).

U.S. Domestic Hemp Production Program, 2021. Laboratory Testing Guidelines.

U.S. Pharmacopeia, 2016. <1111> Microbiological Examination of Nonsterile products: Acceptance Criteria for Pharmaceutical Preparations and Substances for Pharmaceutical Use.

What is QuEChERS? [WWW Document], 2019.

URL: https://www.restek.com/en/video-library/what-is-quechers/

(accessed 5.23.21).

Wyatt, K., 2015. Colorado bill seeks to standardize labs' marijuana testing. The Cannabist.

‡ State and Federal regulations were obtained from most recent published cannabis laws as of May 2020.

Afterword

(Dr. Andrea Holmes and Dr. Mark Orsag)

The textbook *Cannabis: A Comprehensive Overview* has been both a challenging and rewarding project. Our work has spanned, and at times co-mingled, the academic disciplines of plant biology, agricultural science, history, economics, business, law, communications, medicine and chemistry. The vast and highly interdisciplinary nature of the subject and the continuing effects and aftereffects of the harsh regulatory and legal landscape affecting cannabis usage around the globe that destructively restricted and retarded scientific research, education, economic and commercial development proved difficult hurdles to clear. The effective dichotomy between hemp and marijuana also complicated our efforts to complete this book. Some authors were more inclined to focus on hemp, while others wanted to present more of a balance between the two close cannabis cousins. The academic field of cannabis and the overall holistic and highly interdisciplinary environment are evolving at the speed of light in the United States and around the world, but significant segments of the global regulatory, legal and educational systems are still lagging far behind... and most likely will be for many more years.

While we have striven, and we believe succeeded, to make this volume not only *comprehensive* in terms of breadth of coverage but also *current* in terms of keeping pace with the latest fast-moving and multifaceted trends in the vast and complex cannabis field, we also strongly believe that a presumed rapid pace of future cannabis-related events will, in the next few years, push us to rather quickly revisit these volumes and produce updated editions.

The unique and intriguing nature of this plant is what inspired our work's lead author to immerse herself so intensely in the study of cannabis, and, in turn, to lead the considerable effort of producing this two volume work. As Dr. Andrea Holmes herself notes, her deep dive into the cannabis industry in Colorado, Nebraska, the US, Asia and Europe, allowed her to reach professional and personal satisfaction. Nothing has excited her more in her entire scientific career as much as this industry, and she will continue to plow forward and educate, build businesses and new programs, innovate and help improve the health and wellness of humans and animals. The evolving 21st Century relationship between humans and the cannabis plant will indeed, we expect, be as complicated and controversial, full of multifaceted opportunities, important and entertaining to analyze and chronicle...just as it has been for thousands of years.

Andrea Holmes and Mark Orsag

Glossary Volume Two (Alphabetical Order)

Accuracy: How well the method of an instrument is able to get the correct value.

Acne: A skin condition that occurs when your hair follicles become clogged with oil and dead skin cells. It causes whiteheads, blackheads or pimples.

Acidic Phase: The early form or phase of a cannabinoid. Heat, time and light decarboxylate and degrade, respectively, the acidic phase cannabinoid to its neutral phase by removing a carboxyl group. Example: THCA (acidic phase) is converted to THC (neutral phase) when it is heated.

Adaptogen: A Food and Drug Administration (FDA) defined metabolic regulator that has been proved to help the body adapt to its environment and to prevent external harms:
1. plant-originated adaptogens must reduce the harm caused by stressed states, such as fatigue, infection and depression;
2. plant-originated adaptogens must have positive excitatory effects on the human body;
3. in contrast to traditional stimulants, the excitatory effects produced by plant-originated adaptogens must not cause side effects such as insomnia, low protein synthesis or excessive energy consumption;
4. plant-originated adaptogens must not harm the human body.

Adenosine: An organic compound used medically to treat irregular heartbeats (arrhythmias). It can also be used during a heart stress test.

Aerobic Microbial: Organisms that require oxygen to grow.

Agonist: A chemical that binds to a receptor and activates the receptor to produce a biological response.

Allosteric Receptor Modulator: In pharmacology and biochemistry, a group of substances that bind to a receptor to change that receptor's response to stimulus.

Alopecia Areata: Sudden hair loss that starts with one or more circular bald patches that may overlap. Alopecia areata occurs when the immune system attacks hair follicles, and may be brought on by severe stress.

Alopecia Effluvium: A reversible condition in which hair falls out after a stressful experience.

Alzheimer's Disease (AD): A degenerative brain disease and the most common form of dementia. Dementia is not a specific disease. It's an overall term that describes a group of symptoms. Its' hallmark is beta-amyloid plaques that accumulate in the brain.

Amyotrophic Lateral Sclerosis (ALS)" Also called Lou Gehrig's Disease, a nervous system disease that weakens muscles and impacts physical function of idiopathic origin.

The main symptom is muscle weakness. Medication and therapy can slow ALS and reduce discomfort, but there's no cure. It is progressive and leads to death over months to years.

Anorexia: Lack or loss of appetite for food.

Antagonist A substance that interferes with or inhibits the physiological action of another.

Arthritis: Inflammation of the joints that leads to pain, swelling, redness and stiffness.

Aspergillus Fumigatus: The most common fungus species of genus *Aspergillus* found prevalently in the soil. However, it is becoming more commonly found as an airborne fungal pathogen affecting health facilities such as leukemia treatment centers and transplantation units.

Autoimmune Hepatitis: Inflammation in the liver that occurs when the immune system attacks the liver.

Bidirectional Response: Functioning in two directions.

Biphasic: Having two phases.

Cachexia: Weakness or wasting of the body; the muscle wasting and severe weight loss seen in late stage cancer and other diseases.

Candida Albicans: One of the most common fungal pathogens found in humans that causes the yeast infection candidiasis in many places including the mouth, throat, gut and vagina.

Cannabinoids: A class of diverse chemical compounds that act on cannabinoid receptors in the endocannabinoids system and alter neurotransmitter release in the brain.

1. **Endocannabinoids:** Produced naturally in the body by animals.
2. **Phytocannabinoids:** Found in cannabis and some other plants.
3. **Synthetic Cannabinoids:** Artificially manufactured cannabinoids.

Cannabinoid Receptor (CB Receptors): Located throughout the body, are part of the endocannabinoid system, which is involved in a variety of physiological processes including appetite, pain-sensation, mood and memory.

Causalgia: Severe burning pain in a limb caused by injury to a peripheral nerve.

CB1: One of the receptors in the endocannabinoid system that binds to endogenous (naturally formed in the body) and cannabis derived cannabinoids. This receptor helps regulate the nervous system and is located in neurons and other cells. The interaction of cannabinoids with this receptor is responsible for the effects on the human body.

CB2: One of the receptors in the endocannabinoid system that binds to endogenous (naturally formed in the body) and cannabis derived cannabinoid. This receptor helps regulate the nervous system and is located in neurons and other cells. The interaction of cannabinoids to this receptor is responsible for the effects on the human body.

CBC: Cannabichromene, also called cannabichromene, cannabichromene, pentyl cannabichromene or cannabichromene, is one of the hundreds of cannabinoids found in the Cannabis plant and is, therefore, a phytocannabinoid.

CBC (Cannabichromene), CBT (Cannabicitran), CBL (Cannabicyclol), CBDV (Cannabidivarin) and THCV (Tetrahydrocannabivarin): All minor cannabinoids that play an important bioactive role in human health and wellness.

CBD: A nonintoxicating cannabinoid found in cannabis and hemp. Today, this major cannabinoid is the basis, in and of itself, of an important sector of the cannabis industry.

CBG: Cannabigerol (CBG), a non-psychoactive cannabinoid that plays an important role in the biochemistry of the cannabis plant.

CBN: Cannabinol (CBN), a mildly psychoactive cannabinoid found only in trace amounts in Cannabis and is mostly found in aged cannabis.

Certified Reference Material (CRM): A standard of analyte(s) prepared at a known concentration with the greatest precision by an ISO 17034 accredited supplier.

Chemotherapy-Induced Nausea and Vomiting (CINV): Nausea and vomiting that results from the administration of chemotherapy agents used to treat cancer.

Chromatogram: A plot of chromatography signal as the signal as a function of time.

CO2: Carbon Dioxide, a gas used for extraction of cannabinoids.

Coliforms: A sub-family of Enterobacteriaceae that includes *Citrobacter, Enterobacter, E. coli* and others. Typically considered an indicator for unsanitary conditions in many food and beverage industries.

Colony Forming Unit (CFU): A colony that forms from one viable cell from the original sample. Used to quantify organisms present in a product.

Complex Regional Pain Syndrome: Chronic arm or leg pain developing after injury, surgery, stroke or heart attack.

Continuous Calibration Verification (CCV): A QC sample prepared at a calibration concentration with standards that is analyzed daily with samples. It is used as a daily validation of the calibration.

Corrective Action Report (CAR): A report of behavior that should be investigated by the appropriate party and evaluated for any action that should be taken for correction of the problem. This will also include a follow up of the situation to ensure the correction of the behavior.

Cultivar: A plant variety that has been produced in cultivation by selective breeding.

Cytotoxic: Toxic to living cells.

Decarboxylation: A chemical reaction that removes a carboxyl group and releases carbon dioxide (CO_2). Usually, decarboxylation refers to a reaction of carboxylic acids, removing a carbon atom from a carbon chain. With cannabis, this is the process of converting cannabinoids from their acidic forms (i.e., THCA) to their neutral forms (i.e., THC).

Decoction: The liquor resulting from concentrating the essence of a substance by heating or boiling, especially a medicinal preparation made from a plant.

Dermatitis: A general term that describes a skin irritation; a common condition that has many causes and occurs in many forms. It usually involves itchy, dry skin or a rash on swollen, reddened skin or it may cause the skin to blister, ooze, crust or flake off.

Diazepam: A tranquilizing, muscle-relaxant drug used chiefly to relieve anxiety. It is in the class of drugs called benzodiazepines and has high addictive potential.

Dispersive Solid Phase Extraction (dSPE): A column of solid material that is used to remove unwanted compounds from a sample solution.

Docosahexaenoic Acid (DHA): An omega-3 fatty acid that is a primary structural component of the human brain, cerebral cortex, skin and retina. It can be synthesized from alpha-linolenic acid or obtained directly from maternal milk, fish oil or algae oil.

Dopamine: A type of neurotransmitter made by the body. The nervous system uses it to send messages between nerve cells. That's why it's sometimes called a chemical messenger. Dopamine plays a role in how a person feels pleasure. It's a big part of a person's unique human ability to think and plan. It is also given as a drug to support blood pressure in cases of septic shock and heart failure.

Dose Response Curve: The dose–response relationship, or exposure–response relationship, describes the magnitude of the response of an organism, as a function of exposure to a stimulus or stressor after a certain exposure time. Dose–response relationships can be described by dose–response curves.

Duchenne Muscular Dystrophy (DMD): Disease characterized by chronic inflammation and irreversible skeletal muscle damage and degeneration. It is an X-linked recessive genetic disorder. Girls can be carriers and mildly affected, but the disease typically affects boys.

Dystonia: A state of abnormal muscle tone resulting in muscular spasm and abnormal posture, typically due to neurological disease or a side effect of drug therapy.

Electron Ionization (EI): A hard ionization source where a beam of electrons that is a sample is passed through causing ionization and fragmentation of the sample compounds.

Electron Multiplier (EM): A detector used in MS made of surfaces that produce several electrons when electrons, ions or neutrals collide with the surface. This amplifies the electrons to create a current producing a signal for analysis.

Electrospray Ionization (ESI): A soft ionization source where a metal capillary with liquid sample has a strong electric field applied. The electric field causes ionization and dispersion of the liquid.

Eicosapentaenoic Acid (EPA): An omega-3, polyunsaturated fatty acid found especially in fish oils. In humans it is a metabolic precursor of prostaglandins.

Endocannabinoid System: A biological system composed of endocannabinoids, which are endogenous lipid-based retrograde neurotransmitters that bind to cannabinoid receptors, and cannabinoid receptor proteins that are expressed throughout the vertebrate central nervous system and peripheral nervous system.

Endorphin System: Endorphins consist of a large group of peptides, which are produced by the central nervous system and the pituitary gland. Since endorphins act on the opiate receptors in a person's brain, they reduce pain and boost pleasure, resulting in a feeling of well-being.

Endothelial Dysfunction: A type of non-obstructive coronary artery disease (CAD) in which there are no heart artery blockages, but the large blood vessels on the heart's surface constrict (narrow) instead of dilating (opening). This condition tends to affect more women than men and causes chronic chest pain.

Entourage/Ensemble Effect: The theory that all compounds in cannabis work together, and when taken in combination, they produce a better effect than when taken alone.

Enzyme: Proteins that act as biological catalysts, which accelerate chemical reactions. The molecules upon which enzymes may act are called substrates. The enzyme converts the substrates into different molecules known as products.

Epigenetics: The study of changes in organisms caused by modification of gene expression rather than alteration of the genetic code itself.

Epilepsy: A disorder in which nerve cell activity in the brain is disturbed, causing seizures. Epilepsy may occur as a result of a genetic disorder or an acquired brain injury, such as a trauma or stroke.

Escherichia Coli (E. coli): Bacteria commonly found in the gut. Most strains are harmless but there are six pathogenic strains that can cause extreme discomfort if ingested. Most severe symptoms include the development of a life threatening infection. Most common pathogenic strain is Shiga toxin-producing *E. coli* (STEC).

External Standard: A solution prepared with certified reference materials of known concentrations of analyte(s) used for the calibration of instrumentation.

Extracted Ion Chromatogram (XIC): Chromatogram plotted as the select ions versus scan number/time.

FDA: The Food and Drug Administration is responsible for protecting the public health by ensuring the safety, efficacy, and security of human and veterinary drugs, biological products and medical devices; and by ensuring the safety of our nation's food supply, cosmetics and products that emit radiation.

Fibrogenesis: The formation of excessive fibrous tissue, as in a reparative or reactive process.

Fibromyalgia: A chronic disorder characterized by widespread musculoskeletal pain, fatigue and tenderness in localized areas. Fibromyalgia is often accompanied by fatigue and altered sleep, memory and mood.

Flame Ionization Detector (FID): A common detector in gas chromatography that detects carbon containing compounds using a flame for ionization that results in a current produced as the signal for the analyte presence.

Flavonoid: A class of polyphenolic secondary metabolites found in plants and commonly consumed in diets. Flavonoids are the most important plant pigments for flower coloration, producing yellow or red/blue pigmentation in petals designed to attract pollinator animals. In higher plants, flavonoids are involved in UV filtration, symbiotic nitrogen fixation and floral pigmentation. They may also act as chemical messengers, physiological regulators and cell cycle inhibitors.

Fragment Ion: Ion of fragments.

Fragmentation: The breakdown of a molecule into smaller pieces called fragments.

Full Agonist: A drug which is capable of producing a maximum response that the target system is capable of: "When the receptor stimulus induced by an agonist reaches the maximal response capability of the system (tissue), then it will produce the system maximal response and be a full agonist in that system."

Full Evaporation Technique (FET): A sample is heated prior to sampling to evaporate analytes of interest. The headspace of the sample vial is sampled for analysis. Also known as headspace analysis.

GABA: Gamma-Aminobutyric acid, or γ-aminobutyric acid, or GABA, is the chief inhibitory neurotransmitter in the developmentally mature mammalian central nervous system. Its principal role is reducing neuronal excitability throughout the nervous system.

Gas Chromatography: A chromatography technique that uses a carrier gas to move samples and compounds through the instrument for analysis.

Gas Chromatography Mass Spectrometry (GCMS): One instrument that can be used which characterizes the retention time and molecular mass of small and volatile molecules, including cannabinoids. GCMS can also be used to characterize residual solvents and terpenes, which are both getting more and more concentrated during processing and refinement.

Ghrelin: A hormone produced by enteroendocrine cells of the gastrointestinal tract, especially the stomach, and is often called a "hunger hormone" because it increases food intake. Blood levels of ghrelin are highest before meals when hungry, returning to lower levels after mealtimes.

Glutamate: In neuroscience, glutamate refers to the anion of glutamic acid in its role as a neurotransmitter: a chemical that nerve cells use to send signals to other cells. It is by a wide margin the most abundant excitatory neurotransmitter in the vertebrate nervous system.

Glutaminergic/Cholinergic/Serotonergic Systems": Neurotransmission systems that utilize glutamate, acetylcholine and serotonin, respectively.

Gradient: A method in gas chromatography or HPLC that uses a program to change temperature or the mobile phase composition, respectively, during analysis.

H_2SO_4: Sulfuric acid, a chemical used for retting in hemp.

Hepatitis C: A virus that is a small, enveloped, positive-sense and a single-stranded RNA virus of the family Flaviviridae. It is the cause of Hepatitis C and some cancers such as liver cancer and lymphomas in humans.

High Performance Liquid Chromatography (HPLC): The standard method in the cannabis industry to determine the concentration of cannabinoids in any sample.

Hirsutism: Excessive hair growth on unexpected areas of the body, such as on the face, chest and back.

HIV/AIDS: Also called human immunodeficiency virus, acquired immunodeficiency syndrome. HIV causes AIDS and interferes with the body's ability to fight infections.

Homeostasis: The tendency toward a relatively stable equilibrium between interdependent elements, especially as maintained by physiological processes.

Huntington's Disease: Known as HD, it is a progressive brain disorder caused by a defective gene, which causes changes in the central area of the brain that affect movement, mood and thinking skills.

Hypothalamic-Pituitary Axis (HPA): The human central stress response system. The HPA axis intertwines the central nervous system and endocrine system and is responsible for the neuroendocrine adaptation component of the stress response.

Immunomodulation: Encompasses all therapeutic interventions aimed at modifying the immune response. Augmentation of the immune response is desirable to prevent infection in states of immunodeficiency, to fight established infections and to fight cancer.

Inductively Coupled Plasma Mass Spectrometry (ICP-MS): An argon plasma ionization source interfaced with a mass analyzer, typically a quadrupole, used for elemental analysis in samples. It has a wide linear range, very low detection limits and is very sensitive. It can be used to quantify most elements of the periodic table.

Inflammation: A local response to cellular injury that is marked by capillary dilatation, leukocytic infiltration, redness, heat and pain and that serves as a mechanism initiating the elimination of noxious agents and of damaged tissue. Inflammation is part of the body's defense mechanism and plays a role in the healing process.

Inflammatory bowel disease (IBD): Ongoing inflammation of all or part of the digestive tract. Crohn's disease and Ulcerative Colitis are the two primary forms of IBD.

Initial Calibration Verification (ICV): A QC sample prepared at one calibration concentration with standards of a different lot than those used for calibration. It is used to verify a new calibration before proceeding with any testing.

Insomnia: Persistent problems falling and staying asleep.

Insulin Resistance: A pathological condition in which cells fail to respond normally to the hormone insulin. The cells become resistant due to a buildup of dietary fat inside the cell. Insulin resistance is the precursor to Type 2 Diabetes.

Interim Final Rule (IFR): United States Department of Agriculture current ruling for the hemp program setting the production framework and requirements for testing.

Internal Standard: A compound similar to the analyte(s) of interest that is added to the sample and elutes from the HPLC column at a different retention time. It aids in HPLC quantitative analysis.

Interstitial Cystitis (IC) or Painful Bladder Syndrome (PBS): A chronic condition causing bladder pressure, bladder pain and sometimes pelvic pain. The pain ranges from mild discomfort to severe pain. The condition is a part of a spectrum of diseases known as painful bladder syndrome.

Inverse Agonist: In pharmacology, an inverse agonist is a drug that binds to the same receptor as an agonist but induces a pharmacological response opposite to that of the agonist. A neutral antagonist has no activity in the absence of an agonist or inverse agonist but can block the activity of either.

Irritable Bowel Syndrome: A widespread condition involving recurrent abdominal pain and diarrhea or constipation, often associated with stress, depression, anxiety or previous intestinal infection.

ISO 17025: International standard for accreditation for analytical testing and calibration laboratories.

Isocratic: A method in HPLC that has a constant mobile phase throughout analysis.

Isoprene: A unit (C_5H_8) that is found in terpenes.

Isothermic: A method that has one set temperature for the column oven within gas chromatography.

Laboratory Control Sample (LCS): Commonly a QC sample prepared with a matrix blank (a matrix that has no analytes present). In the cannabis industry, it is accepted to prepare a method blank that is spiked with a known concentration of the analyte using standards.

Laboratory Information Management System (LIMS): A system that can be used for recordkeeping all information corresponding to a sample from the time it is submitted to the laboratory for testing to the reporting of results and sample disposal.

Laboratory Replicate Sample (LRS): A QC sample prepared by replicating the preparation of a random test sample. It is used to ensure the repeatability of the method from homogeneous sampling to analysis.

Leptin: A hormone predominantly made by adipose (fat) cells and enterocytes (cells in the small intestine) that helps to regulate energy balance by inhibiting hunger, which in turn diminishes fat storage in adipocytes.

Ligand: A molecule that binds to another (usually larger) molecule. Often a ligand binds to a receptor.

Limit of Detection (LOD): The lowest concentration that an instrument can reliably detect an analyte.

Limit of Quantification (LOQ): The lowest concentration that can be reliably measured for quantification.

Linearity: Determined for a calibration curve of an instrument, it ensures the accuracy of quantification of analytes concentrations within the calibration range. It can also be expressed in linear regression as r^2 where a straight line would be equal to 1.00.

Lipogenesis: The metabolic process through which acetyl-CoA is converted to triglyceride for storage in fat.

Mass Spectrum: A plot of mass spectrometer data as the relative abundance vs m/z.

Mass-to-Charge Ratio (m/z): Mass of the ion (m) divided by the charge of the ion (z).

Matrix Spike Sample (MSS): A QC sample prepared by replicating the preparation of a random test sample that is spiked with a known concentration of analytes using standards. It is used to evaluate the effect of sample matrices on the method performance.

Method Blank (MB): A QC sample prepared following the sample preparation but without a sample. It is used to ensure daily that no analytes or interfering chemicals are introduced during sample preparation or contaminating the instrument.

Migraine: A recurrent throbbing headache that typically affects one side of the head and is often accompanied by nausea and disturbed vision. One aspect of migraine pain theory explains that migraine pain happens due to waves of activity by groups of excitable brain cells. These trigger chemicals, such as serotonin, to narrow blood vessels. Serotonin is a chemical necessary for communication between nerve cells.

Mitochondria: Membrane-bound cell organelles (mitochondrion, singular) that generate most of the chemical energy needed to power the cell's biochemical reactions. Chemical energy produced by the mitochondria is stored in a small molecule called adenosine triphosphate (ATP).

Moisture ContentL The % of mass that is from water present in a sample.

Molecular Ion: Ion that of the molecule with m/z close to the molecular weight of the compound or nominal mass.

Multiple Sclerosis: A disease in which the immune system eats away at the protective covering of nerves (myelin sheath) resulting nerve damage disrupts communication between the brain and the body. Multiple sclerosis causes many different symptoms, including vision loss, pain, fatigue and impaired coordination. The symptoms, severity and duration can vary from person to person. Some people may be symptom free most of their lives, while others can have severe chronic symptoms that never go away.

Murine: Of or relating to a murid genus (Mus) or its subfamily (Murinae) which includes the common household rats and mice; Also of, relating to or involving these rodents and especially the house mouse.

Mycotoxins: Toxins produced by microfungi that are suspected of being carcinogenic and are harmful to both animals and humans. Most common toxins are aflatoxins B_1, B_2, G_1 and G_2 and ochratoxin A.

NaOH: Sodium Hydroxide, a chemical used in retting of hemp.

Negative Allosteric Modulator (NAM): NAM's indirectly change agonist binding by interacting at a secondary site on the receptor to diminish the ability of the agonist to bind to the primary site. It has the net effect of lowering agonist affinity and/or efficacy.

Net Zero Dipole Moment: Dipole moments from the carbon to the oxygen cancel out making it non-polar.

Neuroimmune Modulation: A system of structures and processes involving the biochemical and electrophysiological interactions between the nervous system and immune system which protect neurons from pathogens. Neuroimmune modulation is the exertion of a modifying or controlling influence of the neuroimmune system.

Neuroplasticity: Also known as neural plasticity, or brain plasticity, is the ability of neural networks in the brain to change through growth and reorganization. These changes range from individual neuron pathways making new connections, to systematic adjustments like cortical remapping.

Neuroprotection: Refers to the relative preservation of neuronal structure and/or function.

Neurotransmission: The transmission of nerve impulses between neurons or between a neuron and a muscle fiber or other structure.

Neutral Agonist: Will inhibit the action of both agonist and antagonist compounds.

Neutral Phase: The degraded or decarboxylated form or phase of a cannabinoid. Heat, time and light decarboxylate and degrade, respectively, the acidic phase cannabinoid to its neutral phase by removing a carboxyl group. Example: THCA (acidic phase) is converted to THC (neutral phase) when it is heated.

NIH: The National Institutes of Health (NIH), a part of the U.S. Department of Health and Human Services, is the nation's medical research agency making important discoveries that improve health and save lives.

Nociception: The neural processes of encoding and processing noxious stimuli.

Non-alcoholic Fatty Liver Disease (NAFLD): The accumulation of liver fat in people who drink little or no alcohol. Over time, inflammation and scarring of the liver (cirrhosis) can occur.

Nonconforming Report (NCR): A report of any unusual behavior that occurs within the laboratory that does not necessarily require any action or resolution.

Norepinephrine: A naturally occurring chemical in the body that acts as both a stress hormone and neurotransmitter (a substance that sends signals between nerve cells). It's released into the blood as a stress hormone when the brain perceives that a stressful event has occurred.

NP (Nanoparticle): A carrier like a dendrimer or liposome to make a cannabinoid more bioavailable.

Omega-3 PUFA: Omega−3 fatty acids, also called Omega-3 oils, ω−3 fatty acids or n−3 fatty acids, are polyunsaturated fatty acids (PUFAs) characterized by the presence of a double bond three atoms away from the terminal methyl group in their chemical structure. They are widely distributed in nature, being important constituents of animal lipid metabolism, and they play an important role in the human diet and in human physiology. The three types of omega−3 fatty acids involved in human physiology are α-linolenic acid (ALA), found in plant oils, and eicosapentaenoic acid (EPA) and docosahexaenoic acid (DHA), both commonly found in marine oils.

Omega-6 PUFA: Omega-6 fatty acids (also referred to as ω-6 fatty acids or *n*-6 fatty acids) are a family of polyunsaturated fatty acids that have in common a final carbon-carbon double bond in the *n*-6 position, that is, the sixth bond, counting from the methyl end. Linoleic acid (18:2, *n*−6), the shortest-chain of the common omega-6 fatty acids in the human diet, is categorized as an essential fatty acid because the human body cannot synthesize it. Omega-6 fatty acids are precursors to endocannabinoids, lipoxins, and specific eicosanoids. Mammalian cells lack the enzyme omega-3 desaturase and therefore cannot convert omega-6 fatty acids to omega-3 fatty acids, which is why certain omega-3 fatty acids are also essential.

Overactive Bladder (OAB): The name for a group of urinary symptoms of which the most common symptom is a sudden, uncontrolled need or urge to urinate. Some people will leak urine when they feel this urge.

Palliative Care Pain Management: Is used to manage a disease or medical condition that is serious or life threatening by easing pain and other associated physical, emotional, or psychosocial symptoms.

Parkinson's Disease: A brain disorder that leads to shaking, stiffness and difficulty with walking, balance and coordination. Parkinson's symptoms usually begin gradually and get worse over time. As the disease progresses, people may have difficulty walking and talking. Nerve cell damage in a portion of the brain (substantia nigra) causes dopamine levels to drop leading to the symptoms of Parkinson's.

Partial Agonist: In pharmacology, partial agonists are drugs that bind to and activate a given receptor, but have only partial efficacy at the receptor relative to a full agonist.

Parts-Per-Billion (ppb): One part per 10^9 parts (10^{-9}). Can be descriptive in a liquid sample as 1 ppm is equal to 1 µg of analyte per 1 L of sample.

Parts-Per-Million (ppm): One part per 10^6 parts (10^{-6}). Can be descriptive in a liquid sample as 1 ppm is equal to 1 mg of analyte per 1 L of sample.

Percent Recovery: Calculated to evaluate how close a result is to the expected value;

$$\frac{reported\ value}{expected\ value} * 100\%$$

Peripheral Neuropathy: Weakness, numbness and pain from nerve damage, usually in the hands and feet. A common cause of peripheral neuropathy is diabetes, but it can also result from injuries, infections and exposure to toxins. Symptoms include pain, a pins-and-needles sensation, numbness and weakness.

Petrifilms: Thin, pre-made surface for bacteria culture growth and quantification made by 3M™. They have the appropriate nutrients and growth material to target specific microbial for quantification and dyes to help facilitate CFU counting. Serves as an alternative to agar plates.

Pharmacokinetic (PK) Curves: Pharmacokinetic curves are used by scientists to judge how fast, how much and how long a substance acts on our bodies.

Photodiode Array (PDA): A common detector used in liquid chromatography that produces a current/signal proportional to the UV/Vis light intensity that reaches the detector.

Phytocannabinoids: A molecule synthesized by plants. There are 113 known phytocannabinoids in the cannabis plant, including CBD and CBG.

Poly(lactic-co-glycolic acid) (PLGA): A hydrophobic, non-toxic polymer and gets metabolized and excreted from the body.

Polymerase Chain Reaction (PCR): A method used to quantify the presence of microbial by its DNA.

Polyphenol: A large family of naturally occurring organic compounds characterized by multiples of phenol units, which are abundant in plants and structurally diverse. Polyphenols include flavonoids, tannic acid and ellagitannin. Polyphenols are micronutrients gained through certain plant-based foods and packed with antioxidants and potential health benefits. Polyphenols may improve or help treat digestion issues, weight management difficulties, diabetes, neurodegenerative disease and cardiovascular diseases.

Polyunsaturated Fatty Acid: Fatty acids that contain more than one double bond in their backbone. This class includes many important compounds, such as essential fatty acids. Polyunsaturated fat is found in plant and animal foods, such as salmon, vegetable oils, and some nuts and seeds.

Positive Allosteric Modulator (PAM): Only activates receptors when the endogenous agonist is present. It has the net effect of increasing agonist affinity and/or efficacy.

Post Traumatic Stress Disorder (PTSD): A disorder in which a person has difficulty recovering after experiencing or witnessing a terrifying event. The condition may last months or years, with triggers that can bring back memories of the trauma accompanied by intense emotional and physical reactions. Symptoms may include nightmares or unwanted memories of the trauma, avoidance of situations that bring back memories of the trauma, heightened reactions, anxiety or depressed mood.

Postherpetic Neuralgia: The most common complication of shingles. The condition affects nerve fibers and skin, causing burning pain that lasts long after the rash and blisters of shingles disappear.

PPAR Gamma System: Peroxisome proliferator-activated receptor-gamma (PPAR-gamma), an essential transcriptional mediator of adipogenesis, lipid metabolism, insulin sensitivity, and glucose homeostasis, is increasingly recognized as a key player in inflammatory cells and in cardiovascular diseases (CVD) such as hypertension, cardiac hypertrophy, congestive heart failure and atherosclerosis.

Precision: How reproducible the method for an instrument is able to detect multiple injections of an analyte at the same concentration.

Pruritus: An uncomfortable, irritating sensation that creates an urge to scratch that can involve any part of the body.

Pseudomonas Aeruginosa: A gram-negative bacteria that commonly causes lung infections. These lung infections can become life-threatening for some, especially those with compromised immune systems.

Psoriasis: A skin disorder that causes skin cells to multiply up to 10 times faster than normal. This makes the skin build up into bumpy red patches covered with white scales. They can grow anywhere, but most appear on the scalp, elbows, knees and lower back. It is thought to be a disorder of the immune system.

Quadrupole: A common mass analyzer that has four rods where opposite pairs of rods are connected to opposite ends of a direct current source. One pair is negative and the other positive and they are alternated over time. The rods also connect to an electric source oscillating at radio frequency (RF) resulting in the ion moving through a quadrupole in a "corkscrew" path. Allows for the selection and separation of ions based on the m/z.

Quality Control (QC): A system in place to ensure the reliability of testing and quality of results.

Quality Manual: Comprehensive document that outlines all forms, policies and documents that should be used in the laboratory to uphold all requirements of the ISO 17025 standard.

Quantitation: An accurate measurement of the concentration of the analyte of interest present.

QuEChERS: A method used in the sample preparation for pesticide analysis. First, samples are hydrated and organic solvent added. $MgSO_4$ and sodium acetate are also added and the mixture shaken. Then the sample is cleaned using a variety of steps including dispersive solid phase extraction.

Receptor: In biochemistry and pharmacology, receptors are chemical structures, composed of protein, that receive and transduce signals that may be integrated into biological systems. They are the sites where ligands bind.

Relative Percent Difference (RPD): Calculated to express the similarity of two prepared samples from the same cannabis product;

$$\frac{|(representative\ sample\ measure\ -\ replicate\ sample\ measurement)|}{(representative\ sample\ measurement\ +\ replicate\ sample\ measurement)/2} \times 100\%$$

Reperfusion: The restoration of blood flow to an organ or to tissue. After a heart attack, an immediate goal is to quickly open blocked arteries and reperfuse the heart muscles. Early reperfusion minimizes the extent of heart muscle damage and preserves the pumping function of the heart. The same is true for the brain after an occlusive stroke.

Rett syndrome (RTT): A rare neurodevelopmental disorder, characterized by severe behavioural and physiological symptoms. Rett syndrome is caused by an X chromosome mutation that affects girls with seizures, speech issues and muscle spasticity.

Rheumatoid Arthritis: An inflammatory disease of the joints characterized by pain, stiffness, and swelling, as well as an eventual loss of limb function. Rheumatoid arthritis affects about 1% of the population, primarily women.

Salmonella: Bacteria that causes the common illness "food poisoning". Symptoms include diarrhea, fever and stomach cramps. Children, older adults and immune compromised people are most susceptible to serious illness.

Selected Ion Monitoring (SIM): Mass spectrum is set to only select for specific ions throughout analysis.

Sleep Apnea: A potentially serious sleep disorder in which breathing repeatedly stops and starts. Those affected often snore loudly and feel tired even after a full night's sleep. The main type of sleep apnea is obstructive sleep apnea that occurs when throat muscles relax.

Standard Operating Procedure (SOP): A step-by-step manual of a single method that is performed within a laboratory.

Staphylococcus Aureus: A gram-positive bacteria that commonly causes infections which can become serious if it enters the bloodstream or internal tissues.

Steatosis: Also called fatty change, is abnormal retention of fat (lipids) within a cell or organ. Steatosis most often affects the liver, the primary organ of lipid metabolism, where the condition is commonly referred to as fatty liver disease.

Serotonin: Also referred to as 5-hydroxytryptamine, is a monoamine neurotransmitter. Its biological function is complex and multifaceted, modulating mood, cognition, reward, learning, memory and numerous physiological processes such as vomiting and vasoconstriction.

Specificity: The accuracy of the method of an instrument has to distinguish an analyte from other analytes or compounds that might be present in the sample matrix.

Strain: In botany, refers to variations found within plant cultivars. It also refers to the offspring that descend from modified plants which are either produced by biotechnological methods or through regular breeding.

Stroke: Also called CVA, a cerebrovascular accident, with damage to the brain from interruption of its blood supply.

Tandem MS (MS-MS or MS^n): Mass spectrometers that use a mass analyzer to select ions which are further fragmented and ionized. Ions are separated with a second mass analyzer for detection. This process can be repeated in some instrumentation.

Terpene: A class of natural products consisting of compounds with the formula $(C_5H_8)_n$. Comprising more than 30,000 compounds, these unsaturated hydrocarbons are found in many plants, though many people commonly associate them with cannabis because cannabis plants contain high concentrations of them.

THC: Tetrahydrocannabinol, a crystalline compound that is the main active ingredient of cannabis.

THC-V: Tetrahydrocannabivarin is a compound in cannabis that offers a unique array of effects and medical benefits which sets it apart from other cannabinoids like THC and CBD.

Total Enterobacteriaceae: A large family of bacteria that contains pathogens including *E. coli*, *Salmonella*, *Enterobacter*, *Shigella* and others. This family of bacteria is also known as Bile-tolerant gram-negative bacteria.

Total CBD: [CBD] + 0.877 x [CBDA].

Total Ion Chromatogram (TIC): Chromatogram plotted as the total count from ions of all masses vs scan number/time.

Total THC: [Δ9-THC] + 0.877 x [THCA].

Total Yeast and Mold: Analysis for a broad spectrum of yeast and molds within products for contamination detection.

Tourette's Syndrome: A problem with the nervous system that causes people to make sudden movements or sounds, called tics, that they can't control. For example, someone with Tourette's might blink or clear their throat over and over again. Some people may blurt out words they don't intend to say.

Type 2 Diabetes: An impairment in the way the body regulates and uses sugar (glucose) as a fuel. This long-term (chronic) condition results in too much sugar circulating in the bloodstream. Eventually, high blood sugar levels can lead to disorders of the circulatory, nervous and immune systems. It's precursor is insulin resistance.

Uncertainty: The estimated range of values where the measured quantity is likely to be.

USDA: The U.S. Department of Agriculture (USDA) is made up of 29 agencies and offices with nearly 100,000 employees who serve the American people at more than 4,500 locations across the country and abroad.

Vanilloid System: Compounds which possess a vanillyl group. A number of vanilloids, most notably capsaicin, bind to the transient receptor potential vanilloid type 1 (TRPV1) receptor, an ion channel which naturally responds to noxious stimuli such as high temperatures and acidic pH. This action is responsible for the burning sensation experienced after eating spicy peppers.

Varin: Varin cannabinoids (CBGV, THCV, CBDV, etc.) are derived from parent varin acids (CBGV-A, THCV-A, CBDV-A, etc.) and are homologous to their non-varin counterparts. Cannabinoids have side-chains made up of five carbon atoms, whereas varin cannabinoids have side-chains made up of three carbon atoms. Cannabinoid acids (including varins) have no psychoactive effect until being matured and activated through decarboxylation, though they may be medically beneficial before decarboxylation.

Vis Medicatrix Naturae: The Latin rendering of the Greek Νόσων φύσεις ἰητροί, a phrase attributed to Hippocrates. While the phrase is not actually attested in his corpus, it nevertheless sums up one of the guiding principles of Hippocratic medicine, which is that organisms left alone can often heal themselves.

Water Activity: The amount of free water available to the environment evaluated on a scale from 0.00 to 1.00 where 1.00 is pure water and 0.00 is completely dry.

Brief Author Biographies

Andrea Holmes, Ph.D (Lead Author): Dr. Andrea Holmes is a Professor of Chemistry at Doane University in Crete, Nebraska. Dr. Andrea Holmes is one of the co-founders and Chief Growth Officer of Precision Plant Molecules, a premier hemp extraction company that is focused on THC free and minor cannabinoids located in Denver. In her role at Precision Plant Molecules, Dr. Holmes explores the needs of the current cannabis industry and identifies the markets that still have great potential for growth. Dr. Holmes is also an expert in testing cannabis consumer products for potency, pesticides, terpenes, residual solvents, yeast, molds, salmonella and e-coli.

Dr. Holmes received her Ph.D. in organic chemistry at New York University and was a National Institutes of Health postdoctoral Fellow at Columbia University in New York City. She has received more than $5 million in federal grant funding, including the Presidential Early Career Award funded by the National Science Foundation. Her scholarship led to 3 patents and nearly 40 peer reviewed journal publications. Dr. Holmes is passionate about teaching organic chemistry at Doane University and is an expert in cannabis chemistry and the cannabis industry. Dr. Holmes has given local, national and international lectures and has published articles on cannabis education, terpenes, endocannabinoid system, major and minor cannabinoids, extraction methods, niche markets like using CBD for the pet industry and unique topics that involve the rapidly emerging cannabis industry. She is an affiliate faculty member in the Institute for Human and Planetary Health (IHPH).

Amanda E. McKinney, MD, CPE, FACLM, FACOG: Dr. McKinney is the Executive Director of Doane University's Institute for Human and Planetary Health (IHPH). She obtained her medical degree from the University of Nebraska Medical Center. She completed her residency and fellowship training at the University of California-Irvine. She holds the titles of Associate Dean of Health Sciences and Executive Director for Doane University's Institute for Human and Planetary Health. Dr. McKinney has extensively practiced medicine in clinical settings; she holds Board Certifications in Obstetrics and Gynecology, Female Pelvic Medicine and Reconstructive Surgery and Lifestyle Medicine and possesses training in herbal and cannabis medicine.

She has previously served as the Physician's Governing Board Chair, Chair of the Peer

Review Committee and Director of Lifestyle Medicine while a physician at Beatrice Community Hospital in Beatrice, Nebraska. She has served on the Board of Directors of the American College of Lifestyle Medicine and currently serves on the Board of Directors for the Center for Rural Affairs. Dr. McKinney has given over twenty invited presentations, at times as a keynote or plenary speaker, in the United States and overseas. She has published articles in, among other publications, *The Lancet Planetary Health, The American Journal of Lifestyle Medicine* and the *American Journal of Obstetrics and Gynecology.* She was also featured, along with Samuel L. Jackson, James Cameron and others, in the 2016 documentary film *Eating You Alive.*

 **Allan Jenkins, Ph.D (John C. Marienau Fellow):** Dr. Allan Jenkins, is Professor of Economics, Emeritus and John C. Marienau Fellow at the University of Nebraska Kearney. He received his B.A. with High Honors from the University of Oklahoma and his M.A. and Ph.D. from the University of Nebraska-Lincoln. At UNK, his teaching interests focused on health care economics, public finance and environmental economics. He also created and taught a Morality of Capitalism capstone course for the General Studies program. His research interests include Platte River issues, rural development and rural health care.

Throughout his 34 year career at UNK, Dr. Jenkins was an active participant in state and regional policy discussions. He was involved in the discussions that led to the Three State Platte River Agreement, served as the General Editor of *The Platte River: An Atlas of the Big Bend Region,* sponsored by Omaha World Herald Foundation, (1992) and co-authored an economic impact report on the Platte River for EPA Region 7 (1996). Dr. Jenkins co-authored a staff review of competing economic impact reports for the Nebraska Public Service Commission in their consideration of the $8 billion Keystone XL pipeline (2017). He and his colleague, Dr. Ron Konecny, completed Tax Increment Financing statutory reports for nearly $1.5 billion dollars in proposed investment projects in Nebraska and multiple economic impact reports for legislative proposals from a variety of economic development groups.

After creating a Health Care Economics course in 2006, Dr. Jenkins became involved in rural healthcare. He co-authored Medicaid expansion economic impact reports for South Dakota and Nebraska and testified before the Nebraska Unicameral on this issue. He served as a media contact in the Medicaid expansion debate prior to the 2018 election and made multiple public presentations on the issue. After the ballot initiative passed, supporters recognized Dr. Jenkins as one of the major contributors to the election victory. He helped create a Health Care Minor in the UNK College of Business and Technology, initiated a student internship program with rural hospitals and has been a frequent speaker at health association events. In 2016, Dr. Jenkins' contributions were recognized with the President's Award from the Nebraska Rural Health Association.

Significant service includes creating and securing outside funding for the biennial UNK John C. Marienau Symposium on the Morality of Capitalism. Dr. Jenkins served as chair or co-chair for four of the five symposiums held to date. He has been active in the Nebraska Economics and Business Association since 1985, serving as President 3 times and serving on the Board of Directors for more than 20 years. In 2007, Dr. Jenkins' contributions to the organization were recognized with the NEBA Lifetime Achievement Award. In 1999, Dr. Jenkins was one of ten national recipients of the Sasakawa Foundation Fellowship awarded by the American Association of State Colleges and Universities. The UNK College of Business and Technology has recognized Dr. Jenkins for outstanding teaching and service and presented him with a Career Achievement Award in 2019.

Since 2015, Dr. Jenkins has been a recognized supporter of hemp. In 2016, he was the editor of a hemp advocacy book: *The Return of An Ancient Partner*. The book was given to state senators in Wyoming and Nebraska, print and broadcast media, and identified regional influencers to help the public better understand that hemp is not marijuana. Dr. Jenkins testified twice in favor of legal hemp cultivation before the Nebraska Unicameral. In 2019, he was one of ten Nebraskans selected to grow hemp in the state's pilot project. In 2020, he held a hemp processor's license. Dr. Jenkins has appeared as a panelist or primary speaker at multiple hemp education events in Nebraska, Wyoming and Nevada. He continues his advocacy work and educational presentations today.

Mark Orsag, Ph.D (Editor): Dr. Mark Orsag is Professor of European and Interdisciplinary History at Doane University. He is also an affiliate faculty member in the Institute for Human and Planetary Health (IHPH). Dr. Orsag received a BA from Carnegie-Mellon University, an MA from Pennsylvania State University, and a Ph.D. from Michigan State University. He is the current Chair of Doane University's History Department. His areas of concentration in teaching, professional presentation and published scholarly output have encompassed Ancient, European, Russian, Military and Interdisciplinary history. As a teacher, Dr Orsag has won an unprecedented three Doane University Student Congress Teaching Awards. He has over 30 reviewed/juried articles, books and/or conference presentations.

His current scholarly interests are collaborative projects centered at the nexus of history and the natural sciences. This includes work with Doane University colleague Dr. Amanda McKinney, MD and Dr. DeeAnn Reeder, PhD (Biology) of Bucknell University, on the five articles that compose the "What Caused the Plague of Cyprian? A Proposed Multidisciplinary Solution to a Horrific 1,771 Year-Old Mystery" series. The first two of these articles were presented at the 2021 Association of Ancient Historians Conference (University of Illinois). The whole series has been accepted for presentation at the American Historical Association Annual Meeting in New Orleans (January 2022). Dr. Orsag's other current scholarly projects include an in-progress interdisciplinary monograph (also with Dr. McKinney), *The 21st First Century Crisis: Healing in the Anthropocene.* He also is a chapter lead author, ("The Intriguing History of Cannabis") and serves as the Editor for the forthcoming *Cannabis: A Comprehensive Overview, a* multidisciplinary/multi-author volume being written under the leadership of Doane University Professor of Chemistry and Director of Cannabis Studies, Dr. Andrea Holmes.

 **Blake Colclasure, Ph.D.:** Dr. Blake Colclasure is an Assistant Professor of Environmental Science at Doane University where he teaches foundational courses in natural resources and the agricultural sciences. He is a highly passionate and student-centered educator who incorporates inquiry-based instruction, problem-based learning and real-world learning experiences in the classroom. Dr. Colclasure has teaching experience at diverse levels, including leading high school and community college agricultural programs. He has delivered teacher professional development on teaching methods in agricultural and environmental sciences to practicing secondary and post-secondary teachers and received a teaching award from the North American Colleges and Teachers of Agriculture.

Dr. Colclasure's scholarship lies at the nexus of agriculture, environmental science and human dimensions. He believes in order to solve the complex global challenges of the 21st Century, interdisciplinary research teams must be used to address the critical role people play in both the problem and the solution. Dr. Colclasure is an active researcher with over 35 peer-reviewed publications and presentations, including scholarship focused on hemp education and adoption. Dr. Colclasure holds a PhD in Agricultural Education and Communications from the University of Florida and an M.S. in Natural Resources and Environmental Science and a B.S. in Agricultural and Environmental Science Education, both from the University of Illinois at Urbana-Champaign.

Arin Sutlief, Ph.D.: Dr. Arin Sutlief is the senior laboratory technician at Sweetwater Hemp Company, a cold-water hemp extraction facility in Pleasanton, Nebraska. At this facility, she is involved with many aspects including hemp extraction, hemp-derived product formulation, quality control testing and research and development. Dr. Sutlief was also co-founder of Cannabis Testing Laboratories at Doane University and served as laboratory director.

Dr. Sutlief received her Ph.D. in analytical chemistry at the University of Nebraska-Lincoln. She was a National Institutes of Health Postdoctoral Fellow at Doane University in Crete, Nebraska. She has over twenty peer-reviewed publications and presentations including cannabis educational presentations at forums dedicated to the education and expansion of the cannabis industry in the Midwest. Dr. Sutlief is passionate about bringing a successful cannabis industry to the Midwest and helping people learn more about this amazing plant.

Mahesh Pattabiraman, Ph.D.: Dr. Pattabiraman is a professor of biology at University of Nebraska at Kearney. He has published 24 articles and a book chapter related to photochemistry, supramolecular chemistry, synthesis of phytochemical analogs and their biological effects. His research activities aim to understand the excited reactivity of organic molecules when perturbed with weak interactions (hydrogen bonding, pi-pi, ion-dipole, halogen...halogen, CH-pi, Van der Waals, etc.). As a trained photochemist, he utilizes his expertise to synthesize natural product analogs which have potential antinociceptive and anticancer properties. His work involves extracting and analyzing phytochemicals in plants such as curcuma longa, incarvillea sinensis, green peas and shiitake mushrooms. As a faculty member in a primarily undergraduate institution (PUI), as well as an avid researcher, he blends research and undergraduate education to provide an enriched learning experience for his research students.

Steven J Rothenberger, Ph.D.: Dr. Steven J. Rothenberger is professor emeritus of biology, University of Nebraska at Kearney. He has published more than 35 scientific papers for professional journals and has written popular articles for *Nebraskaland*, the *Midland* and the *Platte Valley Review* among others. He was co editor for the book "A Presidential Visit"

and senior editor and contributing author of "A Prairie Mosaic: An Atlas of Central Nebraska's Land, Culture and Nature" selected in 2001 as an award winning Notable Government Document by *Library Journal*. He considers himself a student of the prairie and the popular culture of the Great Plains. His recent book, "Scottsbluff in '62: A Rock'n'Roll Retrospective of Small Town America (2018)" chronicles the history and music of the remarkable 1960s.

Made in the USA
Monee, IL
03 August 2022

10789548R00169